MICROBIOLOGY TECHNIQUES

Susan G. Kelley, Ph.D.

Frederick J. Post, Ph.D.
Utah State University

Star
PUBLISHING COMPANY

PUBLISHING COMPANY

P.O. Box 68
Belmont, CA 94002
(415) 591-3505

Publisher and Managing Editor: Stuart A. Hoffman
Typography: Gist & Erdmann, Inc.
Art: Sharon Belkin with Photography by Marty Cohen
    Doug Hurd
    Liz Stanley
    Claudia Barazi
Cover Color Separations: Colorprep, Inc.

Printed in the United States of America

0-89863-149-1

0 9 8 7 6 5 4 3   00 01 02 03

TABLE OF CONTENTS

UNIT XV. IMMUNOLOGY

PREFACE

The purpose of *Microbiology Techniques* is to introduce the beginning student to the fascinating field of microbiology. As in *Basic Microbiology Techniques*, the approach is to provide a single exercise illustrating the basic tools of the microbiologist. Each exercise is described in a simple manner with line drawings where experience has shown problems to exist. In addition to the basic tools, a number of exercises have been included showing the range of microbiological applications in industry, agriculture, foods, and health. Most of the exercises are within the range of most beginning microbiology students but a few do require a little more background. The instructor may select particular exercises and omit others depending on the nature of the course. Even if not performed, the student may wish to scan the other exercises to see what areas are covered.

Each exercise was written in a particular format:

1. *Performance objectives* are designed to aid the students in knowing what is expected of them.

2. An *Introduction* describes some of the background for each exercise. Most of these are fairly brief, but some are necessarily longer.

3. A *Materials* section includes the items necessary to perform the exercise including the optimum group size. Many of the exercises should be done alone to improve bench skills. Others work best with groups or pairs. Any arrangement may be selected by the instructor depending on course goals.

4. The *Procedures* section indicates the total time commitment involved for the exercise or section and the details of procedure to carry it out. We generally tried to write these procedures to be performed with a minimum of additional direction. However, there are always some special requirements for each teaching situation that may need to be added. An *Observations* section guides students through the final steps of the procedure, what to look for, and what to record. This *Observations* section is generally combined with the *Procedures* section for 1-day exercises.

5. *Thought Questions* at the end of each exercise are designed to provoke the thinking student into consideration of the principles of the exercise. These questions are usually not answerable from the laboratory manual. Indeed, a specific answer may not be found in some cases. Any textbook of microbiology can be a source for answers to these.

6. The *Results and Observations* form follows each exercise and guides the student into a structuring of the exercise results. You might specifically note how data are to be presented. As part of the report form, a set of questions is found directed for the most part to the objectives set out at the beginning. Again, not all the answers will be found in the exercise itself. These questions are generally less complex than the *Thought Questions* and answers are provided in the accompanying Instructor's Manual.

7. The *Appendices* contain a list of the media, reagents, and organism strains used in each exercise. The students should consult these often to identify the ingredients of media and reagents.

The range of subjects covered in this manual are:

<table>
<tr><td>microscopy</td><td>viruses of bacteria</td></tr>
<tr><td>microbe groups</td><td>genetics of bacteria</td></tr>
<tr><td>cultivation</td><td>identification</td></tr>
<tr><td>staining</td><td>soil microbes</td></tr>
<tr><td>counting microbes</td><td>water microbes</td></tr>
<tr><td>metabolic activities</td><td>medical microbiology</td></tr>
<tr><td>environmental stresses</td><td>immunology</td></tr>
</table>

Instructor's Manual. An Instructor's Manual accompanies this manual. It contains suggestions to the instructor for preparing the exercise materials, sources of videos to accompany the exercises, suggested volumes for cultures and media and container size, and answers to the questions on the report forms. Part of the Instructor's Manual is Appendix IV associated with Exercise 61A. This contains computer programs and dichotomous keys to be used in the identification of an unknown. Instructors may request the Instructor's Manual and computer diskettes from the publisher.

Acknowledgement. The authors wish to thank Dr. Jon Y. Takemoto, Dr. D. Andy Anderson and Dr. John J. Skujins for permission to use procedures they developed, and Dr. Reed P. Warren for reading parts of the manuscript.

We would like to thank the publisher, Stuart Hoffman, for his help and encouragement and especially his patience.

Frederick J. Post
Susan G. Kelley

INTRODUCTION

Within each of the subject areas of this manual a number of interesting and informative techniques are provided, all of them with relevance to everyday life. First you are introduced to microscopy and to the vast range of the microbial world. Then, and perhaps the most important feature for the beginning student, aseptic technique is introduced. Many of the following exercises provide a continuing opportunity to practice and master aseptic technique. One must always be prepared to recognize the sources of contamination when handling cultures. Once contaminated, **no** results are reliable. One important feature of aseptic technique is laboratory safety. Not only do you wish to prevent contamination of yourself and your cultures but you must prevent contamination of your work environment, the air, and your colleagues. For this reason a number of safety precautions are provided on the pages to follow which should be adhered to rigorously. Mouth pipetting is specifically prohibited. Wives, children, and non-class members should be prohibited from the laboratories for their own safety. Most of the organisms called for in this manual are not hazards but keep in mind that almost any bacterium can cause disease if the dose is large enough and given an opportune site.

One thing the beginning microbiologist usually has trouble with is realizing how small many of these microbes appear, especially the bacteria, even with the aid of a powerful microscope. Students often cannot "see" the bacteria on a slide because they don't "think small." Minor changes or differences in color, shape, density of growth, and colony size, among others are often very important in studying microbes. Development of the ability to see detail often overlooked by others is a requirement for microbiologists.

The authors hope that you have a pleasurable as well as a learning experience in using these exercises.

LABORATORY SAFETY

GENERAL REQUIREMENTS

1. All materials and clothes other than laboratory manual and notebook are to be kept off and away from the bench.

2. Wear a lab coat or apron. Dyes and other materials CANNOT be removed from clothing.

3. Read each exercise over carefully BEFORE the period so that you know what is to be done and the basic principles involved.

4. Do not begin work until a brief introduction is given by the laboratory instructor. Good laboratory technique hinges on knowing what you are to do. A good policy is to take notes on procedures, modifications, and principles in your lab manual.

REGULATIONS

1. Sponge off the bench top with the disinfectant solution provided both BEFORE the class starts and AFTER you have finished for the day. Use the same solution to rinse your hands after washing them with soap and water.

2. Mouth pipetting is **NOT** permitted.

3. On every table will be found pipet holders containing disinfectant. Please keep them clean. They are for dirty pipets ONLY.

4. Keep extraneous materials off the desk top and put all materials away at the end of the day.

5. Use waste baskets or other provided containers.

6. Discard glass in trays and glass test tubes in baskets. DO NOT mix glass and plastics. Plastics, cotton swabs, and other disposables are placed in autoclave bags. If appropriate trays, baskets, or bags are not available, see your instructor. DO NOT leave tubes or plates simply lying about.

7. Remove marks from all glassware with xylene available for this purpose.

8. Because the organisms used in this class are potentially pathogenic, aseptic technique is important. Develop proper habits at the beginning. Keep hands and other objects away from your mouth. DO NOT lick labels, NO eating, NO drinking, and NO smoking in the laboratory.

9. Report all accidents such as cuts, burns or spilled cultures to your instructor *immediately*. Students with long hair should be especially cautious around the Bunsen burners.

10. Microscopes should be put away with the low power down and no oil on the lenses. If these are not in proper condition when you take them out, let your instructor know.

11. Media removed from the supply baskets should NOT be returned to the supply baskets under any circumstances.

LABORATORY SAFETY

GENERAL REQUIREMENTS

1. All materials and clothes other than laboratory manual and notebook are to be kept off and away from the bench.

2. Wear a lab coat or apron. Dyes and other materials CANNOT be removed from clothing.

3. Read each exercise over carefully BEFORE the period so that you know what is to be done and the basic principles involved.

4. Do not begin work until a brief introduction is given by the laboratory instructor. Good laboratory technique hinges on knowing what you are to do. A good policy is to take notes on procedures, modifications, and principles in your lab manual.

REGULATIONS

1. Sponge off the bench top with the disinfectant solution provided both BEFORE the class starts and AFTER you have finished for the day. Use the same solution to rinse your hands after washing them with soap and water.

2. Mouth pipetting is **NOT** permitted.

3. On every table will be found pipet holders containing disinfectant. Please keep them clean. They are for dirty pipets ONLY.

4. Keep extraneous materials off the desk top and put all materials away at the end of the day.

5. Use waste baskets or other provided containers.

6. Discard glass in trays and glass test tubes in baskets. DO NOT mix glass and plastics. Plastics, cotton swabs, and other disposables are placed in autoclave bags. If appropriate trays, baskets, or bags are not available, see your instructor. DO NOT leave tubes or plates simply lying about.

7. Remove marks from all glassware with xylene available for this purpose.

8. Because the organisms used in this class are potentially pathogenic, aseptic technique is important. Develop proper habits at the beginning. Keep hands and other objects away from your mouth. DO NOT lick labels, NO eating, NO drinking, and NO smoking in the laboratory.

9. Report all accidents such as cuts, burns or spilled cultures to your instructor *immediately*. Students with long hair should be especially cautious around the Bunsen burners.

10. Microscopes should be put away with the low power down and no oil on the lenses. If these are not in proper condition when you take them out, let your instructor know.

11. Media removed from the supply baskets should NOT be returned to the supply baskets under any circumstances.

I, the undersigned, have read and agree to observe and abide by the above requirements and regulations.

_____   _____
Student Signature   *Date*

UNIT *I*

Microscopy

Since the first observation of microbes by van Leeuwenhoek about 1680, the microscope has assumed a central role in microbiology. A current definition of a microbe is that a microscope must be used to see the entire organism. Some multicellular animals are included in microbiology, because the microscope is the major tool to visualize them (e.g., helminths). This section is intended to introduce the student to a minimum of optics and to the care and handling of the microscope.

1   Care and Use of the Microscope

OBJECTIVES

The student will be able to:

1. identify the parts and respective functions of the microscope.

2. define the terms *total magnification*, *resolving power*, *working distance*, and *numerical aperture*.

3. describe the various features of the microscope.

4. properly handle and care for the microscope.

5. focus the microscope properly. (In conjunction with Exercises 2 and/or 3)

Microbiology holds as one of its principle unifying bases the need of a microscope to observe the organisms involved. There are many types of microscopes: bright field, phase contrast, interference, electron, and others differing in manner of construction and details of operation. Certain principles underly all microscopes, however.

MAGNIFICATION results from the use of one or more lenses. In a compound microscope, the objective lens nearest the object magnifies producing a real image. The eyepiece or ocular lens magnifies the real image producing a virtual image seen by the eye. The magnification of a lens is usually expressed in diameters of apparent increase in size or power: 10X is a ten times increase in size or 10 power. Microscopes generally consist of at least three objective lenses: a low power objective of about 10X, a high power objective of about 40X and an oil immersion lens of about 100X (Figure 1-1). The actual lens magnification depends on the type of microscope and the manufacturer. The total magnification of the microscope is the product of the magnification of the objective and the magnification of the eyepiece.

NUMERICAL APERTURE relates to the resolving power of the lens. The maximum amount of light entering a lens is a function of the lowest index of refraction of the materials between the object and the lens and is expressed as:

$$NA = i \sin\theta$$

where i is the index of refraction between the object and the lens, and θ is the angle between the extreme ray of the axial bundle and the axis of the light entering the objective, i.e. 1/2 the angle of light entering the lens (Figure 1-2). The greater the numerical aperture, the greater the resolving power of the microscope. The index of refraction for air is 1.0. In order to increase the light gathering ability of the lens, something with an index of refraction greater than 1.0 must be placed between the object and the lens. Immersion oil serves this purpose having an index of refraction nearly identical with the glass of the lens, about 1.56 (Figure 1-3).

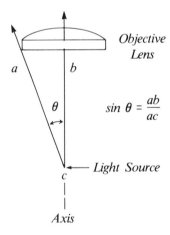

Figure 1-2. sin θ

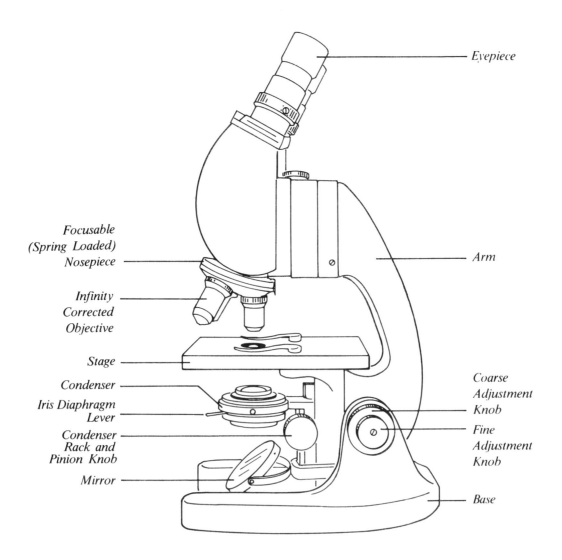

Eyepiece

Arm

Focusable
(Spring Loaded)
Nosepiece

Infinity
Corrected
Objective

Stage

Condenser

Iris Diaphragm
Lever

Condenser
Rack and
Pinion Knob

Mirror

Coarse
Adjustment
Knob

Fine
Adjustment
Knob

Base

Figure 1-1. Compound light microscope

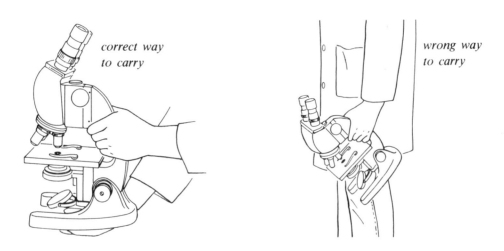

correct way
to carry

wrong way
to carry

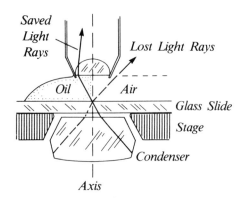

Figure 1-3. Effect of oil on light gathering in a lens

RESOLVING POWER is the ability of a lens or a microscope to distinguish between two closely adjacent points. The theoretical resolving power of a microscope is rarely achieved due to lens abberations and the fact that extraordinary performance on the microscope by the user is required. The resolving power is a function of the wavelength of light used and the numerical aperture of the lens.

Resolving power can be calculated as follows:

$$d = \frac{\text{wavelength}}{\text{NA of objective + NA of condenser}}$$

where d = diameter of the smallest observable object (μm), wavelength of light (μm), NA = numerical aperture (NA is unitless) and results from the use of an objective and a condenser below the stage to collect oblique light to illuminate the specimen. If the condenser NA is unknown, two times the NA of the objective is used.

The resolution should be better as wavelength decreases but is limited by several factors. The human eye is most sensitive to green light and "sees" best at about 500 nm. Green or blue green filters are often used to aid in this. Photography works best at ultraviolet wavelengths and special lenses are used. For optimum resolving power, in addition to an expert microscopist, oil must be interposed between the condenser and the bottom of the slide. This is not usually done in the teaching laboratory.

WORKING DISTANCE is the space between the objective and the specimen when the latter is in focus (Figure 1-3 and 2-1). The higher the magnification, the smaller or the shorter the working distance, and generally speaking, the greater the amount of light required to see the specimen. The diaphragm of the condenser should be almost completely open when using the oil immersion lens. A microscope is **parfocal** when objectives can be exchanged in position requiring only minor adjustments.

Five types of microscopes are widely used in microbiology today: bright field, dark field, phase contrast, interference, and epiluminescence. The bright field microscope is the most widely used usually with stained preparations and is illustrated above. Dark field observation is achieved by attaching an annular ring below the condenser on a bright field microscope (or by using a special condenser). The only light entering the objective is that striking the object on the slide (Figure 1-4). If there is no object, no light enters the objective. This type of microscopy is widely used to examine specimens for spirochetes which are difficult to see with the bright field microscope.

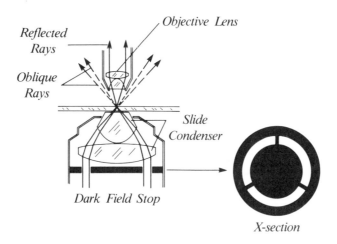

Figure 1-4. Dark field optics

Phase contrast microscopes (Figure 1-5) are widely used to view specimens by increasing the contrast between the object (or subcellular components) and the background. Live objects do not absorb light but delay it about 1/4 wavelength. Light waves delayed by 1/2 wavelength cancel undelayed light from the same light source. This cancellation creates a darkened place in the image that the eye sees. This is accomplished by the use of an annular diaphragm below the condenser and a phase plate cemented in the objective. Without a specimen on the stage, all the light is focused to pass through the thin part of the phase plate. When a specimen is present, image forming light is directed through the thick part of the phase plate and the remaining light through the thin part. The details

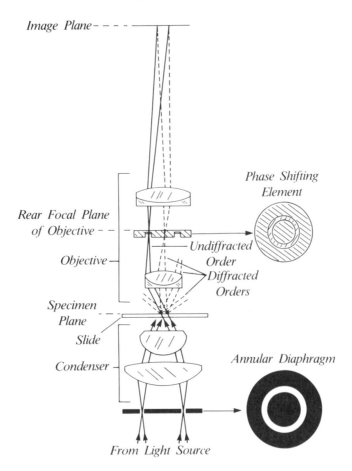

Figure 1-5. Phase contrast

of the specimen delay the wavelength by 1/4 and the thick part by another 1/4. When the image forming light mixes with light from the thin part of the phase ring, it creates a darker image allowing transparent detail to be seen. Unfortunately a halo is also created around the outside of the object image which sometimes interferes with seeing the object. Interference contrast is similar to phase contrast except that a polarizer and a Wollaston prism are used below the condenser to create two light paths, one through the specimen and the other through the background which are then recombined to interfere with one another, thus enhancing contrast without the halos common in phase contrast.

Epiluminecence microscopy is a form of bright field microscopy in which light passes down through the objective, strikes the object and returns upward through the objective again (Figure 1-6).

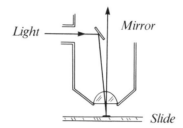

Figure 1-6. Epiluminescence microscope

This type of system is widely used with fluorescence observation in which ultraviolet light causes an object to fluoresce in the visible range with the light returning to the eyes.

Each lens has letters or numbers giving some information about the lens. The letters often refer to the use of the lens. Ph means phase, Fl means fluorescence, Plan means a flat field of view, Achrom means color corrected (achromatic), etc. The number followed by X is the magnification. Sometimes there is no X but a / followed by the numerical aperture, a number between 0 and 1.6. Some older lenses include the focal length, a number followed by mm. Newer lenses do not include this feature.

MATERIALS (per person)

1. Microscope
2. Immersion oil
3. Lens paper

PROCEDURE AND OBSERVATIONS (1 day)

Note: This exercise is intended to be accompanied by Exercises 2 and/or 3 for focusing instruction.

1. A microscope will be assigned to you for use in class. You should use *only* the assigned microscope and its proper care is your responsibility. If you find it improperly stored, with oil on the lens, or a lamp burned out, report it immediately to your instructor. Do not use any other microscope without your instructor's approval.

2. Grasp the microscope by the arm (Figure 1-1) with one hand. Place the other hand under the base and return to your bench. Carry the microscope upright being very careful not to tip the body tube allowing the eyepiece to fall out. Place the microscope on the bench and identify each part using Figure 1-1 as a guide. Study the introduction to this exercise and identify the symbols on the lenses. Since variations are common among manufacturers, your instructor may provide additional information about the symbols or the microscope.

3. Proceed to Exercises 2 and/or 3 for **focusing** of the microscope. These exercises can be done independently if desired.

4. When returning the microscope to its storage place, make sure all oil has been removed from the lenses. Turn the low power objective down. Make sure the dust cover is in place, if required.

5. After completing your study of the microscope, answer the questions and submit them to your instructor.

PRECAUTIONS

1. Clean the lenses only with the special paper provided. Clean the eyepiece lens occasionally as eyelashes leave an oily film.

2. Always remove the slide and clean the lenses when finished.

3. Clean the stage and condenser if oily. Keep clean.

4. Use two hands when carrying the microscope. One hand grasps the microscope arm, the other hand is under the base. Do *not* tilt the microscope when carrying it.

5. Do *not* force parts. Call your instructor if a problem arises.

6. Always raise the objective (or lower the stage) when focusing so that the lens and slide are moving apart.

7. Store your microscope with the *low* power objective *down* and *no* oil on lenses or stage.

THOUGHT QUESTIONS

1. Define working distance.

2. How does oil help in viewing an object? Make a diagram.

3. Would a microscope using electrons instead of light follow the same principles as the light microscope? X-rays? Protons?

Name _____ Date _____ Grade _____

1. Care and Use of the Microscope

QUESTIONS

A. True or False Statements: Circle the correct response.

T (F) 1. When swinging the oil immersion into position after using high-dry, one must raise the objective a little first to avoid damaging the oil immersion lens.

(T) F 2. A lens is in sharp focus on an object. If an adjacent lens is parfocal, it is in approximate focus when it is swung into position over the object.

T (F) 3. The size of the microscopic field remains constant regardless of the magnification of the objective you are using.

(T) F 4. Magnification at eyepoint (i.e., total magnification) equals the magnification of the objective multiplied by the magnification of the ocular.

T (F) 5. The microscope should be stored with the oil immersion lens in the down position.

(T) F 6. Once you have achieved an image, you should move the parts that control the light striking the object as little as possible.

B. Multiple Choice: Select the best answer for the following statements.

___a___ 7. If the total magnification with a 45X high-dry objective is 225X, what would be the magnification of the ocular?

    a. 5X
    b. 10X
    c. 12X
    d. 15X

_____ 8. The resolution of a microscope is increased by:

    a. using a shorter wavelength of light
    b. decreasing the amount of light emerging from the diaphragm
    c. using a condenser with low numerical aperture
    d. removing the condenser from the microscope

C. Short Answer:

_____ 9. Given: Blue light of wavelength 400 nm, a condenser, and an objective with a numerical aperture of 1.2. What is the smallest resolvable object in μm diameter seen with such a microscope? Show work.

$$d = \frac{\lambda}{NA_o + NA_c} = \frac{400\,nm}{1.2\,(2)} = \frac{400\,nm}{2.4}$$

$$d =$$

_____ 10. How does oil help in viewing an object? Answer by making a diagram in the space below.

C. **Matching:** Match the parts of the microscope with their functions.

___b___ 11. Ocular	a.	Opens and closes with a lever controlling the amount of light striking the object
___g___ 12. Revolving nosepiece	b.	A series of lenses that usually magnify 10 times
___e___ 13. Objective	c.	Condenses light waves into a cone, thereby preventing escape of light rays; raised and lowered to control amount of light striking object
___a___ 14. Diaphragm	d.	Raised and lowered in focusing some microscopes
___c___ 15. Condenser	e.	The lens closest to the object
___i___ 16. Mechanical stage	f.	Supports upper portion of microscope
___j___ 17. Base	g.	Rotates to change from one objective to another
___f___ 18. Arm	h.	Moves stage or body tube up and down rapidly for purposes of approximate focusing
___h___ 19. Coarse adjustment	i.	Allows the slide to be moved
___k___ 20. Fine adjustment	j.	Supports entire microscope
___d___ 21. Body tube	k.	Moves stage or body tube up and down very slowly for purposes of definitive focusing

D. **Completion:**

22–30. Complete the following table with regard to *your* microscope.

Objective	Objective Magnification	Ocular Magnification	Total Magnification
Low			
High-dry			
Oil immersion			

2   Calibration of the Microscope (Focusing)

OBJECTIVES

The student will be able to:

1. measure the microscope field of view.

2. calculate the area of view on a slide in cm^2.

3. calibrate an eyepiece scale.

4. measure an object and express its dimensions and volume in μm and μm^3, respectively.

Many uses are made of microscopic measurements in microbiology. The **field size or area**, for example, is used in making direct microscopic counts of food, milk, yogurt (see Exercise 75), cultures, etc. Direct measurement of cells is necessary for determining dimensions, volume, and biomass. In order to make these determinations, the field diameter must be measured and an **ocular micrometer** calibrated. Several eyepiece scales can be used depending on the purpose: for example, oculars with a linear scale or Whipple eyepieces (with a grid). Their calibration is essentially the same. In this exercise the field diameter will be measured and a linear ocular micrometer calibrated.

MATERIALS (per person)

1. Microscope

2. Stage micrometer

3. Ocular fitted with a linear scale

PROCEDURE AND OBSERVATIONS (1 day)

A. **Field measurement.** Do not use the ocular micrometer for this part.

1. Obtain a stage micrometer slide and record the division units and other pertinent microscope data on the results form.

2. Place the slide on the microscope stage coverslip up.

3. **Center** the coverslip over the light hole in the stage as carefully as possible.

4. **Close the diaphragm** about 3/4 and **lower** the low power objective until it cannot be lowered further.

5. Slowly raise the objective (or lower the stage with some microscopes) using the **coarse adjustment** until the scale comes into view.

6. Bring the scale into sharp focus with the **fine adjustment. Lower the condenser** and **readjust the diaphragm** until the scale is sharp and clear. With the low power the condenser will be well down and the diaphragm nearly closed as depicted in Figure 2-1.

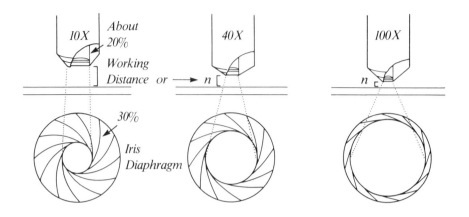

Figure 2-1. Approximate diaphragm openings

7.   Locate the micrometer scale. It should look like Figure 2-2.

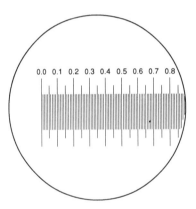

Figure 2-2. Initial appearance of stage scale

8.   Move the stage so that the scale is across the center of the field of view (white circle of light) so that the left margin of the field just touches one of the scale lines as in Figure 2-3.

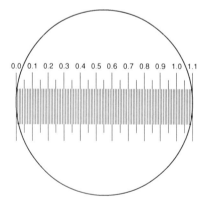

Figure 2-3. Stage scale adjusted to 0.0 on left side of the field

Count the number of divisions across the diameter of the field to the nearest half of a division. In Figure 2-3, each division is 0.01 mm and whole scale (as seen here) is 1.1 mm long. The field in Figure 2-3 measures 1.095 mm. Record the measurement in item three on the Results and Observations form.

9. With the scale across the *exact* center of the field, turn to the **high dry objective. Open the diaphragm** about 3/4 of the way (Figure 2-1) and **raise the condenser** until it is 1-2 cm below the stage. Focus carefully with the **fine adjustment**. Locate the scale across the center of the field as before and estimate the diameter in mm to the third decimal place, for example, 0.013 mm (13 µm). Record the figure in item 3 on the Results and Observations form.

10. Place the scale across the *exact* center of the field and focus carefully. Rotate the nosepiece halfway to the oil lens and place a drop of immersion oil on the center of the slide coverslip. Rotate the oil immersion into place. If the lens is not parfocal, it will touch the coverslip — Stop and see your instructor. Otherwise proceed.

11. **Raise the condenser** to full upright position and open the diaphragm all the way (Figure 2-1).

12. Locate the scale and focus, adjusting the diaphragm for the best image. Scale markings will appear very thick at this magnification. Move the scale so that the left side of the field just touches the right *or* left side of one of the scale lines (Figure 2-4).

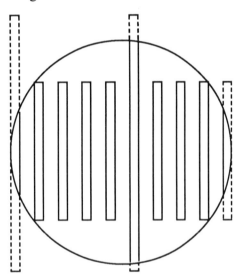

Figure 2-4. Appearance of stage scale under oil immersion

Count the number of marks across the field estimating to the third decimal place, 0.094 in Figure 2-4. Note that the 0.01 mm measurement begins or ends on the *same* side of a line as you positioned the left side of the field. Record the number of mm in item 3 of the Results and Observations form.

13. Convert the measured field data to mm^2 as indicated in the Results and Observations section.

B. **Ocular micrometer calibration**

1. Exchange your standard eyepiece for one with an ocular micrometer in it. Record the eyepiece number on the Results and Observations form. Since lenses and microscopes vary, always use the same eyepiece with your microscope.

2. Since oil is already on the slide from the field measurement, calibrate the oil immersion lens first.

3. Move the stage scale so that the zero mark on the left of the eyepiece scale just touches the left *or* right side of one of the stage scale marks (Figure 2-5).

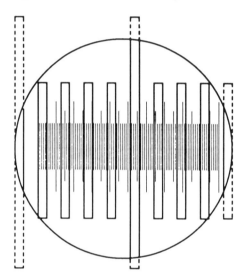

Figure 2-5. Ocular and stage scales

4. Move your attention to the right-most mark on the eyepiece scale (10 in Figure 2-5). If that does not coincide with the *same* side (right or left) of a stage mark as the zero line, go left to the *first* eyepiece line which *does* coincide with the same side of a stage line. Figure 2-5 shows 0.070 stage line coincides with 90 eyepiece lines.

Note: It is important to use as many eyepiece scale lines as possible in this calculation.

5. Record the number of eyepiece marks intercepted and the number of mm on the stage in item 4 on the Results and Observations form. Convert the mm to μm, then divide the number of μm by the number of eyepiece units. The result is the number of μm per eyepiece unit using the oil immersion lens. The example in Figure 2-5 is $70/90 = 0.78\,\mu$m per eyepiece unit. If your value is not in the range of 0.6 to 2.0 μm per eyepiece unit for a 1000X magnifying microscope system, check with your instructor.

6. Clean the oil from the slide and from the oil immersion lens.

7. Repeat the procedure for the high dry and the low power lenses recording the data in item 4 of the report form. This may be omitted if your instructor so desires.

THOUGHT QUESTION

1. Why can't a millimeter rule be used directly in the eyepiece instead of using the procedure of this exercise?

Name _____ Date _____ Grade _____

2. Calibration of the Microscope

RESULTS AND OBSERVATIONS

1. Scale data from the stage micrometer label _____

2. Magnification data:

    eyepiece _____ X

    low power objective _____ X   total _____ X

    high dry objective _____ X   total _____ X

    oil immersion _____ X   total _____ X

3. Field measurements:

	diameter	radius	area
low power	_____ mm,	_____ mm,	$r^2 \times 3.14 =$ _____ mm^2
high dry	_____ mm,	_____ mm,	$r^2 \times 3.14 =$ _____ mm^2
oil immersion	_____ mm,	_____ mm,	$r^2 \times 3.14 =$ _____ mm^2

4. Ocular micrometer calibration:

    eyepiece identification number _____

	stage units intercepted	eyepiece units intercepted	eyepiece μm/division
low power	_____ mm or _____ μm	_____	_____
high dry	_____ mm or _____ μm	_____	_____
oil immersion	_____ mm or _____ μm	_____	_____

QUESTIONS

Completion:

1. Fifteen units of an eyepiece micrometer intercepted 0.02 mm (2 divisions) of the stage scale. Each eyepiece division is _____ μm.

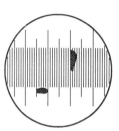

2. The yeast cell (upper irregular cell in the diagram) measures _____ μm wide using the scale from question 1.

3. The rod (lower left cell in the diagram) measures _____ μm long using the scale from question 1.

4. A slide was placed in a stream and removed after 3 days. After staining, it was observed under the microscope using the oil immersion lens. 95 bacteria were counted in one field. If the field diameter is 70 μm, the count on the slide surface is _____ bacteria per cm^2 (round to two significant figures).

5. If a photograph was taken through the microscope of a cell measuring 1.3 μm long and the photograph image was 13 mm long, what is the magnification of the photographic image? _____ X

UNIT *II*

Survey of the Microbial World

The world of microbes is vast, made up of prokaryotic and eukaryotic organisms. A wide range of sizes from viruses (not really cells) to fairly large structures seen with the naked eye. Most are single cells, but a few of the larger forms are multicellular. The fascinating array of these organisms includes free-living forms, saprophytes, parasites, pathogens, and symbionts, all playing major roles in the biosphere. This section will introduce the student to a few representatives of this most interesting group.

Bacteria. These are the smallest of the cells, all prokaryotic and found universally in the biosphere. Important as decomposers and nutrient cyclers. A few are pathogenic.

Cyanobacteria. These photoautotrophic prokaryotes are important oxygen producers and nitrogen fixers.

Algae. Eukaryotic photoautotrophic oxygen producers rivaled in biomass only by the plants.

Protozoa. Eukaryotic unicellular organisms feeding on bacteria and other materials. A few are pathogens.

Fungi. Eukaryotic decomposers found universally in soils and foods and are important antibiotic producers. A few are pathogens.

Helminths. Multicellular eukaryotes usually classified with the animals. Many cause important human and animal diseases (e.g., schistosomiasis).

3 Bacteria (Focusing)

OBJECTIVES

The student will be able to:

1. name some of the morphological forms of bacteria.

2. identify the various form names of the cocci.

2. name the genera of five morphological forms of bacteria.

The **eubacteria** (or bacteria) and the cyanobacteria are the **prokaryotic** cell types among the microbes. The bacteria are the smallest cell types averaging less than one micrometer in diameter. The cyanobacteria average slightly larger. Morphologically the bacteria are fairly limited in types (Figures 3-1, 3-2) and classification is only partially based on shape. The cyanobacteria are much more varied. Extensive branching occurs in morphologically more advanced forms of both groups. The cyanobacteria also contain chlorophyll *a* (only) and combined with accessory pigments often colors the cells a green, blue green or brown. The color may be seen in larger forms under the microscope. Chlorophyll *a* does not occur in the bacteria; it is replaced by bacteriochlorophylls of several varieties. Although colonies are often colored, pigments in bacteria cannot be seen in cells under the microscope.

This exercise is intended to show only a few of the many morphological forms of bacteria occurring in nature. It also provides an opportunity to practice use of the microscope as described in Exercises 1 and 2. It should be noted that few if any intracellular structures can be seen.

Many bacteria are motile with flagella, others are nonmotile. Some bacteria exhibit motility of a gliding type, also found among the cyanobacteria. Gliding occurs **only** when a cell or filament is in contact with a surface, for example, a coverslip or slide.

MATERIALS (per person)

1. Prepared slides of bacteria and a yeast

   Bacillus subtilis
   Proteus vulgaris
   Staphylococcus aureus
   Streptococcus pyogenes
   Spirillum sp.
   Saccharomyces cerevisiae

2. Microscope

3. Immersion oil

4. Lens paper

Figure 3-1.

PROCEDURE AND OBSERVATIONS (1 day)

1. Place the prepared slide on the stage, specimen side **up**.

2. **Center** the specimen over the light hole in the stage as carefully as possible.

3. **Lower the condenser** about 3/4 of the way to the stop and **close the diaphragm** nearly completely (Figure 2-1). **Lower the low power objective** over the specimen until it cannot be lowered further.

4. Look through the microscope looking for colored material indicating stained cells. Focus carefully **using the fine adjustment** *only*. Adjust the condenser and diaphragm if necessary. After centering the specimen (note that no details can be seen, only color), move your eyes to the level of the stage and while looking from the side rotate the **high power** objective over the specimen until it clicks into place. **Raise the condenser** until it is about 2 cm below the stage. **Open the diaphragm** 1/2 to 3/4 of the way (Figure 2-1).

5. Again, look through the microscope focusing with the **fine adjustment** *only*. Adjust the condenser level and diaphragm as needed. Note, at least with the bacteria, only a little more detail can be seen. Center very carefully. Rotate the **oil immersion lens** about half way and place a drop of immersion oil on the specimen over the center of the light path. Then, with your eyes again at the level of the stage, rotate the oil lens into the immersion oil. If there is any resistance, stop immediately and determine why. Most lenses are parfocal so it may mean a problem has arisen. Ask your instructor for help if the cause is not readily determined. **Completely open the diaphragm** (Figure 2-1) and **raise the condenser to full upright position**.

6. Look through the microscope focusing with the fine adjustment *only*. The slide may have to be moved a little to bring cells into the field of view. Adjust the diaphragm opening slightly, if necessary, focus carefully and make your observations.

7. Draw a few representative cells of each organism in a circle on the laboratory Results and Observations form. Note the color of the cells in the space provided. Make drawings of cells reasonably large. **Do not** simply make a pencil line. From Figure 3-1, give the morphological name for each bacterium.

In making drawings, use ink and/or colored pencils, preferably the latter.

THOUGHT QUESTIONS

1. Bacteria are about 0.5 μm^3. What factors might make this about the lower limit in size for a free-living cell?

2. These cells have been stained red or purple. Of what significance is the color?

3. What influence does the cell wall have on the morphology of bacteria?

Cocci (spherical shapes)

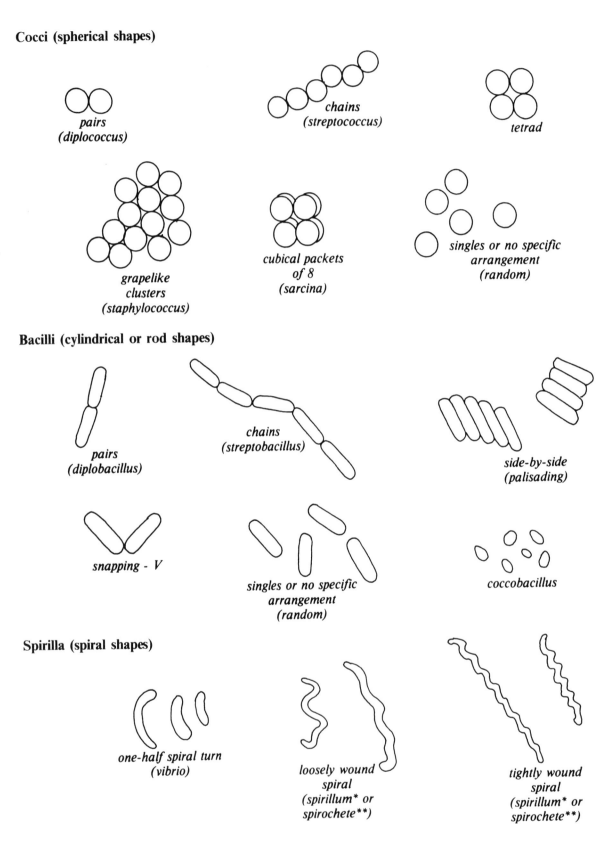

pairs
(diplococcus)

chains
(streptococcus)

tetrad

grapelike
clusters
(staphylococcus)

cubical packets
of 8
(sarcina)

singles or no specific
arrangement
(random)

Bacilli (cylindrical or rod shapes)

pairs
(diplobacillus)

chains
(streptobacillus)

side-by-side
(palisading)

snapping - V

singles or no specific
arrangement
(random)

coccobacillus

Spirilla (spiral shapes)

one-half spiral turn
(vibrio)

loosely wound
spiral
(spirillum* or
spirochete**)

tightly wound
spiral
(spirillum* or
spirochete**)

*spirillum - movement is rotational along the long axis
**spirochete - movement is a helical wave (corkscrew)

Figure 3-2. Bacterial shapes and arrangements (morphology)

Name _____ Date _____ Grade _____

3. Bacteria

RESULTS AND OBSERVATIONS

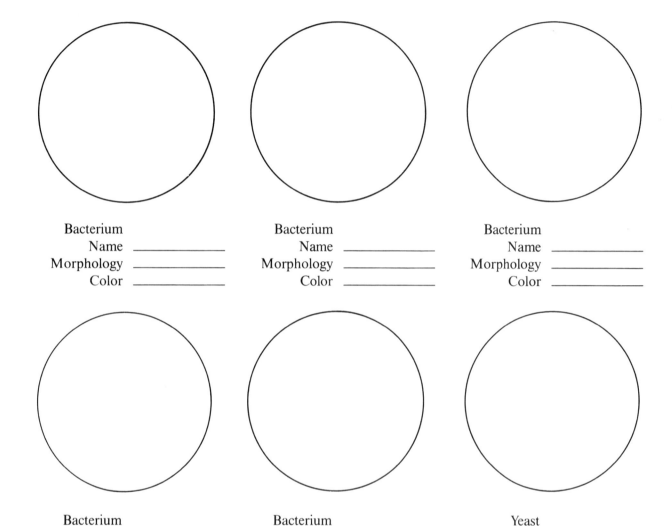

Bacterium
Name _____
Morphology _____
Color _____

Bacterium
Name _____
Morphology _____
Color _____

Bacterium
Name _____
Morphology _____
Color _____

Bacterium
Name _____
Morphology _____
Color _____

Bacterium
Name _____
Morphology _____
Color _____

Yeast
Name _____
Morphology _____

QUESTIONS

Completion:

1. Name one bacterium which is stained red _____ .

2. Name one bacterium which is stained purple _____ .

3. Give the morphological name for each of the following bacterial shapes:

   a. spheres irregularly clustered _____

   b. spheres in a chain _____

   c. spiral S shape _____

   d. one half a spiral turn _____

   e. cells dividing remaining side by side _____

   f. a cylinder shape _____

4. Name the five bacterial genus and species used in this exercise (check your spelling):

   _____

   _____

   _____

   _____

   _____

5. _____ is the fungus used in this exercise.

6. If you observe a microbe which is 2 μm long and 1 μm in diameter, what is its volume, in μm^3?
   _____ μm^3

4   Cyanobacteria

OBJECTIVES

The student will be able to:

1. name nine genera of cyanobacteria.

2. recognize the major morphological forms of the cyanobacteria studied.

3. recognize heterocysts, akinetes, sheaths, and trichomes, and describe the function of each.

The prokaryotic cyanobacteria were long known as the blue-green algae on the basis of photosynthesis using chlorophyll *a* with water as the electron donor and the subsequent production of oxygen as an end product. With increased understanding of the biology of prokaryotes and eukaryotes, it became clear that the cyanobacteria were prokaryotes and more closely related to the true bacteria (eubacteria) than to the eukaryotic algae. In recognition of this relationship, the term cyanobacteria (cyano Gr = dark blue) was coined and the entire group classified with the bacteria. Despite this, many refer to these organisms as blue-green algae.

The taxonomy of the cyanobacteria is subject to many of the same problems as the taxonomy of bacteria and is more and more turning to physiology and biochemistry as the primary tools of classification. The cyanobacteria are, generally speaking, larger and more complex morphologically than the eubacteria. Consequently, morphology is the chief method of classification and is the mainstay of identification by field biologists. A number of special morphological features are used in identification of this group. A few of them are used in the taxonomy of the filamentous eubacteria as well. These features and terms are:

Akinetes are special reproductive cells formed by some of the filamentous forms. They are often enlarged, thick walled, granular, and brown or yellow in color (Figure 4-1g and i).

Heterocysts are specialized, thick walled, clear or light green cells, where nitrogen fixation takes place. The location in the filament is a useful taxonomic character (Figure 4-1g and h).

Trichomes are filaments of cells contained within a sheath (Figure 4-1 several). Wide variation occurs in diameter, length, taper, and may show true branching or false branching.

Sheaths are materials of various types (glycocalyx) formed around individual cells, colonies, or filaments. It is similar to the capsule of bacteria. It may be thick and gelatinous (Figure 4-1j) or so thin as to be almost undetectable (Figure 4-1h). In some it becomes laminated similar to a tube and parallel to the filament (Figure 4-1d).

Granules are often observed inside. These may be storage compounds or gas vacuoles. The gas vacuoles are numerous, highly refractile, and fairly large. Storage products include cyanophycin (a polypeptide) and polyphosphate.

Phycobilins are accessory pigments associated with photosynthesis. Many of these are dark blue-green giving the group its name. Some are red or brown and as a result some species may be colors other than blue-green. These pigments are best seen in living cells with low magnification.

Gliding motility requires live cells to observe. Many filamentous and a few coccoid forms are able to move by a process of gliding but *only* if a part of the cell or trichome is touching a surface, e.g., the slide or coverslip.

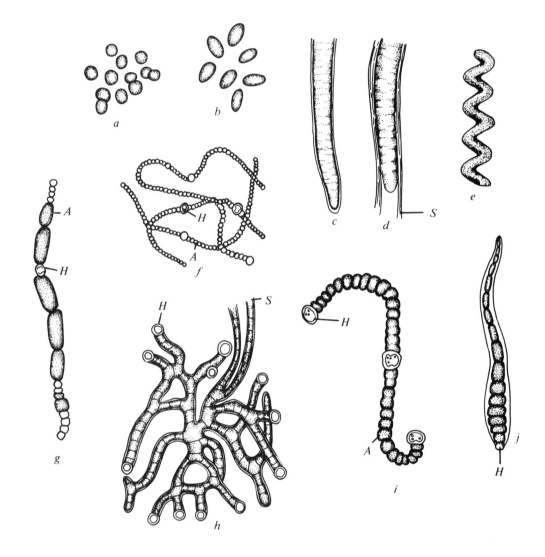

Figure 4-1. Representative cyanobacteria: a) *Aphanocapsa* sp. (X600); **b)** *Synechococcus* sp. (X1000);
c) *Oscillatoria rubescens* (X500); **d)** *Lyngbya majuscula* (X170); **e)** *Spirulina gigantea* (X750);
f) *Nostoc sphaericum* (X300); **g)** *Anabaena oscillaroides* (X400); **h)** *Mastigocoleus testarum* (X200);
i) *Nodularia sphaerocarpa* (X500); **j)** *Calethrix clavata* (X1000). A = akinete; H = heterocyst; S = sheath.
Adapted from G.E. Fogg et al. "Blue-Green Algae", Academic Press, NY, 1973.

Hormogonia are short pieces of trichomes or filaments which become detached and glide away eventually giving rise to a new filament. In some forms (*Oscillatoria*) the filament simply breaks up. These are usually seen only in mature or aged cultures.

Symbiotic forms are common among the cyanobacteria in lichens and ferns among others. The example used in this exercise is the fern *Azolla* widely used in the Orient for fertilizing rice paddies.

This exercise is intended to illustrate some of the characteristic sizes, shapes and special structures of this important group of microbes.

MATERIALS (per person)

1. Prepared slides and/or live cultures of

   Anabaena cells, heterocysts, akinetes
   Anabaena azolla symbiont in *Azolla* fern leaf
   Arthrospira spiral, many cells
   Gleocapsa sheath and colonies
   Lyngbya sheath, like *Oscillatoria*
   Microcystis coccoid single cells in slimy colony
   Nostoc filaments and heterocysts
   Oscillatoria filaments no sheath
   Rivularia tapered filaments with terminal heterocyst
   Spirulina spiral, unicellular

2. Microscope

3. Slides

4. Coverslips

5. Vaseline

6. Toothpicks

7. Calibrated ocular micrometer

PROCEDURE AND OBSERVATIONS (1 day)

A. Prepared slides

1. Use the same procedure for these prepared slides as with the prepared bacterial slides in Exercise 3. However, use the low power or high dry objectives in most cases. Use the objective with which you can see the most.

2. Make drawings of each of the slide preparations making note of the various special structures noted above. Use the Results and Observations section of the laboratory report form.

3. Measure the width and length (where possible) of cells or structures using the ocular micrometer calibrated in Exercise 2.

B. Live cultures (if available)

1. Prepare wet mounts as described for the yeasts (Part II) in Exercise 7.

2. Observe and make drawings on the report form of the structures described above. Be sure to see the color of cells and look for gliding motility. Gliding may take time to occur because cells must contact the glass surface before they can glide.

THOUGHT QUESTIONS

1. Name one genus *in addition* to the ones studied here which forms heterocysts.

2. If the tip of your organism glides across your high dry objective in 5 sec, how fast is it traveling in kilometers per hour? Obtain the field diameter from Exercise 2 data.

3. Cite some similarities and differences between the cyanobacteria and the true algae.

Name ——————————————————————— Date ——————————— Grade ———————————

4. Cyanobacteria

RESULTS AND OBSERVATIONS

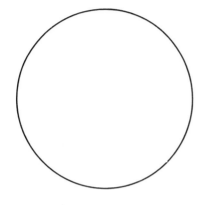 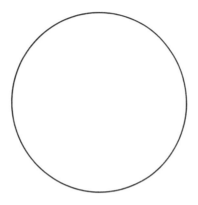 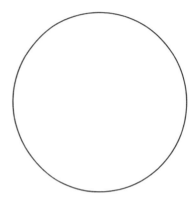

Name ——————————   Name ——————————   Name ——————————
Morphology ——————————   Morphology ——————————   Morphology ——————————

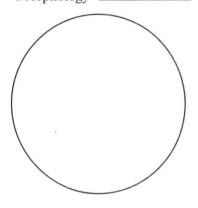 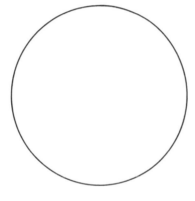 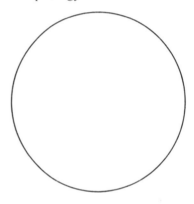

Name ——————————   Name ——————————   Name ——————————
Morphology ——————————   Morphology ——————————   Morphology ——————————

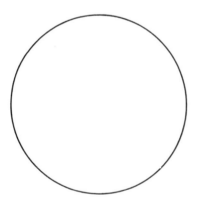 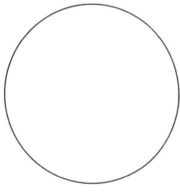

Name ——————————   Name ——————————   Name ——————————
Morphology ——————————   Morphology ——————————   Morphology ——————————

Name _____ Name _____ Name _____
Morphology _____ Morphology _____ Morphology _____

QUESTIONS

Completion:

1. From your observations of *Anabaena azolla*, the fern is used as a fertilizer because it

   _____ (two words). You know this because this cyanobacterium

   has _____.

2. A reproductive structure found in some of these organisms is called a _____ .

3. Name the nine genera of cyanobacteria used here:

   _____

   _____

   _____

4. The mucilage around a filament is called a _____ .

5. The only type of motility exhibited by the cyanobacteria is _____ .

6. The motility of cyanobacteria requires _____ for it to occur.

7. Another name for a filament is _____ .

8. These organisms contain chlorophyll *b* (yes or no) _____ .

5 Algae

OBJECTIVES

The student will be able to:

1. describe the meaning of the term "Protist."

2. explain the apparent overlap of classification of the motile photosynthetic protists.

3. describe the morphology of the major groups of algae.

4. name a genus representative of the euglenids, the diatoms, and the green algae.

The protozoa and the algae are **eukaryotic** microbes classified in a single group (except some green algae) called the Protists or Protoctista. The Fungi, Animalia, and Plantae make up the rest of the eukaryotic organisms. The close relationship between the protozoa and the algae is evident in the dual classification of the motile (and some nonmotile) photosynthetic (and some not) single celled organisms. In many cases two genus names are given to a single species, one in the protozoa and one in the algae classification. Fortunately, the species name is usually the same. The more "advanced" algae are clearly not protozoa and vice versa, and there is no problem of dual taxonomy.

The algae are photosynthetic eukaryotes possessing a membrane bound **chloroplast** (thus excluding the cyanobacteria previously called the blue-green algae). They are a diverse group of organisms ranging from unicells (motile or nonmotile) to very large multicellular plant-like organisms. All of them possess chlorophyll a and at least one other chlorophyll type b, c, or d contained in the chloroplast (Table 5-1). This is in marked contrast to the cyanobacteria which contain only chlorophyll a found throughout the cell. Algal cells may be motile by one or more flagella (a trait of the protozoan Mastigophora), exhibit gliding motility as in the diatoms, or are nonmotile. Many of the flagellated types possess a more or less prominent **red eyespot**.

Algae are important **primary producers** in fresh and marine waters, soil surfaces, symbioses (e.g., lichens), and a few special environments such as hot springs, saturated salt lakes, etc. They are important oxygen-generating organisms and constitute a significant portion of the plankton in water. As primary producers, they also serve as the start of the food chain for other organisms. A very simple classification used by aquatic biologists (Table 5-2) divides the algae into pigmented flagellates, nonmotile forms, and diatoms. This scheme is also used for the flagellated protozoa.

Algae and protozoa are best observed as live specimens, however, this presents a few problems: speed of movement and time. For examination of live specimens, especially if flagellates or ciliates are present, it is necessary to slow movement. This is done by adding a small amount of a viscous material to the slide preparation. A ring of **methycellulose** (10%) is made on the slide and a drop of the sample placed in the center. The methylcellulose diffuses into the sample after the coverslip is in place and slows the motile organisms sufficiently for study.

The second problem is the time required to make observations. A large number of samples may require days to complete. Preservatives may be used in such cases to fix the organisms for later observation. Most features remain intact in these agents. Several are recommended: a water-95% alcohol-formalin (6:3:1) solution is added in equal quantity to the sample; 1 ml of Lugol's iodine (60 g KI, 40 g I_2 per L) is added per 100 ml of sample and stored in the dark.

This exercise is intended to demonstrate a few of the many morphological forms of algae, parasitic and free living. As with the other organism groups in this section, specialized courses in phycology are usually available.

MATERIALS (per class)

1. Prepared slides[a] of a selection of protozoa and algae

    Synedra diatom (Chrysophyta)
    Spirogyra filamentous (Chlorophyta)
    Chlamydomonas (Chlorophyta-Mastigophora)
    Euglena (Euglenophyta-Mastigophora). Also with protozoa.
    Peridinium (Pyrrophyta-Mastigophora)
    Ochromonas two unequal flagella (Chrysophyta-Mastigophora)
    Chara multicellular (stonewort) (Chlorophyta)
    Mixed flagellates

    [a] Carolina Biological Supply Co.
    Other supply houses also have prepared slides.

2. Live cultures may be available. These will be selected by your instructor.

3. Pond or other sample with live algae and protozoa (seasonal)

4. Slides and coverslips if live cultures available

5. Methylcellulose, 10% in dropper bottle for live cultures

6. Calibrated ocular micrometers

PROCEDURE AND OBSERVATIONS (1 day)

Two procedures are presented here, one with prepared slides, the other with live preparations. The instructor may select one or the other, or some of both.

A. Prepared slides

1. Place the prepared slide on the microscope stage and focus as described in Exercise 3 using the low power.

2. Depending on the specimen, switch to the high power, focus and, if necessary, go to the oil immersion lens.

3. Make drawings and label on the report form in the space provided. Additional paper may be used if necessary.

4. Measure the specimens with the calibrated ocular.

B. Live specimens

1. Prepare wet mounts of each organism or the pond sample as described for the fungi in Exercise 7.

2. If the organisms are actively motile, place a thin ring of methylcellulose around the drop of specimen. In these preparations, oil immersion will not usually be useful.

3. Observe specimens under low power, high power, and oil immersion objectives as needed.

4. Make drawings on the report form and measure with the calibrated ocular.

THOUGHT QUESTIONS

1. What are the major differences between the algae and the cyanobacteria?

2. What are some of the properties of the diatoms? What role do they play in geology?

3. What are some differences in the photosynthetic process between the algae and eubacteria (NOT the cyanobacteria)?

Table 5-1. Major algal groups

Group Name	Pigment System Chlorophylls	Others	Cell Wall Composition	Reserve Material	I_2 Test
Brown algae Phaeophyta	*a, c*	carotenoids	cellulose and algin	lamarin and fats	−
Diatoms Chrysophyta	*a, c*	carotenoids	silica in diatoms	leucosin and oils	−
Dinoflagellates Pyrrophyta	*a, c*	carotenoids	starch and cellulose	starch and oils	−
Euglenids Euglenophyta	*a, b*		no wall (pellicle)	paramylum and fats	−
Green algae Chlorophyta	*a, b*		cellulose	starch	+
Red algae Rhodophyta	*a, +/−d*	phycobilins	cellulose	starch-like	−

Table 5-2. Comparison of three major groups of aquatic algae

Feature	Pigmented Flagellates **All Pyrrophyta All Euglenophyta All Chlorophyta and Chrysophyta with flagella**	Green Algae **Nonmotile Chlorophyta and Chrysophyta**	Diatoms **Bacillarophyceae**
Color	Green (brown)	Green	Brown, light green to yellow-green
Starch	Present or absent	Present	Absent
Motility	Flagella	Nonmotile	Gliding in many
Flagellum	Present	Absent	Absent
Cell wall	Thin or absent	Semi-rigid smooth or with spines	Very rigid with regular markings
"Eye" spot	Present	Absent	Absent

Name _____ Date _____ Grade _____

5. Algae

RESULTS AND OBSERVATIONS

1. Make drawings of the various organisms and preparations below. Use additional paper if necessary.

QUESTIONS

Completion:

1. The common name of those organisms with a silica cell wall is _____ .

2. A simple chemical test for starch in cells is the use of _____ .

3. The red algae have the accessory pigments _____ as do the prokaryotic _____ .

4. The most commonly found secondary chlorophyll among the algae would appear to be
    _____ .

5. The nucleus of the protozoa and algae, and the chloroplast of the algae are surrounded by a unit
    _____ .

6. Name a genus of: diatoms _____ , the euglenids _____ ,
    the dinoflagellates _____ the green algae _____ .

7. _____ is the chemical used to slow motility of algae and protozoa.

8. In which group of algae is gliding motility found? _____

9. A filamentous green alga is _____ .

10. An eyespot is commonly found in motile/nonmotile (cross out incorrect word) cells of the groups
    _____ , _____ , _____ , and _____ .

11. An important waste product of algal photosynthesis is _____ .

12. If chlorophyll were observed to be uniformly distributed in the cytoplasm, the organism would belong
    to the _____ .

13. Some algae are symbiotic with fungi in group known as _____ .

6   Protozoa

OBJECTIVES

The student will be able to:

1. describe the meaning of the term "Protist."
2. indicate which organisms overlap in classification of the motile photosynthetic protists.
3. name and describe the morphology of the major groups of protozoa.
4. name at least four human diseases caused by protozoa and to which groups they belong.
5. name a genus representative of the four protozoan groups.

As indicated in the introduction to the algae exercise, the protozoa are **eukaryotic** microbes placed in a single kingdom, the Protista, along with the algae. The motile flagellates are often classified as either algae or protozoa.

Protozoa are divided into four groups based on the method of motility. The **Mastigophora** are motile by means of one or more flagella (the algal flagellates), the **Sarcodina** by means of amoeboid movement, the **Ciliata** by means of shortened modified flagella called cilia; and the **Sporozoa** which are nonmotile (and entirely parasitic). Protozoa occupy almost all the habitats in which algae are found as well as many others where light is absent. Protozoa are considered the primary consumers, eating algae, bacteria and organic particles. Some are symbionts (e.g., cockroach and termite intestines), and a few are pathogens with one group entirely parasitic (Sporozoa) causing many human and animal diseases.

Protozoa and algae are best observed as live specimens. As with the algae, it is necessary to slow movement. This is done in the same manner as described for the algae by using methycellulose. The same preservatives used with algae also may be used for the protozoa.

This exercise is intended to demonstrate a few of the many morphological forms of parasitic and free-living protozoa. It may be done at the same time as Exercise 5. As with the other organism groups in this section, specialized courses in protozoology are usually available.

The prepared slides include four representatives of the many human and animal pathogens among the protozoa. **Malaria** is the most important, considered by some to be the world's most important infectious disease. There are four types caused by different species of *Plasmodium*. The most serious is *P. falciparum* which is often fatal and is now showing drug resistance. *P. vivax, P. ovale*, and *P. malariae* cause less severe infections. Mixed infections are not uncommon. Animal malaria is caused by other species. Malaria infection begins when infective *Anopheles* mosquitoes bite a human (Figure 6-1). **Sporozoites** in the saliva of the mosquito are injected into the bloodstream. These migrate to the liver invading parenchymal cells where they undergo schizogony forming **merozoites** which are released into the blood. These penetrate red blood cells undergoing further schizogony releasing more merozoites and repeating this process again and again. It is the rupture and release of the merozoites which produce the symptoms of malaria. The process is not continuous but cyclic resulting in periods free of symptoms followed by symptoms again. The period between these is in part a function of the parasite species and the feeding habits of the particular *Anopheles* species involved. Some of the merozoites undergo gametogenesis becoming **gametocytes** which are infectious to the mosquito. In the mosquito stomach, sperm and ova develop, fertilize each other forming oocysts on the stomach wall. Within the oocysts, sporozoites are formed. Upon rupture of the oocyst, the sporozoites migrate to the salivary glands, ready to begin another cycle. The sexual cycle takes place in the mosquito, the asexual cycle in humans. Diagnosis is made by observing red blood cells for ring forms, mature trophozoites, or gametes.

Trypanosoma gambiense causes **trypanosomiasis** or African sleeping sickness. It is transmitted by the bite of the tsetse fly and is often fatal. Several forms occur in cattle and wild animals with some transmissible to humans. American trypanosomiasis (Chagas' disease) is caused by a different species and is transmitted by triatomid (kissing) bugs.

Giardiasis (Figure 6-2) is the diarrheal disease caused by *Giardia lamblia*. This disease is associated with drinking untreated water in mountainous areas of the United States or failures in treatment of domestic supplies. The parasite infects a number of animals besides humans including beaver and possibly sheep and cattle.

Trichomonas vaginalis is a common cause of **vaginitis** in humans and occasionally causes a urethritis in males (Figure 6-3). It is a sexually transmitted disease.

An excellent reference for symptoms, occurrence, treatment and other aspects of these diseases is "The Control of Communicable Diseases in Man," 15th edition. A.S. Benenson, ed. American Public Health Association, Washington, D.C., 1990.

MATERIALS (per class)

1. Prepared slides[a] of a selection of protozoa and algae

   Euglena (Euglenophyta-Mastigophora)
   Giardia lamblia intestinal (Mastigophora)
   G. lamblia, cysts
   Trichomonas vaginalis vaginitis (Mastigophora)
   Trypanosoma gambiense (Mastigophora)
   Plasmodium falciparum (Sporozoa)
   Amoeba proteus (Sarcodina)
   Paramecium caudatum (Ciliata)
   Vorticella sp. (Ciliata)

   [a] Carolina Biological Supply Co.
   Other supply houses also have prepared slides.

2. Malaria life cycle chart (Carolina Bioreview Sheet No. 42-4170) and/or other illustrations

3. Live cultures may be available. These can be obtained from Carolina Biological Supply Co.

4. Pond or other sample with live algae and protozoa (seasonal)

5. Slides and coverslips if live cultures available

6. Methylcellulose, 10% in dropper bottle for live cultures

7. Calibrated ocular micrometer

PROCEDURE AND OBSERVATIONS (1 day)

Two procedures are presented here; one with prepared slides, the other with live preparations. The instructor may select one or the other, or some of both.

A. Prepared slides

    1. Place the prepared slide on the microscope stage and focus as described in Exercise 3 using the low power.

    2. Depending on the specimen, switch to the high power, focus and, if necessary, go to the oil immersion lens.

    3. Make and label drawings on the report form in the space provided. Additional paper may be used if necessary.

    4. It is usually difficult to find all the stages of the life cycle on the malaria slides (*Plasmodium* sp.). The Bioreview sheets or other aids supplied by the instructor should help in this.

    5. Measure the cells with calibrated oculars.

B. Live specimens

    1. Prepare wet mounts of each organism or the pond sample as described for the fungi in Exercise 7.

    2. If the organisms are actively motile, place a thin ring of methylcellulose around the drop of specimen. In these preparations, oil immersion will not usually be useful.

    3. Observe specimens under low power, high power, and oil immersion objectives as needed.

    4. Make drawings on the report form and measure with the calibrated ocular.

    5. Note that the photosynthetic flagellated protozoa also can be described using Tables 5-1 and 5-2.

THOUGHT QUESTIONS

    1. Diagram the life cycle of malaria.

    2. What is the relationship between the fever and malaria reproduction.

    3. Name several other protozoan diseases of humans and diagram the life cycle of each.

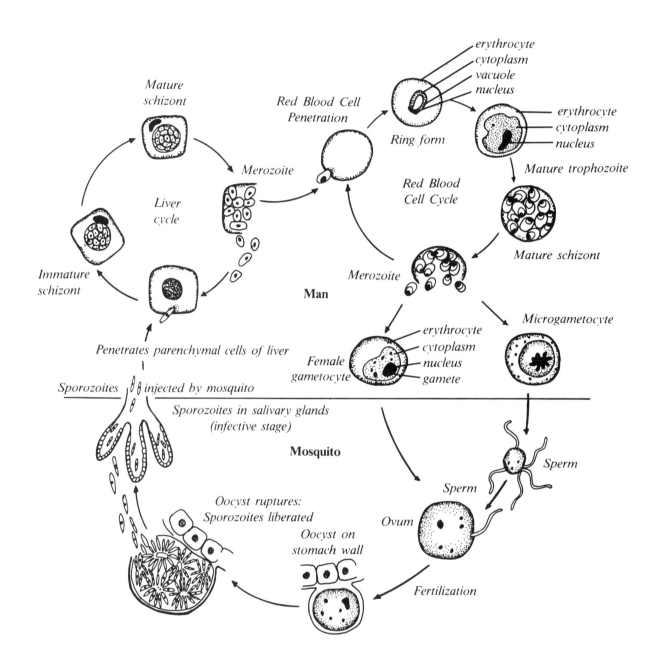

Figure 6-1. Life cycle of the malaria parasite and blood picture

LIFE CYCLE OF GIARDIA LAMBLIA

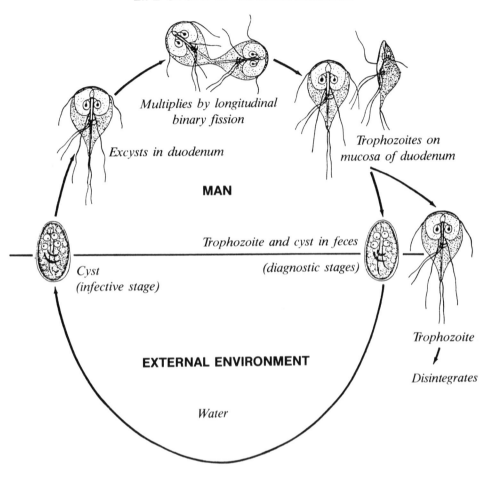

Multiplies by longitudinal binary fission

Excysts in duodenum

Trophozoites on mucosa of duodenum

MAN

Trophozoite and cyst in feces

(diagnostic stages)

Cyst (infective stage)

Trophozoite

Disintegrates

EXTERNAL ENVIRONMENT

Water

Figure 6-2. Life cycle of giardiasis

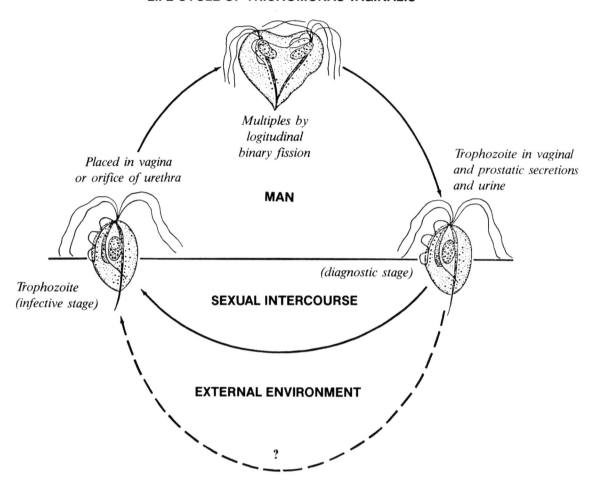

LIFE CYCLE OF TRICHOMONAS VAGINALIS

Multiples by logitudinal binary fission

Placed in vagina or orifice of urethra

Trophozoite in vaginal and prostatic secretions and urine

MAN

Trophozoite (infective stage)

(diagnostic stage)

SEXUAL INTERCOURSE

EXTERNAL ENVIRONMENT

?

Figure 6-3. Life cycle of trichomoniasis in humans

6. Protozoa

RESULTS AND OBSERVATIONS

1. With the aid of the diagrams below place a check mark next to each structural element as you observe it. You may not be able to see all of the structures in a particular specimen.

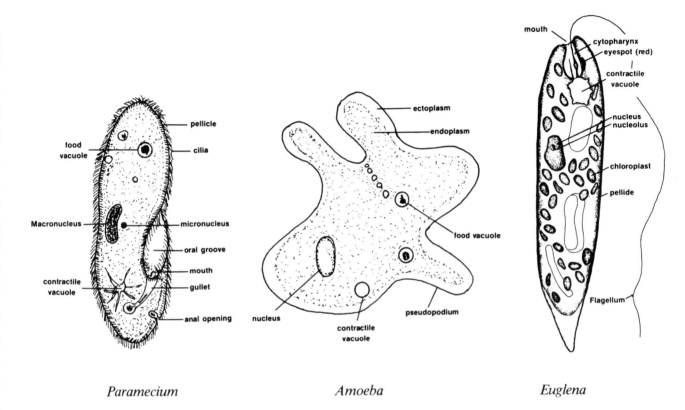

Paramecium   *Amoeba*   *Euglena*

2. Other microscopic observations

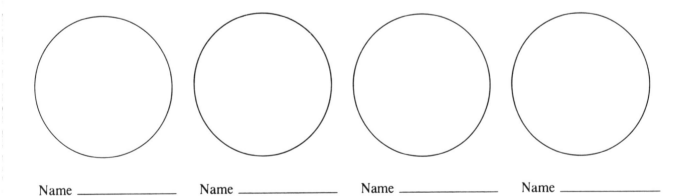

Name _____   Name _____   Name _____   Name _____

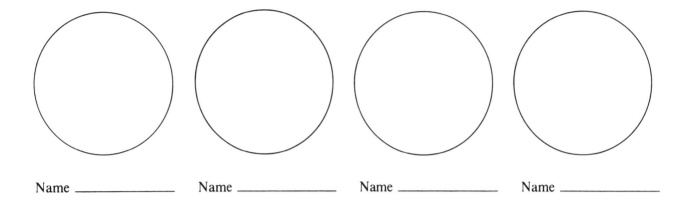

Name _____   Name _____   Name _____   Name _____

QUESTIONS

Completion:

1. You would expect to find the flagellated algae classified among the _____ as protozoa.

2. Name a parasite in the group Mastigophora _____ , Sarcodina _____ , Sporozoa _____ .

3. The chemical used to slow motility of algae and protozoa is _____ .

4. Which group of protozoa is entirely parasitic? _____

5. To what group does *Amoeba proteus* belong? _____

6. The malaria life cycle requires two hosts, man and a _____ of the genus _____ .

7. *Giardia lamblia* is an intestinal parasite causing diarrhea. It is transmitted to man in _____ .

8. *Trypanosoma gambiense* causes the human disease known as _____ .

9. A very common cause of vaginitis in the female or urethritis in the male is _____
_____ .

10. African sleeping sickness is caused by _____ .

11. The malaria parasite undergoes sexual/asexual (cross out the incorrect term) reproduction in humans.

12. Ring-form cells are usually human _____ cells (kind of cell).

13. Protozoa may be symbionts in _____ .

14. *Vorticella* belongs to the _____ (group name).

15. The vector of sleeping sickness is _____ .

7 Fungi

OBJECTIVES

The student will be able to:

1. prepare a slide culture of fungi.

2. make a wet mount for microscopic observation.

3. distinguish septate from nonseptate fungi.

4. recognize the microscopic appearance of fungi and their asexual spores.

5. differentiate yeasts from molds.

The fungi are a complex group of **eukaryotic** microbes ranging from the unicellular yeasts to the extensively mycelial molds. Some are able to form visible sexual fruiting structures variously called mushrooms or toadstools. The fungi are placed in the Kingdom Fungi in the five kingdom system of taxonomy. The fungi are important as contaminants in the laboratory, in creating new foods, in producing antibiotics and industrial chemicals, as pathogens, as a food, and in their own right.

The growth form of most fungi is a tubular cell called a **hypha** (pl. hyphae) which grows from the tip and may form many branches. This many-branched hypha (**mycelium**) can become large enough to be seen with the naked eye when it is often referred to as a mold. The term "mold" is not rigorously defined. One morphological characteristic dividing the fungi is whether or not the hyphae possess **septa** (cross walls) (Figure 7-1). The lower fungi (previously called the Phycomycetes) have no septa and the cytoplasm and nuclei migrate freely through the hyphae. This condition of free movement is called **coenocytic**. The other group has discernible septa across the hypha at intervals but these cross walls are not complete. A hole is present in the center of each septum allowing the coenocytic condition.

Fungi are classified on the basis of the type of sexual reproduction. If sexual spores are formed in a basidium, they are classified as **Basidiomycetes**. Typical representatives are the mushrooms and toadstools. If sexual spores are formed in a structure called an ascus, they are classified as **Ascomycetes**. Typical representatives are *Aspergillus* and *Penicillium*. Enclosed sexual spores of other types are classified among the lower fungi. Examples are *Rhizopus* (bread mold) and *Saprolegnia* (water mold). If no sexual stage has been observed, the organism is placed in the **Deuteromycetes** (or Fungi Imperfecti).

Although the hyphal form is common among the fungi, some exist only as single cells or at most as a pseudohypha a few cells long, possibly even exhibiting a little branching. These are known as the yeasts. Perhaps the best known is *Saccharomyces cerevisiae* (Ascomycetes), the bread, beer, and wine yeast. Many fungi have two morphological forms, a yeast-form under some conditions and a mycelial form under other conditions. Such fungi are called **dimorphic**. Some important human and animal pathogens are dimorphic.

Asexual spores are formed by most fungi and vary widely in morphology and mode of formation. Asexual spores of most lower fungi are enclosed, while the higher fungi form free asexual spores (Figure 7-2). Many aquatic lower fungal spores, both sexual and asexual, are motile with flagella indicating a close affinity with the flagellates of the protists. The asexual spores are often brightly pigmented giving the colony a characteristic color (e.g., red, green, blue, black, brown, etc.). A good example is the blue spores of *Penicillium roqueforti* found in blue or Roquefort cheese. As with the other organisms in this section, specialized courses in mycology are available. This exercise consists of two independent parts, one illustrating a method of growing filamentous forms, and the other, a wet mount technique for observing yeasts.

This exercise will introduce the student to the fungi and several methods for observing them. The instructor may choose to do all or only one or two of the three independent sections below.

PART I. GROWTH OF FUNGI IN A MOIST CHAMBER

MATERIALS (per person)

1. 1 sterile glass Petri plate with fitted filter paper, glass slide, and coverslip

2. A small amount of Sabouraud's glucose (or maltose) agar, sterile

3. 2 sterile Pasteur pipets with bulb

4. Vaspar, melted, sterile

5. 1 sterile 99 ml dilution blank of distilled water

6. Forceps

7. Mold cultures

PROCEDURE (7 days)

Period 1

1. Obtain one sterile glass Petri plate with coverslip, slide, and filter paper in it.

2. Using a sterile Pasteur pipet, add 1 to 2 drops of melted Sabouraud's glucose (or maltose) agar on the center of the glass slide and let it solidify.

3. Using a flamed and cool loop, cut the solid agar drop in half. Push one of the halves off the slide onto the filter paper.

4. Inoculate the cut face of the drop on the slide with one of the fungus cultures or unknowns provided.

5. Flame sterilize the forceps and allow to cool. Pick up the coverslip with the forceps and place it on top of the agar drop. Make sure the surface is parallel with the slide.

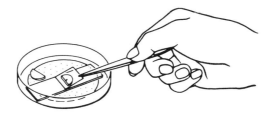

6. With a sterile Pasteur pipet, seal the coverslip-slide space around three sides leaving the side opposite the inoculated cut side open to the air. Avoid getting vaspar on the top of the coverslip.

7. Add just enough sterile water to the filter paper to completely wet it. Check the dish each day and keep the paper moistened until sufficient growth is present.

8. Incubate the covered plate at 20-30°C until desired growth is obtained. About one week is usually sufficient.

OBSERVATIONS

Period 2

9. Place the incubated slide on the microscope stage and examine the growth with the 10X objective.

10. Focus the microscope on the hyphae and spores just below the surface of the coverslip. Carefully rotate the 40X objective into position but be careful not to crush the coverslip with the objective. **DO NOT** attempt to use the oil immersion lens.

11. Make drawings of hyphae and spores for each fungus on the report form looking carefully at hyphae, septa, branching, fruiting bodies, spores, rhizoids, stolons and other structures. Use Figures 7-1, 7-2, and 7-3 as a guide.

PART II. WET MOUNT AND YEAST MORPHOLOGY

MATERIALS (per person)

1. *Saccharomyces cerevisiae* and other yeast cultures on Sabouraud's glucose (or maltose) agar or acetate agar
2. Coverslips
3. Slides
4. Pasteur pipets
5. Loeffler's methylene blue stain
6. Prepared slide of ascus with ascospores

PROCEDURE (1 day)

1. Prepare a wet mount from the yeast cultures provided by ringing a coverslip with a thin bead of vaseline. Place a small blob of vaseline on the rear of the palm of your hand opposite the thumb. Touch one edge of a coverslip to the vaseline and carefully scrape the edge along the rear of the palm until a small ridge of vaseline forms along the edge. Repeat for each edge of the coverslip until all four sides have a small bead. The bead must be thin and uniform. The vaseline may also be added to the edge by drawing a vaseline coated toothpick along each edge. This method often leads to too thick a bead, however.

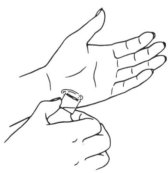

2. Place a small drop of distilled water in the center of the coverslip using a Pasteur pipet. The drop *must* be small.

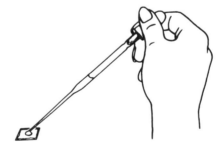

3. Add a very small amount of Leoffler's methylene blue stain to the drop with an inoculating loop.

4. With a sterile inoculating loop, emulsify a small amount of growth from a slant culture in the drop until it appears slightly murky but not milky.

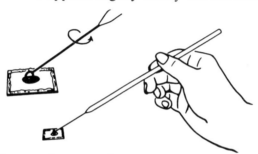

5. Center a slide over the coverslip and press down gently to seal the edges.

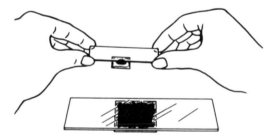

6. Invert the slide and examine it under the microscope. Make drawings using the oil immersion lens. Be careful that the oil lens does not contact the coverslip when rotating it.

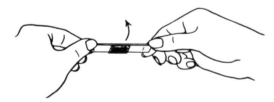

7. Look for the various stages of the life cycle of *S. cerevisiae*. Use Figure 7-4 as a guide.

8. If prepared slides are available, make observations and drawings of these.

PART III. GROWTH OF AN AQUATIC SAPROLEGNIALES

MATERIALS (per group of suitable size)

1. *Saprolegnia* culture
2. Petri plate
3. Sterile dilution bottle for water sample
4. Flask of distilled water
5. Hemp seed
6. Tweezers
7. Scalpel
8. 50 ml beaker
9. 125 ml beaker
10. Depression slide
11. Vaseline and toothpicks
12. Coverslips
13. Calibrated ocular micrometer

PROCEDURE (1–2 weeks)

Period 1

1. Collect a sample of water from a local stream in a sterile container.
2. In a clean flask, boil the stream sample.
3. To a 50 ml beaker, add a small amount of distilled water and one or more hemp seeds. Boil over a flame for 1–2 min.
4. Flame sterilize the tweezers and remove a hemp seed. Place it in a Petri plate and cut it in half with a flamed scalpel.
5. Pour the boiled stream water into the Petri plate until about half full.
6. Inoculate the water in the Petri plate with a loopful of the *Saprolegnia* culture provided.
7. Incubate the covered plate at room temperature for 1–2 weeks or until a cottony growth is seen around the seed.

OBSERVATIONS

Period 2

8. Remove the hemp seed and attached growth to a depression slide. Remove the hemp seed cutting it away with a scalpel if necessary.

9. Place a small amount of vaseline on the four edges of a coverslip (see Part II) and place it over the depression. Press it down gently but firmly.

10. With the low power of the microscope, look for the structures illustrated in Figure 7-5. Measure these and make drawings on the report form.

THOUGHT QUESTIONS

1. Indicate one major morphological difference between the lower and the higher fungi.

2. How do yeasts and molds differ from one another?

3. Draw and label the life cycle of *Saprolegnia*.

4. Find some information on at least three plant diseases caused by fungi.

Nonseptate hyphae

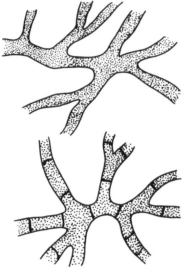

Septate hyphae

Figure 7-1. Septate and nonseptate hyphae

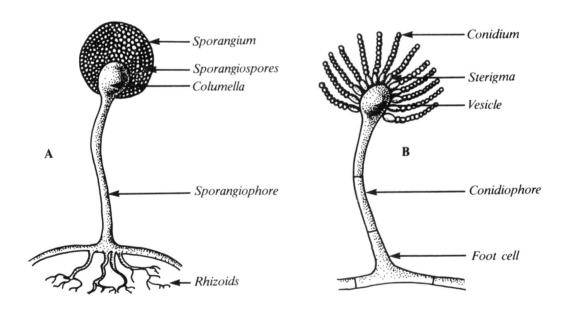

Figure 7-2. Asexual reproductive structure of *Rhizopus*, A; and *Aspergillus*, B

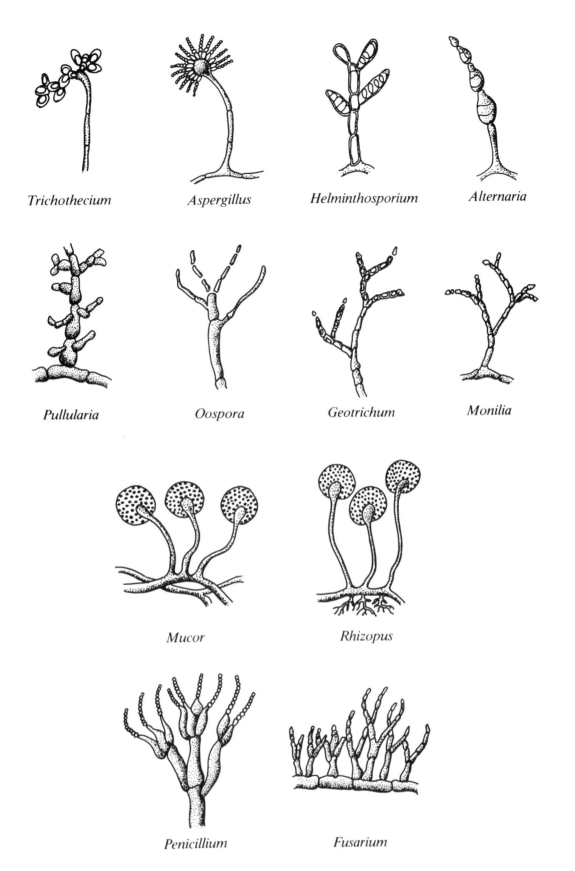

Trichothecium

Aspergillus

Helminthosporium

Alternaria

Pullularia

Oospora

Geotrichum

Monilia

Mucor

Rhizopus

Penicillium

Fusarium

Figure 7-3. The asexual reproductive structures of commonly found fungi

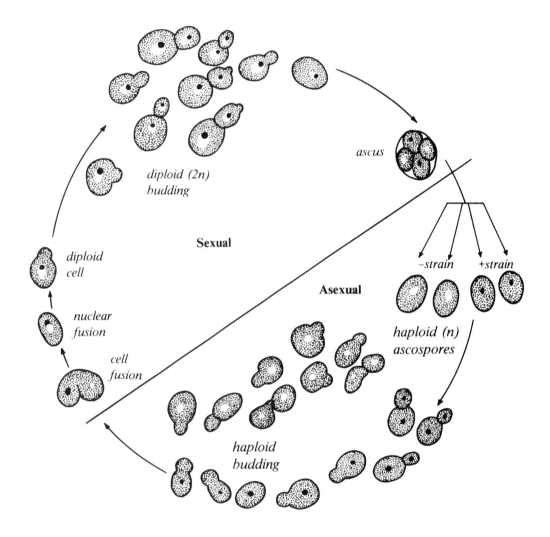

Figure 7-4. Diagram of life cycle of *Saccharomyces cerevisiae*

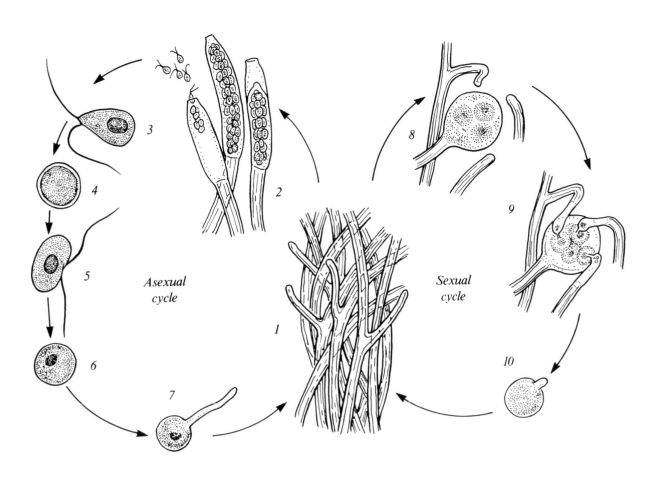

1. Somatic hyphae
2. Sporangia
3. Primary zoospore
4. Cyst (primary)
5. Secondary zoospore
6. Cyst (secondary)
7. Germination
8. Developing sexual structures
9. Fertilization
10. Germination

Figure 7-5. Saprolegnia life cycle

Name ——————————————————— Date ——————— Grade ———————

7. Fungi

RESULTS AND OBSERVATIONS

I. Fungal slide culture drawings

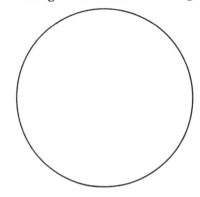

Name ———————————

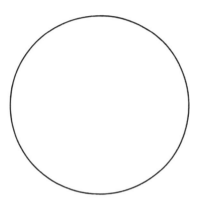

Name ———————————

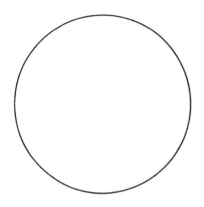

Name ———————————

II. Yeast wet mount drawings

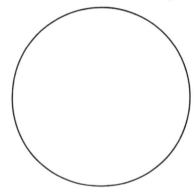

Name ———————————

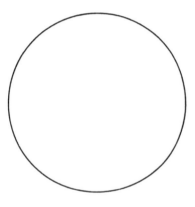

Name ———————————

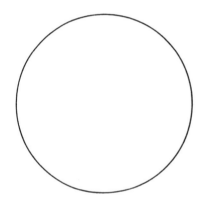

Name ———————————

III. *Saprolegnia* observations

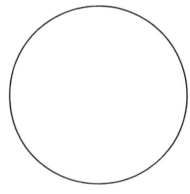

Name ———————————

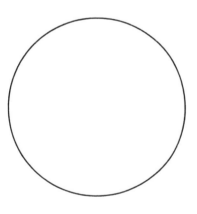

Name ———————————

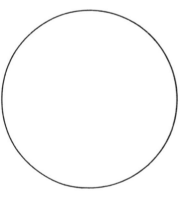

Name ———————————

QUESTIONS

Completion:

1-3. The tubular part of fungus growth is called a _____ .

After much branching, the mass of tubes is called _____ .

When the mass of tubes is visible to the eye as a cottony growth it is commonly called a

_____ .

4. If a fungus growing underground produces an above ground sexual fruiting structure, the structure is called a _____ .

5. The hyphae of fungi may or may not have a _____ across it.

6. When cytoplasm and nuclei move freely through the hyphae it is called the _____ condition.

7-8. The colored part of a fungus colony (e.g., *Penicillium*) is due to _____ which are sexual/asexual (cross out incorrect word).

9-12. The names of the three groups of "higher" fungi are _____ , _____ , and _____ ; these are named on the basis of the spore structure formed in the _____ cycle.

13. A fungus which can sometimes appear mold-like and yeast-like at other times is said to be

_____ .

14. An asexual spore of *Aspergillus* is called a _____ .

15. *Rhizopus* is anchored to substrates by structures called _____ .

16. Haploid and diploid cells of the yeast *Saccharomyces cerevisiae* reproduce by _____ .

17-19. The name of the material used to seal the edge of wet mount coverslips is _____ and on mold culture slides is called _____ .

In the latter case, caution should be taken to avoid overheating while melting because the vapor is

_____ .

8   Helminths

OBJECTIVES

The student will be able to:

1. describe the nature of helminths and explain why it is a topic in a microbiology course.

2. define *cestode, trematode, proglottid, scolex, ovum, monoecious, dioecious, cysticercus, miracidium, cercariae.*

3. diagram and discuss the life cycle of the parasites in schistosomiasis, clonorchiasis, taeniasis, hookworm, pinworm, and trichinosis.

The name **helminth** (helminth*ology* = study of) is a collective term including several metazoan animal phyla of medical and veterinary importance. Members of the phylum Platyhelminthes (**flatworms**) cause the commonly called **fluke** (Trematoda) and **tapeworm** (Cestoda) diseases while members of the phylum Nematoda are the causative agents of **roundworm** diseases. These parasites cause disease in most vertebrates including man. Although rare in the United States, helminth disease is a serious problem in tropical areas of the world. Most cases in the United States are seen in recent immigrants, migrant workers, foreign students, and travelers returning from tropical areas. Helminth diseases occurs worldwide in animals other than man and are frequently a problem in domestic animals.

Helminths are included in microbiology courses because identification of these agents is done in clinical laboratories by microscopic examination of stools, body fluids, and biopsy. Helminthology is a broad subject and cannot be examined in much detail. As with many of the microbial taxonomic groups, special courses are available in this subject. The objective here is to introduce the student to a few of the many important helminth agents of human disease.

An excellent reference for symptoms, occurrence, treatment and other aspects of these diseases is "The Control of Communicable Diseases in Man," 15th edition. A. S. Benenson, ed. American Public Health Association, Washington, D. C., 1990.

TREMATODA

Flukes are generally referred to as intestinal, liver, blood, or lung flukes because of their primary site of residence as adults. Generally the flukes are monoecious (one animal is both male and female) except the blood flukes which are dioecious (separate male and female animals). Many require an alternate host to complete the life cycle. We will be able to study only a few of the many important species in this group.

Schistosomiasis is the disease caused by blood flukes, members of the genus *Schistosoma*. This is one of the world's most important infectious diseases, perhaps second only to malaria in seriousness and the number of persons infected. The life cycle (Figure 8-1) of the human schistosomes (except for the host, others are nearly identical) begins with the formation of an **egg** which is deposited in the venules of intestinal wall, bladder and other sites. These work their way into the feces or the bladder. The eggs have a hook (Figure 8-1a) which often causes damage to the intestinal wall or bladder and urethra and in the latter case results in bloody urine and pusy discharge, a condition illustrated in early dynasty Egyptian hieroglyphics. Once excreted into water, the eggs hatch into a ciliated intermediate stage called a **miracidium** (Figure 8-1b). The miracidium is infectious only to certain species of aquatic snails in which it undergoes transformation to a **sporocyst** (Figure 8-1c). Daughter sporocysts periodically give rise to vast numbers of free swimming fork-tailed **cercariae** (Figure 8-1d). Upon contact with human skin (Figure 8-1e), the cercariae burrow through the skin to the capillaries then migrate via the bloodstream into the mesenteric vessels and intestinal wall and liver, there developing into adult male (large with a ventral groove) and female (small and narrow) animals (Figure 8-1f). As depicted in Figure 8-1, transmission of the human schistosomes is by contact with water containing human waste and aquatic snails. **All** water contact, swimming, wading, working, washing clothes, and drinking are methods of acquiring an infection. Travelers should be wary even of putting their hands in water in areas known to be endemic for this disease. A few animal schistosome cercariae can penetrate the human skin but fail to develop further. A second exposure leads to an immune response resulting in intense itching, the so-called swimmer's itch. This occurs widely in lakes along the Canadian-USA border. Diagnosis is made by finding typical eggs in the feces, urine, or biopsy. A serological test is also available.

Clonorchis sinensis, the Chinese liver fluke (Figure 8-2), is an important parasite in the Orient and is often seen in immigrants from that area. This fluke requires two intermediate hosts. Eggs are shed via the bile duct to the feces and then excreted. An egg hatches when ingested by certain aquatic snails producing a sporocyte which releases a large number of cercariae. These burrow into certain freshwater fish and encyst in the muscles. When raw or undercooked fish is ingested by man or other fish-eating mammals, they excyst and migrate to the liver via the bile duct where they develop into adults. Diagnosis is made by finding eggs in feces.

CESTODA

Tapeworms (cestodes) consist of a **scolex** or head with or without hooks to attach to the intestinal wall. The head produces a long chain of **proglottids**, each being **monoecious**, which break off the terminal end as they reach maturity and are shed in the feces (Figure 8-3). An intermediate host is usually involved.

Taenia solium, the pork tapeworm, has 22-32 hooks on the scolex (Figure 8-3b) with a distinctive proglottid (Figure 8-3a). The pig is infected when eggs are ingested with food contaminated with human feces. The eggs hatch into a stage which migrates through the intestinal wall and, via the blood, to the liver where further development takes place. The cysticerci leave the liver, enter the mesenteries and muscles where they encyst. Man is infected by eating undercooked or raw meat. The cysts are released in the intestinal tract during digestion where they develop into adults (Figure 8-3c). In contrast to *T. saginata*, the beef tapeworm, man can be infected by *T. solium* eggs. When the cysticerci encyst in muscles, they do little harm; however, when they encyst in nervous tissue or sense organs, they can cause considerable damage, even causing death if in the brain. Diagnosis is made by finding characteristic proglottids or eggs (rarely in the case of *T. solium*) in feces. Finding the scolex after treatment is definitive.

Diphyllobothrium latum, the fish tapeworm, occurs widely in North America. Hosts include bears, cats, dogs, man, and other fish-eating carnivores. Human infections have produced tapeworms up to 60 feet in length. Eggs produced from mature proglottids in the mammal host hatch when shed into water producing a ciliated stage infectious to certain copepods in which they develop. When the copepod is eaten by certain freshwater fish (pike, walleye, salmon, perch, turbot, and others), this stage burrows through the intestine to reach the body wall or viscera where further development takes place. When raw or undercooked fish is eaten by the final host, this stage develops into the adult form in the intestine. Eggs are formed in the proglottids, released and shed with the feces, thus completing the life cycle. Diagnosis is made by finding proglottids and eggs in the feces.

NEMATODA

Roundworms of the phylum Nematoda are responsible for a number of very important human and animal diseases. Among them are pinworm, hookworm, ascariasis, river blindness (onchocerciasis), trichinosis, whipworm, heartworm of dogs, filariasis, anisakiasis, and loa loa to name a few. Intermediate hosts and vectors are sometimes involved.

Pinworm (*Enterobius vermicularis*, Figure 8-4) is perhaps the most common helminth infection in the United States, principally in school age children, K to 3rd grade, and secondarily in their immediate family members. The adult worm lives in the intestine, migrating to the anus during the night to lay eggs. The anal area is often irritated causing the child to scratch the area continuously, interrupting sleep and causing general irritability. The eggs are passed to the clothing, bedding, and generally to house dust. Ingestion of eggs from dust and fingers is relatively easy, often infecting all household members. The eggs hatch into larvae in the intestine, where they develop into adults. The finding of eggs or adults in the anal area is diagnostic.

Hookworm disease is common in Africa (*Ancylostoma duodenale*, Figure 8-5) and parts of the western hemisphere including the southern states in the United States (*Necator americanus*). The disease is frequently characterized by chronic **anemia** due to loss of blood, especially in children. Eggs are deposited on moist ground and hatch, passing through several larval stages in the soil. This development requires warm, moist, and humid conditions and the disease is limited to tropical areas of the world as a result. Humans are infected when the larvae penetrate the skin, usually through bare feet, and cause dermatitis (ground itch). The larvae pass, via the blood and lymph systems to the lungs, migrating up the larynx to the trachea whereupon they are swallowed. Reaching the intestine, they attach to the wall and develop to maturity, producing eggs in 6-7 weeks. Diagnosis is by observing eggs in feces.

Trichinosis (*Trichinella spiralis*) is a roundworm parasite of carnivorous and omnivorous animals. The larvae encyst in muscle tissue (Figure 8-6), and it is transmitted by eating raw or undercooked meat. In humans, pork and pork products are the most common vehicles. In the USA, bear meat is often the source. Larvae develop into adults in the small intestine mucosa. Fertilized females then produce larvae which penetrate the lymphatics and are disseminated throughout the body. Larvae migrate into muscle and encyst. Finding larvae in muscle biopsy is the usual diagnostic procedure. A serological test is also available.

Anisakiasis is caused by several genera of the family Anisakidae including *Anisakis*. It is transmitted by eating raw or inadequately treated (salted, frozen, smoked) saltwater fish or squid (sushi, sashimi, ceviche), and herring. The larvae burrow into the intestinal wall causing nausea, vomiting, diarrhea, and pain. The larvae, about 2 cm long, often migrate into the throat where they can be removed with the fingers. Diagnosis is by recognition of the larvae removed from the throat or gastroscopic examination.

MATERIALS (per class)

1. Prepared slides[a] of

Organism	Ova
Schistosoma mansoni, female PS1316	*Schistosoma mansoni* PS1310
Schistosoma mansoni, male PS1315	*Schistosoma japonicum* PS1301
Schistosoma mansoni, cercariae PS1314	
Schistosoma mansoni, miracidium PS1311	
Clonorchis sinensis, PS1210	*Clonorchis sinensis* PS1218
Taenia solium, scolex PS1861	*Taenia solium* PS1865
Taenia saginata, proglottid PS1851	
Taenia solium, cysticercus PS1866	
Diphyllobothrium latum, scolex PS1605	*Diphyllobothrium latum* PS1625
Enterobius vermicularis PS2100	*Enterobius vermicularis* PS2105
Necator americanus PS2360	*Necator americanus* PS2385
Trichinella spiralis, encysted larvae PS2435	
Trichinella spiralis, migratory larvae PS2445	

[a] PS numbers refer to catalog numbers of Carolina Biological Supply Co. Other supply houses also have slides available.

2. Preserved specimens may also be made available

3. Microscopes

4. Stereo dissecting microscopes

PROCEDURE AND OBSERVATIONS (1 day)

(*Note:* Each person works alone making drawings as indicated on the report form.)

1. Examine the prepared slides under either the low power of your microscope or under the dissecting microscope. Your instructor will indicate which is most appropriate for each specimen.

2. Compare what you see with the drawings in this exercise. Eggs are shown in Figure 8-7.

3. Make a drawing of what you see. Label structures as far as you can determine them. It is more important that you be able to recognize the parasite later.

4. Write a short description of each disease and its epidemiology in the space provided on the report form.

THOUGHT QUESTIONS

1. In what parts of the world does each of the diseases described in this exercise occur?

2. What medicines or drugs are used to treat these diseases?

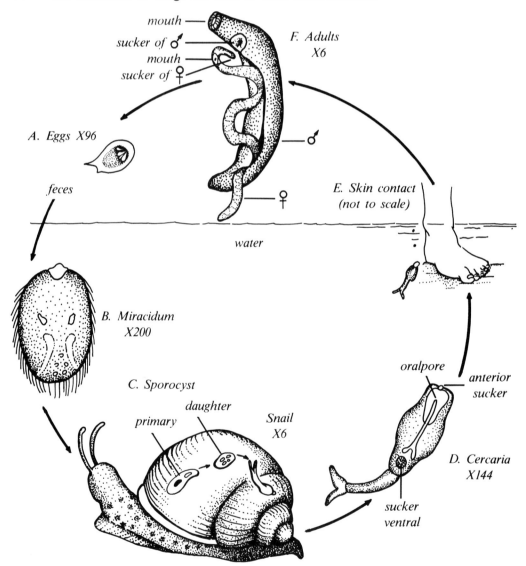

Figure 8-1. Generalized life cycle of the schistosomes

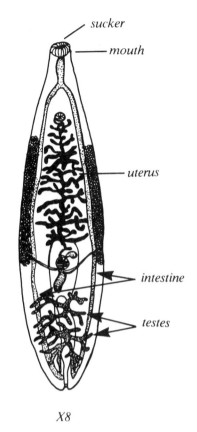

sucker
mouth

uterus

intestine

testes

X8

Figure 8-2. *Clonorchis sinensis*

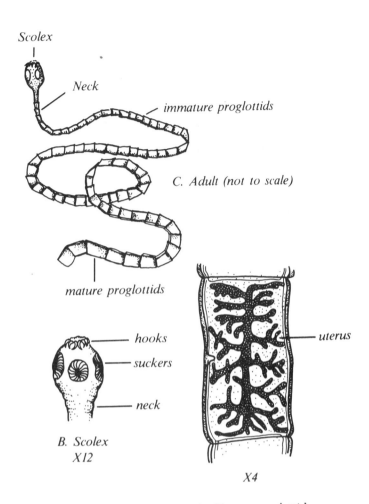

Scolex

Neck

immature proglottids

C. Adult (not to scale)

mature proglottids

hooks
suckers

neck

uterus

B. Scolex
X12

X4

A. Mature proglottid

X6   X6
♀   ♂

Figure 8-3. *Taenia solium.* Adult scolex is about 1 mm diameter and length may reach 15-16 meters

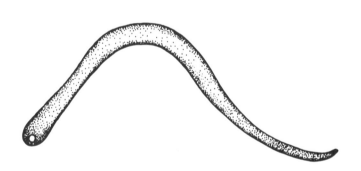

Figure 8-4. The pinworm, adults

Figure 8-5. The hookworm, adults (up to 8 mm long)

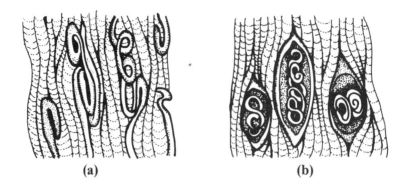

Figure 8-6. (a) *Trichinella spiralis* larvae migrating into human tissue; (b) encysted larvae in porcine muscle (X75)

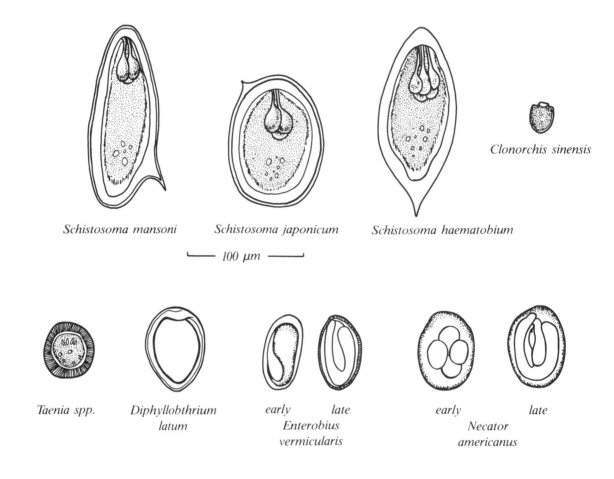

Schistosoma mansoni   *Schistosoma japonicum*   *Schistosoma haematobium*   *Clonorchis sinensis*

⊢ — *100 μm* — ⊣

Taenia spp.   *Diphyllobthrium latum*   *early   late   Enterobius vermicularis*   *early   late   Necator americanus*

Figure 8-7. Helminth eggs, all to same scale

Name _____ Date _____ Grade _____

8. Helminths

RESULTS AND OBSERVATIONS

Schistosoma mansoni

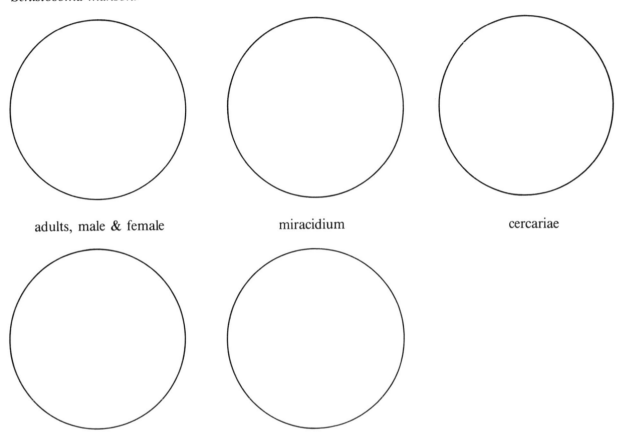

adults, male & female   miracidium   cercariae

ova *S. mansoni*   ova *S. japonicum*

Disease _____
_____
_____
_____
_____

Clonorchis sinensis

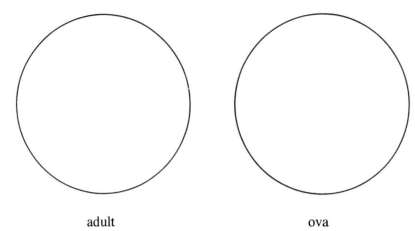

adult   ova

Disease _____

_____

_____

_____

_____

Taenia

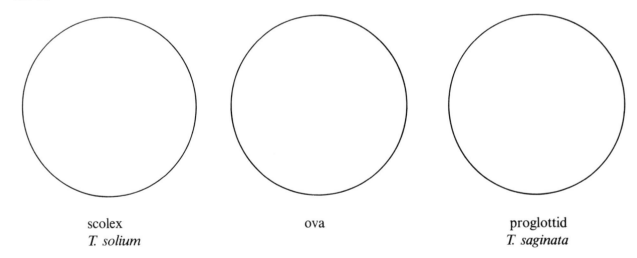

scolex   ova   proglottid
T. solium   *T. saginata*

Disease _____

_____

_____

_____

Diphyllobothrium latum

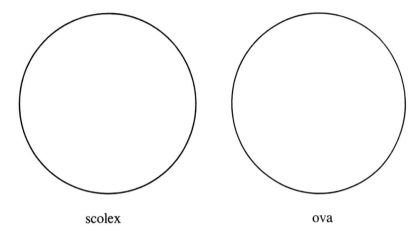

scolex   ova

Disease _____

_____

_____

_____

Enterobius vermicularis

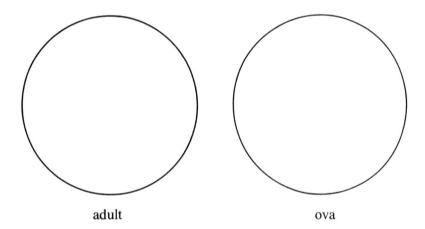

adult   ova

Disease _____

_____

_____

_____

Necator americanus

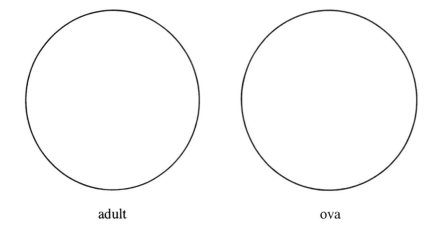

adult   ova

Disease _____

_____

_____

_____

_____

Trichinella spiralis

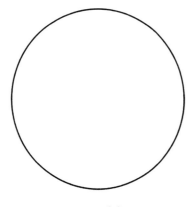 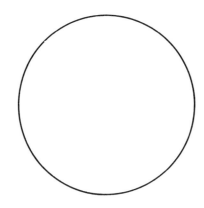

encysted larvae   migratory larvae

Disease _____

_____

_____

_____

_____

QUESTIONS

A. **True or False Statements:** Circle the correct response.

T   F   1.   *Clonorchis sinensis* occurs only in humans.

T   F   2.   A scolex is characteristically found in trematodes.

T   F   3.   The fish tapeworm is acquired by eating raw fish.

T   F   4.   Pinworm commonly causes young children to scratch the anal area.

T   F   5.   Man is infected by *Trichinella spiralis* eggs from pork.

T   F   6.   Hookworm disease is found only in Africa.

T   F   7.   Anisakis infections are obtained from eating raw marine fish.

T   F   8.   Beef tapeworm eggs may be infectious to humans.

T   F   9.   The blood fluke stage, the miracidium, can penetrate the skin of man.

T   F   10.   Blood fluke infection has been known since early Egypt.

B. **Completion:**

11–14. Name the four stages of the life cycle of the schistosomes.

11. _____   13. _____

12. _____   14. _____

15–23. Name two trematode, three cestode, and four nematode diseases.

15. _____   16. _____

17. _____   18. _____   19. _____

20. _____   21. _____   22. _____   23. _____

24–30. Define the following terms:

24. monoecious

25. dioecious

26. proglottid

27. flatworm

28. cestode

29. cysticercus

30. scolex

UNIT **III**

Isolation and Cultivation Techniques

In order to treat disease, learn about the spread of pathogens (epidemiology), genetically engineer organisms, one must first isolate the organisms of interest as a pure culture. The German bacteriologist, Robert Koch, was the first to put pure culture rules into practice in demonstrating that a particular organism is the cause of a specific disease. These rules have come to be known as Koch's Postulates. In this section the student will gain practice isolating organisms, recognizing a pure culture, and observing growth patterns.

9 Aseptic Technique and Broth Culture

OBJECTIVES

The student will be able to:

1. describe the importance of aseptic technique.

2. transfer a culture to broth using proper aseptic technique.

3. recognize and describe the various growth patterns in broth culture.

4. describe other growth characteristics such as relative amount, chromogenesis, and consistency.

Microorganisms require suitable nutrients as well as a favorable environment for growth. First, the **culture medium** must contain those nutrients essential for the growth of a given microorganism. Second, this medium must provide suitable surroundings for growth — the proper pH, osmotic pressure, oxygen, temperature, etc. Many different substances will serve satisfactorily as a culture medium. Essentially, all culture media are one of two forms: (1) **liquid** (broth) or (2) **solid** (agar and other gelling agents).

Since most of your laboratory study will be made with **pure cultures** (i.e., a single species of microorganism), a culture medium must be sterilized and maintained in a sterile condition, free of living forms. You must also be able to inoculate this sterile medium with a pure culture of microorganisms without outside contamination. This last procedure is commonly referred to as **aseptic technique**.

A freshly prepared medium contains numerous microorganisms found in the ingredients, the water used to prepare it, and from the utensil surfaces and glassware; therefore, it must be **sterilized** (i.e., heated to a point where all organisms present are destroyed). Otherwise, a mixture of organisms would result. Prior to sterilization, the container is usually plugged with cotton or loosely capped. This prevents the entry of new contaminants but permits free interchange of air or gases.

Media containing moisture, whether broth or agar, are most often sterilized by the use of steam under pressure called **autoclaving** or **pressure cooking**. The temperature of free-flowing steam (and thus boiling water) is 100°C at sea level. However, this temperature is not high enough to sterilize, since only vegetative forms of microorganisms are destroyed and not the spores of sporeforming bacteria. Applying 15 pounds of pressure per square inch (psi) to free-flowing steam increases the boiling temperature to 121°C. Maintaining the temperature at 121°C for 15-20 minutes will sterilize the media.

To grow a microbial culture in a sterilized medium, cells (the **inoculum**) are transferred (**inoculated**) into the medium, using special precautions to maintain the purity of the culture being transferred.

When a wire needle or loop inserted into a holder is used to transfer microorganisms in the inoculation procedure, it should be sterilized by heating to redness by flaming immediately *before* and *after* making a transfer. Hold the wire portion in the flame in a manner to heat first the entire length of the wire and then the lower part of the holder (Figure 9-1).

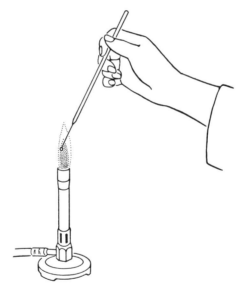

Figure 9-1. Sterilizing the wire inoculating loop in the flame of a Bunsen burner

During the transfer of cells, hold the culture tube in the left hand as nearly horizontal as feasible (if you are right-handed) and grasp the cap between the fingers of the right hand (Figure 7-2). CAUTION: Never lay a cap down! The mouths of the tubes from which cultures are taken and into which they are transferred must be passed through the burner flame immediately *before* and *after* the inoculating loop or needle is introduced and removed. This is to kill organisms on the lip and create heat currents to keep airborne organisms away from the opening. Don't overheat the glass and don't leave the tube open any longer than necessary. Flame the lip of the tube and reseat the cap.

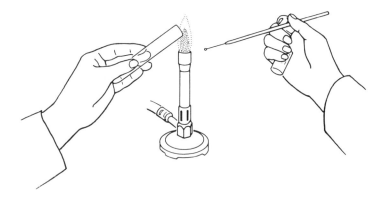

Figure 9-2. Flaming an open culture tube prior to inoculation. The tube is held almost horizontally and the cap held in the little finger of the right hand which holds the inoculating loop.

Pick up the tube to be inoculated, remove the cap, flame the lip and insert the sterile loop or needle. Move the wire back and forth once or twice, remove the loop or needle, and flame it as described above. Flame the lip of the inoculated tube and replace the cap. With a little practice, both tubes can be held in one hand and done at the same time.

Since most of a microbiologist's work is done with pure cultures, you should appreciate the importance of the techniques involved in inoculation and master them early in the course.

Following inoculation, a culture is **incubated** in an environment providing suitable growth conditions. "Growth" here means the development of a population of cells from one or a few cells. The mass of daughter cells becomes visible to the naked eye either as a cloudiness (**turbidity**) in liquid broth or as an isolated population (**colony**) on solid media. The visible appearance of growth is sometimes an aid in differentiating microbial species.

BROTH MEDIA

Use of broth media is a convenient way to handle bacteria in stock culture and organisms often grow in a characteristic manner in the broth medium.

Cells may grow dispersed showing interruption of the light path or cloudiness called **turbidity**. This may be slight to moderate to heavy. Cells may settle to the bottom to form a **sediment** or button. Cells may be attracted to each other to form clumps which settle to the bottom. These clumps may be adherent or slimy when dislodged from the bottom. A small button often may be the only sign of growth. Examine a tube first by looking up from the bottom. Then gently tap the tube near the bottom. A slight sediment will swirl upward. A button is not always growth but simply may be inoculum cells which have settled out. If there is no increase with time, this is probably the case. Many organisms grow in a film across the surface called a **pellicle** which may be heavy or light and membranous. Some organisms form a **ring** of growth around the glass-broth-air interface, seen by tilting the tube slightly. Handle tubes carefully when first observing them because heavy pellicles often fall to the bottom when disturbed. These growth patterns often give information about an organism's relation to air and its surface activity.

This exercise will provide the student with experience in transferring cultures and observing growth patterns.

MATERIALS (per person)

1. 18-24 hour broth cultures of *Escherichia coli, Micrococcus luteus, Bacillus subtilis, Enterococcus (Streptococcus) faecalis,* and *Serratia marcescens*

2. 6 tubes of tryptic soy broth, sterile

PROCEDURE (2 days)

Period 1

1. Label one tube "control" and leave uninoculated.

2. Inoculate each of the other tubes with one loopful of the appropriate stock cultures.

3. Incubate at 32°C for 48 hours.

OBSERVATIONS

Period 2

4. Compare inoculated tubes with the control by placing them against a bright background and also a dark background. Make observations using the diagrams in Figure 9-3.

5. Insert a loop into each broth culture and slowly withdraw it. Note any tendency to form strings or slime.

6. Complete the table in the laboratory report form.

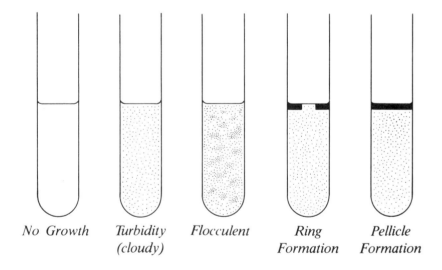

No Growth   *Turbidity (cloudy)*   *Flocculent*   *Ring Formation*   *Pellicle Formation*

Figure 9-3. Cultural characteristics of broth cultures

THOUGHT QUESTIONS

1. About how many cells do you think it would take in a broth culture to see turbidity?

2. What kind of forces would permit a pile of cells to collect in the bottom of a broth tube?

3. Can broth be used to isolate a pure culture?

Name _____ Date _____ Grade _____

9. Aseptic Technique and Broth Culture

RESULTS AND OBSERVATIONS

Broth Culture

Bacterial Species	Control	Serratia marcescens	Bacillus subtilis	Enterococcus faecalis	Micrococcus luteus	Escherichia coli
Sketch of growth						
Type of surface growth*						
Amount of turbidity*						
Amount of sediment*						
Chromogenesis/ Consistency						

* None = 0; Slight = +; Moderate = ++; Heavy = +++
† Refer to Figure 9-3

QUESTIONS

A. True or False Statements: Circle the correct response.

T   F   1.   An inoculum is a small amount of growth which is used to inoculate sterile media.

T   F   2.   The best method for sterilization of liquid media is the hot air oven.

T   F   3.   Aseptic technique is important when transferring microorganisms both to prevent contamination of the microorganisms you are transferring and to prevent self-infection.

T   F   4.   Room temperature is approximately 37°C.

T   F   5.   Pressure is the most important factor to consider when sterilizing by autoclaving.

T   F   6.   Water remains a liquid at 121°C in the autoclave because the atmospheric pressure has been increased.

T   F   7.   In sterilizing your transfer loop, the holder end does not need to be heated.

T   F   8.   It is acceptable practice to set the culture tube cap down on the lab bench.

T   F   9.   Cells which settle to the bottom of a broth tube are collectively referred to as sediment.

T   F   10.   Flocculent growth occurs as a film on the broth surface.

B. Completion:

11.   When growth on or in a medium contains only a single species of microorganism, it is called a

_____ .

12.   A term often used to describe cloudiness in broth media is _____ .

13.   When an object is rendered free of living microbes the process is referred to as

_____ .

14–15. Autoclaving is done at _____ °C and _____ psi for 15–20 minutes.

16.   A household utensil which can accomplish the same sterilizing effect as an autoclave is the

_____ .

17.   When a bacterial culture grows across the surface of a broth, the growth is referred to as a

_____ .

18.   Growth around the margin of the surface of a broth tube but not across it is referred to as a

_____ .

10 Agar Slant Culture

OBJECTIVES

The student will be able to:

1. describe the nature and role of agar in media.

2. transfer a culture to an agar slant without gouging the agar and using proper aseptic technique.

3. recognize and describe the various growth patterns on agar slants.

4. describe other growth characteristics as relative abundance, chromogenesis, and consistency.

A common means of providing a solid medium is to add a solidifying or gelling agent to a broth medium during preparation which hardens as it cools after autoclaving. By far the most common solidifying agent in use is **agar**, a polysaccharide obtained from red algae and available in a dried, purified form. Agar is rehydrated by mixing into broth, melting it by heating to boiling while constantly stirring, distributing it into tubes or flasks and then autoclaving it. After cooling, it solidifies again.

Agar is a colloidal gelling agent, chemically a galactan sulfuric acid ester, which is soluble (melts) in boiling water but not in cold water. Only a few specialized marine bacteria can digest agar, so it is used for its gelling property rather than as a nutrient. It is usually used at a concentration of 1.5%. A concentration of 1.8-2.5% gives a harder, less easily gouged medium, but less water is available for growth. Concentrations of 1% or less are often used in specialized media (e.g., motility media).

Although different agars may vary considerably in their physical properties, the usual melting point is 97-100°C. Thus, solid agar media are liquefied for use by boiling. On cooling, media containing agar solidify at about 42°C. If the media are to be inoculated before hardening, they are usually cooled to 45-47°C, a temperature that is not harmful to many microorganisms for a short time. Once solidified, agar may be incubated over the entire range a microbiologist is likely to use (up to 70°C, perhaps) without melting.

Agar slants are prepared by melting a small amount of a solid medium (broth + 1.5% agar) in a tube and allowing it to solidify in a slanted position. Pure cultures of bacteria are streaked on the surface to serve as a stock culture for future use in inoculating media or to observe cultural characteristics on the slant. This last use will be described here. Note that the terms given in Figure 10-1 for agar slant culture patterns are not widely used in culture descriptions any longer because so many variables affect the pattern (e.g., inoculum size, amount of surface moisture, the medium, amount of agar included, the vigorousness of the organism's motility, and how steady the technician draws the loop up the slant). Other aspects such as pigmentation (**chromogenesis**) and consistency are still widely used, however.

This exercise will give the student more practice in aseptic technique and introduces some terms used to describe cultures.

MATERIALS (per person)

1. 18-24 hour broth cultures of *Escherichia coli, Micrococcus luteus, Bacillus subtilis, Enterococcus (Streptococcus) faecalis,* and *Serratia marcescens*

2. 6 tubes of sterile tryptic soy agar to be slanted, sterile

PROCEDURE (2 days)

Period 1

1. Melt the 6 tubes of the medium in boiling water and let solidify in a slanted position. The slant should begin below the cap and end about 1 cm above the curved bottom of the tube. Label the tubes.

2. Using a loop, inoculate the first slant with *Escherichia coli.* Streak the surface *in one straight line* from bottom to top while holding the loop vertically to the slant as illustrated in Figure 10-2. Holding the loop horizontally will gouge the agar. Rest the loop **very** lightly on the slant so as not to gouge. If the entire surface is to be covered, use the loop parallel to the agar surface and move it rapidly back and forth while drawing the loop up the slant. Great care must be taken to avoid gouging the agar.

3. Repeat step No. 2. with the other cultures and tubes.

4. Leave one slant as your uninoculated "control" for comparison.

5. Incubate at 32°C for 48 hours.

OBSERVATIONS

Period 2

6. Examine the cultures using the diagrams in Figure 7-1.

7. Touch the growth with a sterile loop and observe the consistency of the growth, whether it is brittle, soft, gummy, tough, buttery, or any other description you might use.

8. Complete the table in the laboratory report form.

THOUGHT QUESTIONS

1. Are there more cells on an agar slant culture than in a broth culture? Why?

2. Why is chromogenesis more readily seen on slants than in broth?

Agar Slant Culture Patterns

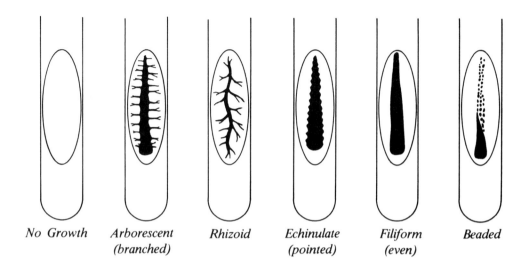

No Growth   *Arborescent (branched)*   *Rhizoid*   *Echinulate (pointed)*   *Filiform (even)*   *Beaded*

Figure 10-1. Cultural characteristics of agar slant cultures

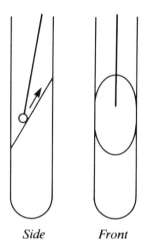

Side   *Front*

Figure 10-2. Holding the loop for making a slant culture

Name _____ Date _____ Grade _____

10. Agar Slant Culture

RESULTS AND OBSERVATIONS

Agar Slant Culture

Bacterial Species	Control	Serratia marcescens	Bacillus subtilis	Enterococcus faecalis	Micrococcus luteus	Escherichia coli
Sketch of growth						
Amount of Growth*						
Form of Growth†						
Chromogenesis/ Consistency						

* None = 0; Slight = +; Moderate = ++; Heavy = +++
† Refer to Figure 10-1

QUESTIONS

A. **True or False Statements:** Circle the correct response.

    T   F   1.   Agar comes from a type of seaweed.

    T   F   2.   Agar is a polysaccharide which contains sulfur.

    T   F   3.   Once agar solidifies it cannot be remelted.

    T   F   4.   Agar will not melt during autoclaving.

    T   F   5.   Agar is the only gelling agent used for making solid media.

B. **Completion:**

6. A substance added to a liquid medium to make it solid, yet not melt at room temperature is

    _____ .

7. Standard nutrient agar has about _____ % agar added before sterilization.

8. A flame-sterilized inoculating _____ is used to inoculate the agar.

9. Agar melts at approximately _____ °C and solidifies at about _____ °C.

10. An isolated population of bacteria growing on a solid medium is called a _____ .

11–13. List three factors which might influence the cultural characteristics of an organism growing on an agar medium.

    11. _____

    12. _____

    13. _____

11 Streak Plate

OBJECTIVES

The student will be able to:

1. describe the application of aseptic technique to preparing agar plates.

2. prepare an uncontaminated plate for streaking.

3. streak and isolate the species within a mixed culture.

4. describe typical colonies with terms applied to colony morphology.

Adding a solidifying substance to a broth medium and then inoculating with bacterial cells traps individual cells in place. Instead of swimming or floating around when they multiply, as in a liquid medium, they are restricted to one place forming a visible mass or colony. If the original cells are trapped some distance apart, each viable cell or clump of cells develops into a separate, distinct **colony**. Because colonies differ in size, shape, texture and color with different microorganisms, colony appearance is a useful aid in identification of species as well as a means of isolating the progeny of one cell — a **pure culture**.

You have thus far used solid media only in the confined area of a test tube. However, by increasing the surface area by using a broad, circular Petri plate, new ways of handling microbial cultures become possible.

How to prepare agar plates

After melting an agar medium, it is then cooled to 45-47°C and 15-20 milliliters of the cooled, but still liquid, agar are poured into a sterile, covered Petri plate. Prior cooling prevents excess condensation of moisture in the Petri plates when the liquid agar solidifies.

Several precautions (i.e., aseptic technique) are necessary to prevent contamination. When you take the melted agar from the holding water bath, the outside of the container should be wiped with a cloth or paper towel. Otherwise, the water will run into the plate and introduce contaminants. When removing the plug or cap to pour the agar, flame the mouth of the container to kill microorganisms on the outside lip. In pouring the agar from the container to the plate, raise the cover of the plate only on one side and just sufficiently to admit easily the mouth of the container. You must also take care not to scrape the container on the Petri plate or its cover when pouring the agar.

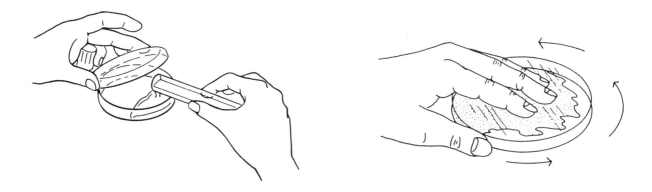

Figure 11-1. Using aseptic technique, lift the cover of the Petri plate high enough to insert the mouth of the tube to pour the melted medium into it. Do not touch the plate with the tube.

Figure 11-2. Rotate the Petri plate in a figure-8 so that the medium covers the bottom. Do not move the plate again until the medium has solidified.

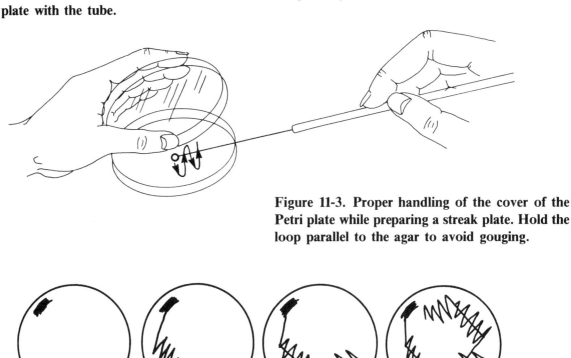

Figure 11-3. Proper handling of the cover of the Petri plate while preparing a streak plate. Hold the loop parallel to the agar to avoid gouging.

Figure 11-4. Steps in the preparation of a streak plate. The inoculating loop is sterilized in between each set of streaks.

How to inoculate agar plates

You may now apply microbial cultures to the surface of the agar and spread them by a loop or bent needle. This is called **streaking** and a plate so prepared is called a **streak plate**. There are several techniques you may use for streaking plates. However, the purpose of the streak plate is to produce well-separated colonies of bacteria from concentrated suspensions of cells. During inoculation, the closely packed cells at the start of the streak form colonies that run together, but as streaking continues, fewer and fewer cells remain on the loop or needle. As these are removed and grow on the surface, colonies develop. A few hasty streaks will not produce isolated colonies. A good plate results from the progressive movements of the loop or needle, repeated many times.

The inoculating loop should be held with the open face parallel to the agar surface rather than vertically as illustrated in Figure 11-3. Hold the handle so that the loop rests lightly on the agar surface. Slide the loop rapidly from side to side in arcs of 2-3 cm while drawing it toward you **but without pressure** (Figure 11-4). This reduces the likelihood of gouging the agar.

Rapidly growing or very prolific organisms may require flaming the loop between each streak or every other streak. If the organism grows poorly, then flaming between streaks can be omitted.

How to incubate agar plates

Because of the high concentration of water in agar, some water of condensation forms in Petri plates during cooling and incubation. Moisture is likely to drip from the cover to the surface of the agar and spread out, resulting in a confluent mass of growth and ruining individual colony formation. To avoid this, Petri plates are routinely incubated **bottom-side up** (i.e., inverted).

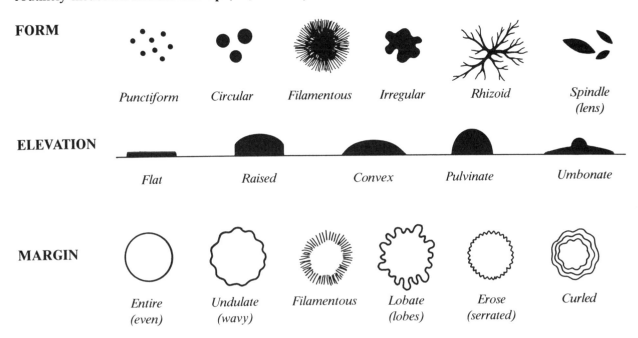

FORM

Punctiform   Circular   Filamentous   Irregular   Rhizoid   Spindle (lens)

ELEVATION

Flat   Raised   Convex   Pulvinate   Umbonate

MARGIN

Entire (even)   Undulate (wavy)   Filamentous   Lobate (lobes)   Erose (serrated)   Curled

Figure 8-5. Cultural characteristics of isolated bacterial colonies

MATERIALS (per person)

1. 18-24 hour mixed broth suspension of *Escherichia coli* and *Micrococcus luteus*
2. 3 nutrient agar deeps, sterile
3. 3 sterile Petri plates

PROCEDURE AND OBSERVATIONS (3 days)

Period 1

1. Pour one Petri plate of nutrient agar using good aseptic technique. Allow it to solidify.

2. Flame the inoculating loop and allow it to cool for a few seconds. Take a loopful of a mixed broth suspension of *Escherichia coli* and *Micrococcus luteus* and streak back and forth over a small area near the side of the agar plate (Figure 11-4). Be careful not to cut the agar or touch the side of the plate. Lift the lid of the Petri plate only far enough to allow insertion of the loop.

3. Flame the loop and allow it to cool briefly. Pass the loop completely through the previously streaked area once and then back and forth in a restricted area as shown in Figure 11-4.

4. Repeat step No. 3 until there is no further room on the plate.

5. Incubate at 30°C for 24 hours.

Period 2

6. Have your instructor criticize your streak performance on the plate before proceeding. This is an important part of developing good technique. (*Note:* The exercise may be terminated at this point by making the observations called for in Period 3.)

7. Prepare two nutrient agar plates as you did in Period 1.

8. Select two well isolated and distinctly different colonies. Streak one for isolation on one agar plate and the other colony on the second plate. Touch only the center of the colony if possible.

9. Incubate both plates at 30°C for 24 hours.

Period 3

10. Make observations on isolated colonies as follows:

    Using the magnifying lens of the Quebec colony counter (Figure 11-6), make detailed drawings and record descriptions of growth for each species as called for in the table provided in the laboratory report form. Use the drawings in Figure 11-5 to aid in your description of the appearance of growth.

THOUGHT QUESTIONS

1. Why does the diameter of bacterial colonies of bacteria stop enlarging after 24 hours or so?

2. How certain can you be that an isolated colony on your first streak plate is the result of division of a single cell?

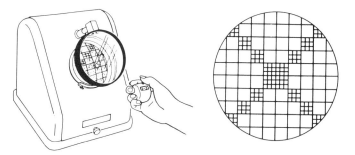

Figure 11-6. Quebec colony counter

Name _____ Date _____ Grade _____

11. Streak Plate

RESULTS AND OBSERVATIONS

Bacterial Species	*Micrococcus luteus*	*Escherichia coli*
Sketch of Colonies		
Size (mm)		
Form		
Elevation		
Margin		
Chromogenesis[a]		
Light Passage[b]		

[a] Pigmentation

[b] Translucent - light passes through but cannot read print through colony

Transparent - can read print through colony

Opaque - no light passes through colony

QUESTIONS

True or False Statements: Circle the correct response.

T   F   1.   Contamination of cultures will arise if asepsis is not practiced in the laboratory.

T   F   2.   A colony touching another colony is considered pure as long as they both look alike.

T   F   3.   Streak dilution of bacterial cells means that the original inoculum has been diluted with sterile saline.

T   F   4.   Bacterial growth means an increase in the bacterial numbers, instead of in the size of one cell.

T   F   5.   A magnifying glass is helpful in determining the margin type of a colony.

T   F   6.   When you incubate a Petri plate, it should always be placed in a container with the cover side up.

T   F   7.   A mass of cells growing on an agar surface is called a colony.

T   F   8.   The mass of cells of question No. 7 is usually a single kind of organism.

T   F   9.   To be certain of pure culture, a colony should be restreaked for isolation several times to ensure purity.

T   F   10.   Flaming the end of the holder is not important in taking cells from a culture tube for streaking.

T   F   11.   Streaking a plate with the loop oriented vertically to the agar surface is a good way to gouge the agar.

T   F   12.   Colony shapes would be the same whether it was composed of a single organism or several species.

T   F   13.   There is only one correct way to streak a plate.

T   F   14.   Agar should be poured into a plate at a fairly cool temperature to avoid excess condensation on the inside of the lid.

12 Pour Plate

OBJECTIVES

The student will be able to:

1. perform a successful loop-dilution pour plate series.

2. explain why subsurface and surface colonies have different morphologies.

3. explain the principle of the loop-dilution pour plate method.

The technique of the **pour plate** gives you a second way of obtaining pure cultures from a mixture of organisms. It differs from the streak plate in that the agar medium is inoculated while it is still liquid (but cool — 45° C) and colonies develop throughout the medium, not just on the surface. In order to have isolated colonies on the plate, there is the problem of getting the proper concentration of cells into the plates poured. If there is too many, the colonies are crowded and the plate is useless. The idea is to make successive dilutions of the cells and then on at least one of the poured plates colonies will be separated well enough to see them as isolated. The plates that are too crowded and those with too few can be discarded. One limitation of this technique is that species with low numbers are not observed when other species are present in high numbers. They are overwhelmed by sheer numbers.

The **loop-dilution** method will yield useful plates with many samples and is based on a roughly quantitative dilution of the original sample in an agar medium. A loop of 3 mm internal diameter, touching but not crossing the shank will hold approximately 0.001 ml. A more quantitative procedure will be introduced in Exercise 23 and used in several later exercises.

MATERIALS (per person)

1. 18-24 hour mixed broth suspension of *Escherichia coli* and *Micrococcus luteus*

2. 3 nutrient agar deeps, sterile

3. 3 Petri plates, sterile

PROCEDURE (2 days)

Note: This exercise requires that you move very rapidly to inoculate, mix and pour plates. Read the procedure thoroughly so you know **exactly** what to do for each step. If medium solidifies in the tubes, remelting them **kills the organisms** and reinoculation is required.

Period 1

1. Label 3 nutrient agar deeps No. 1 through No. 3 and place them into a boiling water bath for melting. Then allow them to cool to 45°C. While the tubes are cooling, label 3 Petri plates No. 1 through No. 3.

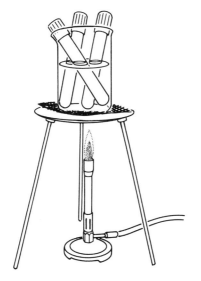

Figure 12-1. Melting tubes

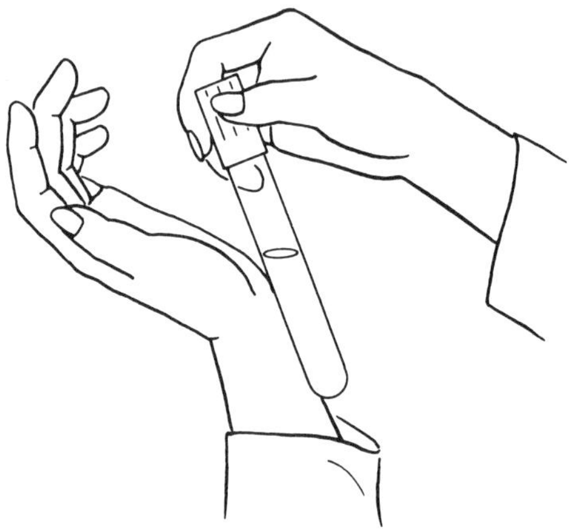

Figure 12-2. Testing agar temperature. Slightly warm to the touch but not hot.

2. Prepare your loop carefully. It must be 3 mm in diameter and the loop closed so that the wire tip touches the wire shank. If not touching, a film does not form and the number of cells transferred is greatly reduced.

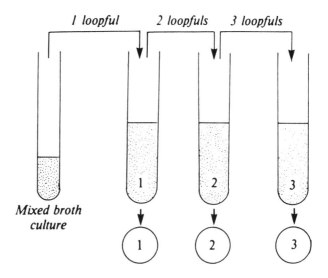

Figure 12-3. Steps in the loop-dilution pour plate method

3. Flame the inoculating loop and allow it to cool briefly. Transfer 1 loopful of the mixed culture of *Escherichia coli* and *Micrococcus luteus* to the first agar deep (Figure 12-3). Resterilize the inoculating loop. Mix by tapping the bottom of the tube rapidly with your forefinger and by rotating the tube between the palms of your hands (Figure 12-4).

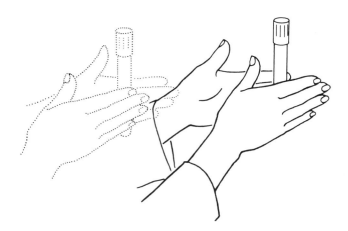

Figure 12-4. Rotate the tube back and forth to insure distribution of the inoculum

4. Flame the inoculating loop. Holding the first and second nutrient agar deeps, transfer 2 loopfuls of the suspension from tube No. 1 to tube No. 2. Reflame the loop. Mix tube No. 2 in the same manner as before.

5. Pour the contents of tube No.1 into the Petri plate labeled No.1. Swirl the agar so it covers the bottom of the plate.

6. Flame the inoculating loop. Holding the second and third nutrient agar deeps, transfer 3 loopfuls from tube No. 2 to tube No. 3. Reflame the loop. Mix tube No. 3 in the same manner as before.

7. Pour the contents of tube No. 2 into the Petri plate labeled No. 2 and swirl the agar gently.

8. Pour the contents of tube No. 3 into the third labeled Petri plate and treat as before.

9. After the agar has solidified, label the bottom of each plate with your name, the date and the exercise number.

10. Incubate at 30°C for 24 hours.

OBSERVATIONS

Period 2

11. Examine each of the plates for isolated colonies using the magnifying lens of the Quebec colony counter. Make a sketch from a section of each of the three plates to illustrate the amount of growth, distribution of growth and size of colonies. Note the appearance of subsurface colonies as compared with colonies growing on the agar surface (Figure 11-5).

THOUGHT QUESTIONS

1. Why do the subsurface colonies appear as small lens shaped structures?

2. If a cell were to come to rest *between* the agar and the plastic dish bottom and then grew, what do you think the resultant colony would look like? Why?

3. Is there any more guarantee that an isolated colony will be the resulting growth of a single cell with this technique than with the streak plate method? Why?

12. Pour Plate

RESULTS AND OBSERVATIONS

Plate No. 1   **Plate No. 2**   **Plate No. 3**

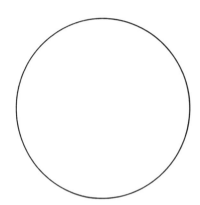   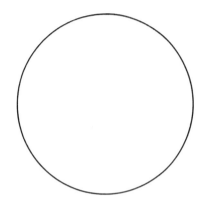   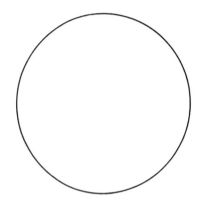

QUESTIONS

A. True or False Statements: Circle the correct response.

T F 1. You should be able to pour several plates from a container holding a large amount of melted medium before you reflame the neck of the container.

T F 2. Pour plates can be used to study colony morphology.

T F 3. When you are sure the melted agar covers the bottom of a Petri plate, you can move it to the incubator before solidification.

T F 4. The water level in the melted agar holding bath must always be just above the level of the media in your tubes or bottles.

T F 5. After inoculation of the melted agar, good distribution of the bacteria will occur by diffusion if allowed to sit at room temperature long enough.

T F 6. When you incubate a Petri plate, it should always be kept cover side down.

T F 7. Colonies embedded in the agar of a pour plate are smaller than surface colonies because they are younger and little oxygen is available to them.

T F 8. You should flame the neck of the inoculated melted agar tube before you pour the contents into a sterile Petri plate.

T F 9. The original inoculum contains many more cells per milliliter than does a milliliter of the first dilution.

T   F   10. If your inoculated tubes in this exercise solidify before you can pour your plates, all you need do is heat them again and pour your plates.

T   F   11. A freshly poured plate should be rotated carefully in a figure-8.

T   F   12. It doesn't matter if the plate rotation is so fast that agar slops up on the cover.

B. Completion:

13.   What is the predominant shape (i.e., form) of subsurface colonies? _____

14.   Which method of separating organisms, streak or pour plating, seems to achieve the best separation?

_____

15–16. Give 2 reasons why the nutrient agar must be cooled to 45°C before inoculating and pouring:

15. _____

16. _____

17.   The name of the instrument used to help count colonies on plates is the _____

_____ .

13 Enrichment Culture

OBJECTIVES

The student will be able to:

1. prepare an enrichment medium with a single carbon source.

2. isolate an organism able to use that carbon source.

3. explain the principle of "enrichment."

Virtually all organic matter entering the soil or water environment is ultimately degraded by microorganisms, even substances considered toxic such as phenol. Many complex organic substances are attacked by only a few microbes and these may often be in a decided minority numerically in any habitat under study. Attempts to isolate these are often unsuccessful when the conventional streak or pour plate techniques are used since these methods rely on the presence of fairly large numbers of a dominant organism. To improve the chance for isolation an **enrichment** technique may be used. A substrate is provided and organisms able to degrade it are stimulated to increase in numbers while other organisms can't grow. Successive transfers to a medium of the same composition further stimulates these special organisms and greatly improves chances for streak or pour plate isolation. The success of enrichment and the time involved in culturing and subculturing depends on the substrate used. In the interest of time, starch will be the substrate for this exercise although the principle is the same for more refractory materials such as phenol, petroleum, and cellulose. If time is available, one of these substrates may be used instead. The procedure used in this exercise will enrich for one or more organisms able to utilize starch as the sole carbon source with ammonium as the nitrogen source.

MATERIALS (per group)

1. 1 flask of *Solution A*: NH_4SO_4 0.2 g; KH_2HPO_4 0.1 g; soluble starch 2.0 g; 69 ml distilled water before autoclaving in 250 ml flask, sterile

2. 1 flask of *Solution B*: $CaCl_2$ 0.002 g; $FeSO_4 \cdot 7H_2O$ 0.001 g; 69 ml distilled water before autoclaving in 250 ml flask, sterile

3. 1 flask of *Solution C*: $MgSO_4 \cdot 7H_2O$ 0.04 g; $MnCl_2 \cdot 4H_2O$ 0.02; 69 ml distilled water before autoclaving in 250 ml flask, sterile

4. 1 flask water agar (agar 2 g in 69 ml distilled water before autoclaving in a calibrated 250 ml flask)

5. 5 Petri plates, sterile

6. 1 nutrient agar slant, sterile

7. 2 sterile 1 ml pipets

8. Soil sample

PROCEDURE AND OBSERVATIONS

This exercise may take 10 to 20 days to complete depending on the actual times of transfer.

Period 1

1. Melt the water agar and temper it to about 50°C.

2. Using aseptic technique pour solutions A and B into the C flask, mix well, and temper to 50°C.

3. Add about 50 ml of the combination to the water agar, mix well, and immediately divide the agar among 5 Petri plates.

4. Divide the remaining solution among flasks A, B, and C so that the volumes are about equal in all three.

5. Add about 5 g of soil to flask A (Figure 13-1). Reserve the other flasks for later subculturing.

6. Incubate the flask at 30°C for 2–3 days or until growth is well developed.

Period 2

7. Mix the growth well by swirling the flask in a circle.

8. Subculture 0.1 ml of the growth into flask B.

9. Incubate at 30°C for 2–3 days.

Period 3

10. Mix well as before and subculture 0.1 ml from flask B to flask C.

11. Incubate at 30°C for 2–3 days.

Period 4

12. Mix flask C as before and streak *one* of the agar plates reserved from the first period (Figure 13-1).

13. Incubate the plate at 30°C for 2 days.

Period 5–19

14. Add a small amount of Gram's iodine between the colonies on the plate and note whether starch is hydrolyzed (a clear zone develops around the colony — see Exercise 25 for more details). Avoid getting iodine on the colony.

15. Touch a colony showing starch hydrolysis with a sterile loop and streak a second plate for isolation.

16. Incubate as Period 4.

17. Repeat steps No. 14–16 three more times.

Last Period

18. From the last plate, transfer a colony to a nutrient agar slant and incubate it at 30°C for 1–2 days (Figure 13-1).

19. If desired this stock culture may be Gram stained (Exercise 16) and an endospore stain made (Exercise 18). This last procedure is important since this enrichment is very likely to produce a *Bacillus* sp. as an isolate.

THOUGHT QUESTIONS

1. Explain the meaning of "enrichment." What is the underlying principle?
2. All the substrates mentioned in the introduction are carbon compounds. Could any of these be used alone? What else is necessary?

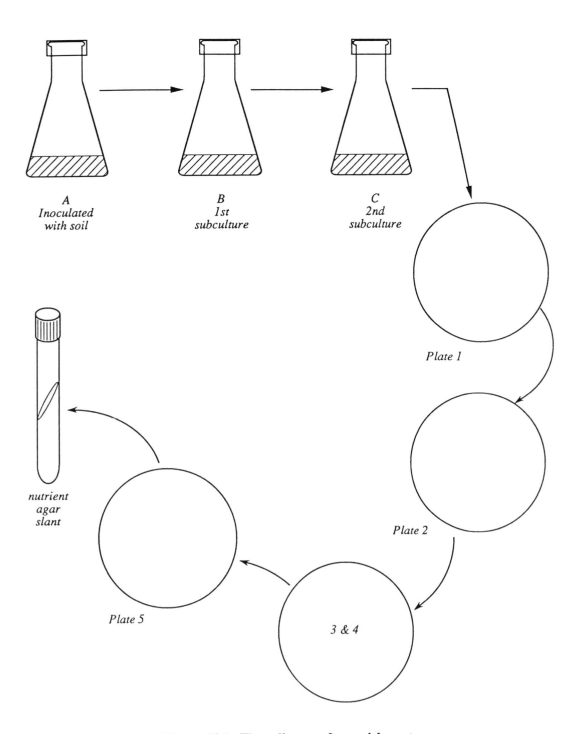

Figure 13-1. Flow diagram for enrichment

Name _____ Date _____ Grade _____

13. Enrichment Culture

RESULTS AND OBSERVATIONS

1. Sketch the appearance of growth in the flasks:

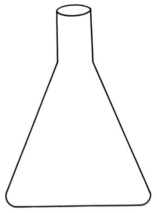 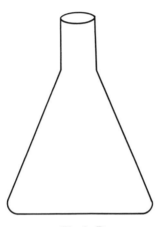 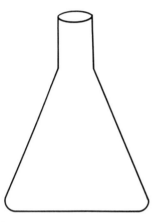

Flask A   Flask B   Flask C

Time of
incubation _____   _____   _____

Appearance of colonies on at least two plates. Include iodine.

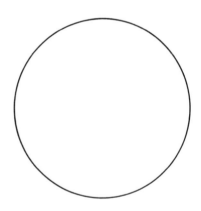 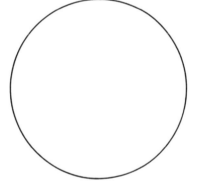

Microscopic description of isolates:

Gram reaction _____   Morphology _____

Endospore stain _____

Other _____

QUESTIONS

A. **True or False Statements:** Circle the correct response.

    T   F   1.   Starch contains nitrogen in the molecule.

    T   F   2.   Repeated streaking and restreaking of isolated colonies on agar plates is likely to produce pure cultures.

    T   F   3.   Starch is readily attacked by many organisms, phenol is not. Thus use of phenol as a sole carbon source would take longer to find a suitable organism.

    T   F   4.   Assuming a starch-using organism grows in the liquid medium, other organisms will not be able to grow.

B. **Completion:**

5. The procedure of encouraging the growth of an organism with a special biochemical capability is called _____ .

6. The shelf chemical used as the source of nitrogen in this exercise is _____ .

7. Of the alternate carbon sources suggested in this exercise, _____ would require homogenization or blending to make it readily available for microbial attack.

14 Media from Common Items

OBJECTIVES

The student will be able to:

1. recognize sources of media from various retail outlets.

2. use readily available kitchen items in preparing media.

3. prepare bacteriological media.

4. sterilize media without recourse to an autoclave.

Elementary and secondary school teachers frequently have need to prepare small amounts of materials for classroom demonstration of microbes, often with a limited budget. Such materials need to be readily available and inexpensive. This exercise is designed to show how teachers and others with limited resources can prepare bacteriological media in small quantities from readily available items. The student is expected to supply all of the materials from local retail stores or home in the quantities needed. This exercise can be done by the student at home if so desired.

MATERIALS (per person)

1. Media: The following ingredients can be obtained from local retail outlets such as a grocery store, drugstore, or health food store.

   a) Agar is sold under the generic name of agar-agar used in cooking, as a laxative or bulking agent. It may be difficult to find. Oriental food stores are the most likely source. Health food stores may carry it under the name of Erewhon Agar-Agar (Erewhon, Inc., Boston, MA 02210 or Los Angeles, CA 90230) or Westbrae Agar Flakes (Westbrae Natural Foods, Berkeley, CA 94706). These retail products may be more expensive. A less expensive source is Difco Agar (Difco, Detroit, MI 48232) which can be ordered from Difco, most chemical supply houses, or through your pharmacy.

   b) Gelatin purchased at your local grocery store may be used as a substitute for agar but melts at temperatures above 30°C. "Jello" or similar type products may be used, especially for molds, but these products are often too acid for bacteria without some neutralization.

   c) Broth media can be made from bouillion cubes (a meat extract), canned beef (or chicken) bouillion (these have the added advantage of being already sterile), powdered skim milk, etc. Do not use canned milk without first diluting it as it is often inhibitory.

   d) Special additives: Sugars such as cane or beet (sucrose), milk (lactose), invert (glucose + fructose), fructose, glucose (dextrose), corn syrup (glucose, high fructose), or maltose may be added to the above. Starch (for starch hydrolysis) later developed with tincture of iodine can also be used (see Exercise 25). Mixed protein powders are available at health food stores as well.

2) Equipment: Almost any heat resistant ("Pyrex®") kitchenware can be used as containers. Especially recommended are Mason jars, jam jars, or stainless steel pans which can be heat sterilized. Petri plate substitutes include saucers, cups, cut-off bottoms of tin or aluminum cans, and metal lids to food jars (e.g., mayonnaise) with the cardboard insert removed. Aluminum foil is used as a cover to prevent contamination, or the foil may be molded to form a dish.

3) Sterilizing: For liquids, a pressure cooker is most useful. However, simple boiling on three successive days (Tyndallization) can be used instead. For dry materials (no liquid whatever) such as glass jars, covers, cups, potential Petri plates, etc. covered with aluminum foil can be dry heat sterilized in a kitchen stove oven at 160°C (320°F) for 1 hour.

PROCEDURE (1–4 days)

Period 1

1. In the absence of a balance, weights of materials to be added can be estimated by assuming that water weighs one gram per ml and adding all ingredients in proportion. For example, agar is usually prepared at 1.5%, thus 1.5 tablespoons of agar are added to 100 tablespoons of liquid. The following proportions are commonly used: agar 1.5%, gelatin 12%, and sugars 1% in a nutrient broth or agar; skim milk 2–5%; protein powders 5–10%; canned bouillon soup is used as instructed on the product label.

2. The student should experiment with different formulations and equipment. The following is an example of preparing a nutrient agar:

   a) Dissolve one bouillon cube in the recommended amount of water in a heat stable container.

   b) Add 1.5% (1.5 parts to 100 parts) agar.

   c) Add 1% invert sugar or glucose (dextrose).

   d) Add 5% protein powder.

   e) Bring the mixture to a boil with *constant* stirring to avoid charring the agar. Be ready to remove the container from the heat upon boiling as the agar frequently causes the mixture to over the container edge. Continue boiling gently with constant stirring for 2–3 minutes until the agar is melted (appears clear).

   f) Cover with a piece of aluminum foil.

3. Sterilization can be done by pressure cooker or by Tyndallization.

   a) Place the container in a pressure cooker following the unit's directions and process for 15 minutes after reaching pressure (1 atm or 15 lbs). After cooling, the medium can be poured into previously sterilized containers (step No. 2 above).

   b) Tyndallization was named after John Tyndall, a physicist who developed the process in 1876. After the container of agar is boiled (step 2e above), it is incubated at room temperature for 24 hours after which it is heated to boiling again. This procedure is repeated at least one more time before the medium is used (i.e., poured into previously sterilized containers). The procedure allows heat resistant spores to germinate or become heat sensitive and are thus killed by the second or third boiling. Solidified agar media must be remelted by placing the container in a pan of boiling water until it melts. Direct exposure to flame or heat source will cause the agar to char since the agar does not melt until about 95°–98° C. This procedure is best for gelatin as well.

Period 2

4. Inoculation of the medium can be made with a small amount of soil, food, river water, one's elbow, or a throat swab. Streaking can be done with a sterile toothpick (place a container in the oven and sterilize) or a bent paper clip dipped in alcohol and flamed.

Period 3

5. Incubation should be at room temperature (20°–25° C) particularly if gelatin is used.

    Notes: After use *all* media should be sterilized by pressure cooking or Tyndallization. **DO NOT** simply discard into the trash as a health problem might arise.

THOUGHT QUESTIONS

1. Why does the placing of children's hands on an agar plate and then letting bacteria grow create a potential health hazard in disposing of the plates?

2. How should you dispose of such plates?

Name _____ Date _____ Grade _____

14. Media from Common Items

RESULTS AND OBSERVATIONS

Equipment   *Ingredients used*   *Sterilizing methods*

Observations:

QUESTIONS

A. **True or False Statements:** Circle the correct response.

T   F   1.   Agar melts at 50°C.

T   F   2.   Invert sugar is pure sucrose.

T   F   3.   Milk contains the sugar lactose.

T   F   4.   Dishes into which sterile medium is poured must themselves be sterile to prevent unwanted growth.

T   F   5.   In the absence of a balance, the ratio of one cup of agar to 100 cups of water is the same as one tablespoon of agar is to 100 tablespoons of water.

T   F   6.   A pressure cooker can be opened immediately after removal from a heat source.

T   F   7.   Tyndallization depends in part on the outgrowth of spores after heat treatment.

T   F   8.   Heat treatment of media and equipment after use, especially those with organisms from the human body, is essential to prevent the spread of possible pathogens.

B. **Completion:**

9–10.   Invert sugar consists of the monosaccharides _____ and _____ .

11.   The technique of intermittent application of heat to liquid media is named after the famous English physicist, John _____ .

12.   Agar melts at about _____ °C.

13–14.   Dry sterilization in a home oven is accomplished at _____ °C or _____ °F.

15–16.   If an organism does not hydrolyze starch on a medium including this carbohydrate, there is a _____ color around the colony when tincture of iodine is added. If the organism hydrolyzes starch, there (is/is not) _____ a color reaction around the colony.

17.   An older but still often encountered synonym of glucose is _____ .

UNIT *IV*

Staining Techniques

Although the microscope revealed to Leeuwenhoek a new world of "animalcules," this world remained functionally invisible until staining techniques were developed to distinguish the microorganisms from their environment, as well as from each other.

Unstained microorganisms are nearly transparent when observed by light microscopy and, subsequently, are difficult to see. Although modern microscopy has helped through the development of phase contrast and interference microscopes among others, staining of the cells to make them more visible still remains the standard tool. In addition to making cells more visible, special stains have been developed to detect special structures or chemicals. Various staining techniques are available (1) to permit easier visualization microscopically by providing contrast between microorganisms and their backgrounds, (2) to allow a more detailed examination of cells by utilizing higher magnifications, (3) to identify internal structures of the cell, and (4) to provide a means of differentiation of microbial species.

Staining is achieved by the use of benzene derivatives called **aniline (coal tar)** or **synthetic dyes**. Each dye molecule has two functional chemical groups with properties that respond to the electromagnetic energy of the light spectrum. The visual detection of color from these dye compounds is due to the **chromophore group**, which consists of unsaturated bonds that absorb specific wavelengths of light. The **auxochrome group** is an ionizing radical that gives the dye molecule increased solubility and salt-forming characteristics and the ability to react with the substrate.

Dyes are classified as **acidic** or **basic**, depending upon whether the chromophore is an anion (negatively charged) or cation (positively charged), respectively. Since the terms acidic and basic really are misnomers, it is more appropriate to refer to dyes as being **anionic (acidic)** or **cationic (basic)**.

Cationic dyes (e.g., methylene blue, crystal violet, carbolfuchsin) will react with substrate groups which ionize to product a negative charge. Anionic dyes (e.g., eosin, nigrosine) will react with substrate groups which ionize to produce positive charges. Since bacterial cells possess a variety of both kinds of staining substrate groups, they have the ability to combine with cationic or anionic dyes.

For practical purposes, bacterial stains can be divided into three groups: simple, differential, and special/structural stains. **Simple stains** (e.g., methylene blue) are single dyes used primarily to help visualize the normally transparent bacteria and do not differentiate between kinds of bacteria. The basis for simple staining is the fact that bacterial cells differ chemically from their surroundings; therefore, the cells can be stained to contrast with the environment. Chemical and physical differences among bacteria provide the basis for **differential stains**. The Gram and Ziehl-Neelsen stains are commonly used differential stains that separate bacteria according to their selective staining properties. **Special** or **structural stains** are used to provide the contrast necessary to visualize bacterial cell structures (e.g., capsules, flagella, endospores, inclusion granules, etc.). These latter stains are used more selectively as aids in the definitive identification of isolated bacteria. In this section students will have an opportunity to learn about and practice various staining procedures.

15 Smear Preparation and Simple Staining

OBJECTIVES

The student will be able to:

1. prepare a smear of proper density from a slant culture.

2. fix a smear with heat.

3. use a simple stain on a smear from teeth and gums.

4. describe the morphology of mouth and saliva organisms.

Unstained microbial cells are nearly transparent when observed by light microscopy and hence are difficult to see. Various staining techniques are available to permit easier visualization microscopically, a more detailed examination of cells, observation of internal cellular components, and a differentiation of cell types.

In order to stain microorganisms, a thin layer of cells called a **smear** must be made first. This is a simple process of spreading an aqueous suspension of cells on a glass slide and allowing it to air dry. This is followed by **fixation** (causing the cells to adhere to the slide) and the application of the staining solutions. **Stains** are generally made on smears from colonies or slants since the mass of cells is very great. The main problem is getting too many cells in the smear. Making smears of the right density can only be learned by experience. Smears can be made from broth cultures but several problems arise. The number of cells is usually very small making them hard to find on the slide. Nutrient carry over causes difficulty in fixing the cells to the slide and organic matter and salts may interfere with the staining process. Smears can also be made from other materials providing there are enough cells present to see under the microscope. At least 500,000 per ml are necessary for oil immersion. In this exercise, saliva and teeth scrapings are stained as well as pure culture smears.

This exercise has two objectives: one, to practice making a smear of the right density for staining; and two, to use a simple stain on a smear of material from around the teeth.

MATERIALS (per person)

1. 18-24 hour slant culture of *Escherichia coli*

2. 3 microscope slides

3. Cleanser

4. 95% ethyl alcohol

5. 13 mm clean test tube (need not be sterile)

6. Loeffler's methylene blue stain

PROCEDURE AND OBSERVATIONS (1 day)

A. Cleaning of Microscope Slides

Clean, grease-free slides are essential for obtaining good stained preparations. Before beginning any staining procedure, slides should be cleaned as follows:

1. Wet the tip of your index finger and rub it on some abrasive cleanser (e.g., Bon Ami, Comet, Ajax).

2. Spread the paste formed over both surfaces of the slide.

3. Wash the slide thoroughly with running water.

4. Apply several drops of 95% ethyl alcohol to the slide and allow it to air dry.

5. Flame the "up" side of the slide for a moment in the Bunsen burner. Allow it to cool.

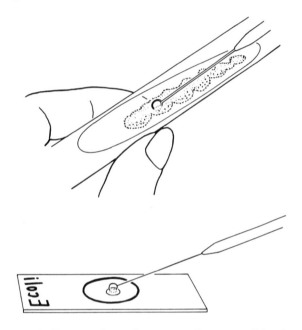

Figure 15-1. Preparation of a smear from a solid culture

B. Smear Preparation from a Solid Culture

1. Place 2 to 3 loopfuls of tap water on a previously labeled slide.

2. Flame the inoculating loop and cool for a few seconds.

3. Touch the growth on the slant with *one* side of the loop (Figure 15-1).

4. Very briefly touch the side of the loop with the cells to the drop and move it back and forth *once*.

5. Spread the cells to an area the size of a dime using the *other* side of the loop where no cells were present.

6. Resterilize the inoculating loop.

7. Allow the smear to air dry for at least 30 minutes. When dry, the smear may appear faintly cloudy or very little may be seen depending upon the amount of growth in the tube.

8. The smear must be "heat fixed" to be certain that the cells will adhere to the slide and not be washed off during staining procedures. This is accomplished by passing the slide (smear side up) back and forth through the flame of the Bunsen burner slowly three times (Figure 15-2). Do *not* overheat the slide. You should be able to touch the underside of the slide comfortably to the back of your hand.

9. Have your instructor critique the smear after drying. This is important since first smears are often too heavy for good staining.

10. This smear may be saved for use in Exercise 16, if desired.

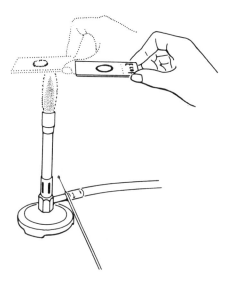

Figure 15-2. Heat fixation of an air dried specimen

C. Smear Preparation from Teeth

1. Force a little saliva rapidly back and forth across your front teeth and collect it in a test tube.

2. With a sterile inoculating loop, transfer 2 loopfuls to a clean slide and spread to form a thin film.

3. Resterilize the inoculating loop.

4. Allow the smear to air dry.

5. Heat fix as in step No. 8 of Part B.

6. Place the slide on a staining rack and flood with Loeffler's methylene blue for 30-60 seconds.

7. Rinse *quickly* with water and blot dry. Too long in the water removes most of the stain.

8. Examine under oil immersion and make drawings.

THOUGHT QUESTIONS

1. Do you think stained cells will be larger or smaller than live cells in a liquid medium? Why?

2. How is it possible to use non-sterile tap water containing bacteria in making stains?

3. What are the large nucleated cells doing in your saliva?

15. Smear Preparation and Simple Staining

RESULTS AND OBSERVATIONS

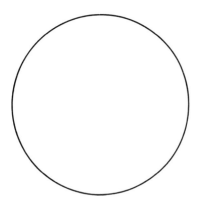

Organism ____**Smear from teeth**____

Morphology _____

Magnification _____

Stain _____

QUESTIONS

True or False Statements: Circle the correct response.

T F 1. Bacterial cells especially are difficult to see because their index of refraction is very similar to air.

T F 2. In making a smear, it is necessary to have as many cells in it as possible to find them better.

T F 3. A broth culture is a better source of organisms for staining than is a slant culture.

T F 4. Grease on the slide helps to make a good smear.

T F 5. Tap water can be used to make smears because there are too few bacteria (about 10,000 per ml) to see under oil immersion.

T F 6. To make the stain better, a smear has to be heated to a high temperature to make cells stick to the
slide.

T F 7. Virtually everyone has bacteria in their saliva.

T F 8. Assuming the number of cells cited in the introduction will result in about 1 cell per oil immersion field, if you had ten cells per field, you would have about 5,000,000 bacteria per ml of your saliva.

T F 9. Lymphocytes are found in saliva.

T F 10. Methylene blue is difficult to remove from cells.

16 Gram Stain

OBJECTIVES

The student will be able to:

1. prepare a Gram stain with consistent results.

2. know the Gram reaction of the organisms in this exercise.

3. recognize and describe the purpose and results of each step of the procedure.

4. list the reagents used and the timing of application.

Simple staining depends upon the fact that bacterial cells differ chemically from their surroundings and thus can be stained to contrast with their environment. Microorganisms also differ from one another chemically and physically and, therefore, may react differently to a given staining procedure. This is the basic principle of **differential staining** — a method of distinguishing between types of bacteria.

The Gram differentiation is based upon the application of a series of four chemical reagents: **primary dye**, **mordant**, **decolorizer**, and **counterstain**. The purpose of the primary dye, crystal violet, is to impart a purple or blue color to all organisms regardless of their designated Gram reaction. This is followed by the application of Gram's iodine, which acts as a mordant by enhancing the union between the crystal violet dye and its substrate by forming a complex. The decolorizing solution of acetone-alcohol extracts the complex from certain cells more readily than others. A safranin counterstain is applied in order to see those organisms previously decolorized by removal of the complex. Those organisms retaining the complex are Gram-positive (purple or blue), while those losing it are Gram-negative (pink or red).

MATERIALS (per person)

1. 18–24 hour slant cultures of *Escherichia coli, Bacillus cereus* and *Staphylococcus aureus*

2. Gram's crystal violet (with ammonium oxalate added)

3. Gram's iodine (Hucker modification)

4. Acetone-alcohol

5. Gram's safranin

PROCEDURE AND OBSERVATIONS (1 day)

1. Prepare smears of *Escherichia coli, Bacillus cereus* and *Staphylococcus aureus*. Air dry and heat fix. You may put all 3 smears on a single slide or on separate slides (Figure 16-1). However, be sure to label the smears carefully so that you can distinguish one organism from another. Smears on a single slide are most suitable since all smears are treated the same. This will be important later in controlling the staining procedure.

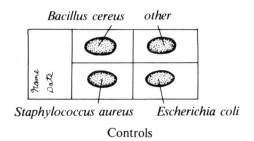

Controls

Figure 16-1. Preparation of a smear to be Gram stained

2. Apply Gram's crystal violet for 1-2 minutes.

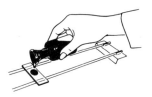

3. Wash off the excess stain by holding the slide under a stream of water. Do *not* tilt the slide until it is under the water.

4. Flood the slide with Gram's iodine and allow it to react for 1 minute or longer.

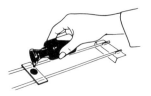

5. Rinse as in step no. 3. Shake the excess water off or blot lightly, but *not* to dryness.

6. Holding the slide at an angle, carefully add the decolorizing solution one drop at a time. As soon as color stops coming off the slide, after about 8-10 seconds, rinse with water to stop the decolorizing action.

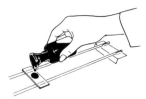

7. Flood the slide with Gram's safranin and allow it to react for 30-60 seconds.

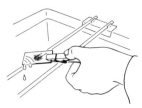

8. Drain the excess stain from the slide and thoroughly wash it.

9. Carefully blot the stained slide using a paper towel. Do *not* rub.

10. Examine with the oil immersion objective. Make a representative drawing of each organism, noting Gram reaction and morphology.

THOUGHT QUESTIONS

1. What is the nature of the cell walls of Gram-positive and Gram-negative organisms?

2. What effect is the wall structure thought to have on the ability to loose the dye-iodine complex?

3. How do you account for Gram-variable bacteria?

4. Why isn't the Gram stain useful for organisms other than eubacteria?

16. Gram Stain

RESULTS AND OBSERVATIONS

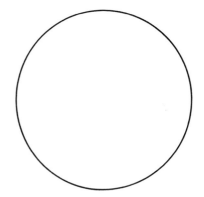

Organism _____*Escherichia coli*_____

Morphology _____

Gram Reaction_____

Organism _____*Staphylococcus aureus*_____

Morphology _____

Gram Reaction _____

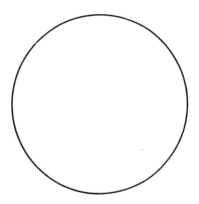

Organism _____*Bacillus cereus*_____

Morphology _____

Gram Reaction _____

QUESTIONS

A. **True or False Statements:** Circle the correct response.

T (F) 1. Over decolorization in the Gram staining method results in all the cells being Gram-positive.

T F 2. The cell wall of Gram-positive organisms appears to be less permeable to the effects of the decolorizer, because it has a lower lipid content than the cell wall of Gram-negative organisms.

T F 3. Gram-negative and Gram-positive cells look the same under the microscope after decolorization of the first two reagents of the Gram stain.

T F 4. Sporeforming bacteria are, for the most part, Gram-negative.

(T) (F) 5. The Gram reaction of a specific bacterial species will never vary if the staining procedure is consistent.

(T) F 6. Gram reactions are reliable only for cultures 24 hours old or younger.

(T) F 7. Excessive washing can remove the primary dye or dye-iodine complexes within the cells.

(T) F 8. All smears are heat fixed unless contraindicated by the procedure.

(T) F 9. The amount of inoculum is the most important factor in making a "good" smear.

T F 10. *Staphylococcus aureus* and *Pseudomonas aeruginosa* are Gram-positive organisms.

T (F) 11. The most critical step in making the Gram stain is the application of safranin.

T F 12. The organisms in a Gram-variable smear usually belong to the Gram-positive group.

(T) F 13. A culture which is too old may be Gram-variable when stained.

B. **Completion:**

14. A preparation made by mixing a loopful of water and a bit of agar slant culture on a glass slide is called a ___smear plate___.

15. The Gram stain is a ___differential___ (type) stain.

16. All members of the genus *Neisseria* are Gram- _____ .

17. Endospores usually appear _____ in a completed Gram stain.

18–33. Fill in the table below to show the changes in Gram-positive and Gram-negative bacteria during each major step of the staining process.

Reagent	Purpose	Microscopic Appearance of	
		G+ Organisms	G– Organisms
Crystal Violet	Primary Dye – Colors all tubes	violet	violet
Iodine (Hucker Mod)	Mordant – Set primary dye forming Complex	violet	~~clear~~ violet
Acetone – Alcohol	Decolorizer extract complex from some cells	violet	clear
Safranin	Counterstain – highlights decolorized cells – G+(p/v)G(pk/red)	violet	red

17 Acid-Fast Stain

OBJECTIVES

The student will be able to:

1. perform an acid-fast stain.

2. list the reagents used and the method of application for each step of the procedure.

3. describe the purpose and result of applying each reagent.

4. name the genera in which the acid-fast property is found.

5. name two human diseases caused by acid-fast organisms.

6. describe the morphology and chemical characteristics of acid-fast organisms.

Acid-fastness is a characteristic limited to the members of the genus *Mycobacterium* and a few *Nocardia* species.

In the **Ziehl-Neelsen** method, carbolfuchsin is utilized as the primary stain. Because of the waxy, impermeable cell wall, heat is required to drive the dye into the acid-fast bacilli. The acid-alcohol decolorizer removes the red of the carbolfuchsin from all organisms except the acid-fast bacilli. Counterstaining with methylene blue colors the non-acid-fast organisms blue, while the acid-fast organisms appear red.

MATERIALS (per person)

1. 18-24 hour slant culture of *Staphylococcus aureus*

2. 72 hour slant culture of *Mycobacterium smegmatis*

3. Ziehl-Neelsen carbolfuchsin

4. Acid-alcohol

5. Loeffler's methylene blue

PROCEDURE AND OBSERVATIONS (1 day)

1. Prepare a mixed smear of *Staphylococcus aureus* and *Mycobacterium smegmatis*. Air dry and heat fix.

2. Flood the smear with the Ziehl-Neelsen carbolfuchsin and allow it to stand for about 1 minute.

3. Heat the preparation to steaming by inverting your Bunsen burner and passing the flame over the stain, or under the slide, moving back and forth the width of the stain (Figure 17-1).

4. Remove the burner when you see steam rising from the stain. When the steam stops rising, pass the flame over or under the stain again as necessary to keep the smear just at steaming. Steam for 5 minutes. Do not boil nor allow the smear to dry. Add the carbolfuchsin as needed to prevent loss of the stain by evaporation.

Steam comes from slide

5. Allow the slide to cool to prevent breaking. Keep adding stain as the slide cools, since the stain continues to evaporate.

6. Wash with water.

7. Holding the slide at an angle, carefully add the acid-alcohol solution one drop at a time to the smear until the red color stops coming off the slide. Immediately rinse with water to stop the decolorizing action.

8. Counterstain with Loeffler's methylene blue for 1 minute.

9. Rinse the slide with water.

10. Carefully blot the stained slide using a paper towel. Do *not* rub.

11. Examine with the oil immersion objective. Draw representative cells in the circle provided on the laboratory report form. Acid-fast organisms tend to clump together because of the waxy cell wall. It may be necessary to examine a large number of fields to find cells.

THOUGHT QUESTIONS

1. What is the nature of the cell wall of these organisms?

2. These organisms are highly hydrophobic. What consequence would this have on the ecology and growth patterns of free-living forms?

Figure 17-1. Steam but avoid boiling

Name _____ Date _____ Grade _____

17. Acid-Fast Stain

RESULTS AND OBSERVATIONS

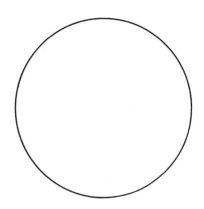

Staphylococcus aureus
+
Organisms ___*Mycobacterium smegmatis*___

Magnification _____

Stain _____

QUESTIONS

A. True or False Statements: Circle the correct response.

T (F) 1. Bacterial species which are acid-fast are quite common.

T F 2. Acid-fast organisms are relatively resistant to drying and to disinfectants.

T F 3. The Gram stain decolorizing agent is stronger than the one used in the Ziehl-Neelsen acid-fast procedure.

T (F) 4. Methylene blue serves as the primary stain in the acid-fast stain.

(T) F 5. The inoculating loop must be resterilized between cultures when preparing a mixed smear.

B. Completion:

6. Carbolfuchsin is prepared by adding _Phenol Carbolic acid_ to basic fuchsin.

7-9. The acid-fast stain identifies microorganisms with a high _Cell-wall lipid_ content. The primary stain is not washed out by the _Acid-alcohol_ decolorizer and the cells are said to be _acid-fast_ .

10. Members of the genus _Mycobacterium_ are usually acid-fast.

11-14. Name 2 pathogenic acid-fast bacteria and the disease that each one causes.

Organism		Disease	
11. *M. tuberculosis*		12. *tuberculosis*	
13. *M. leprae*		14. *leprosy.*	

15-26. Fill in the table below to show the changes in acid-fast and non-acid-fast bacteria during each major step of the Ziehl-Neelsen acid-fast method.

Reagent	Purpose	Appearance of Cells	
		Acid-Fast	Non-Acid-Fast
Carbolfuchsin	stain µBes.	Red	Red
Acid-Alcohol	decolorizer	Red	Clear
Methylene Blue	Counterstain	Red	blue

18 Endospore Stain

OBJECTIVES

The student will be able to:

1. perform an endospore stain.

2. list the reagents used and the method of application for each step of the procedure.

3. describe the purpose and result of applying each reagent.

4. name two of the genera in which endospores are found.

5. name two diseases caused by endospore formers.

6. describe the morphology of endospore formers.

Species of the Gram-positive genera *Bacillus* and *Clostridium* produce a structure referred to as the **endospore**. Unlike the vegetative cell producing it, the endospore is highly resistant to a variety of physical and chemical agents, such as high temperatures, drying, radiation and disinfectants. The location, shape, and whether swelling the cell or not (Figure 18-1) are useful in identifying the species of this group.

The endospore, however, is *not* formed as a response to adverse conditions but is due to a change in the nutritional environment. The endospore is a part of the life cycle of the sporeforming bacteria.

The nature of the endospore requires vigorous treatment for staining. Once stained, the endospore resists decolorization and counterstaining. The Schaeffer-Fulton method uses hot malachite green as the primary dye to drive the dye into the endospore. After a decolorizing wash with water, safranin is applied as the counterstain. Vegetative cells accept the counterstain and appear red, while the endospores appear as small, green structures.

MATERIALS (per person)

1. 18-24 hour slant culture of *Staphylococcus aureus*

2. 12-18 hour slant culture of *Bacillus cereus* on manganese agar

3. 5% aqueous malachite green

4. 0.5% aqueous safranin

PROCEDURE AND OBSERVATIONS (1 day)

1. Prepare a mixed smear of *Staphylococcus aureus* and *Bacillus cereus*. Air dry and heat fix.

2. Cut a piece of paper toweling to cover the smear, yet not hang over the sides of the slide. Place the paper strip on the slide (Figure 18-2).

3. Saturate the paper and smear with malachite green and allow it to stand for about 1 minute (Figure 18-3).

4. Heat the preparation to steaming by inverting your Bunsen burner and passing the flame over the stain, or under the slide, moving back and forth the width of the stain (Figure 18-4).

5. Remove the burner when you see steam rising from the stain. When the steam stops rising, pass the flame over or under the stain again as necessary to keep the smear just at steaming. Steam for 5 minutes. Do not boil nor allow the smear to dry. Add malachite green as needed to prevent loss of the stain by evaporation.

6. Allow the slide to cool to prevent breaking. Keep adding stain as the slide cools, since the stain continues to evaporate.

7. Wash with water. Discard paper toweling.

8. Apply the 0.5% safranin counterstain and allow it to react for 30-60 seconds.

9. Wash with water and blot dry using a paper towel. Do *not* rub.

10. Examine with the oil immersion objective. Draw representative cells in the circle provided on the laboratory report form. Note the position of the spore within the vegetative cell. Also label the different structures appropriately (i.e., endospore, vegetative cell).

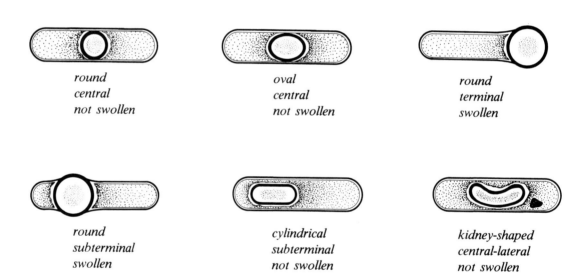

round
central
not swollen

oval
central
not swollen

round
terminal
swollen

round
subterminal
swollen

cylindrical
subterminal
not swollen

kidney-shaped
central-lateral
not swollen
parasporal body

Figure 18-1. Endospores — shape, location, and swelling. Intermediate locations and shapes often occur.

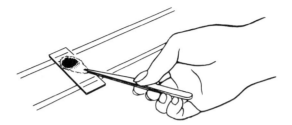

Figure 18-2. Apply paper towel

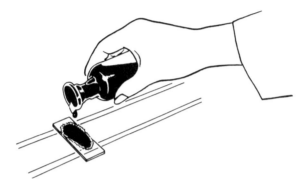

Figure 18-3. Add malachite green

Figure 18-4. Steam but avoid boiling

THOUGHT QUESTIONS

1. The endospore is often described as not being a reproductive spore. What does this mean?

2. What are the steps involved in the development of an endospore?

3. Why is the endospore so heat resistant?

18. Endospore Stain

RESULTS AND OBSERVATIONS

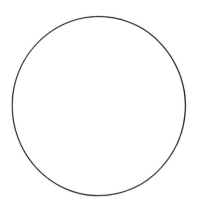

Staphylococcus aureus
+
Bacillus cereus

Organisms _____

Position of Spore _____

Magnification _____

Stain _____

QUESTIONS

A. **True or False Statements:** Circle the correct response.

T F 1. Water functions as the decolorizer in the Schaeffer-Fulton method.

T F 2. The bacterial endospore is more resistant to adverse environmental conditions than is the vegetative cell.

T F 3. Sporulation is triggered by a change in the nutritional environment of certain organisms.

T F 4. Safranin is the primary stain in the Schaeffer-Fulton method.

T F 5. The endospore is the dormant or resting phase of the bacterial cell.

T F 6. Manganese agar stimulates the formation of endospores.

T F 7. Because the spore coat is so resistant, the stained spore tends to decolorize rapidly if the smear is washed too much before the counterstain is applied.

T F 8. The size and location of the spore within the vegetative cell are dependent upon physical and chemical conditions in the environment during sporulation.

B. Completion:

9–20. Fill in the table below to show the changes in sporeforming and non-sporeforming bacteria during each major step of the Schaeffer-Fulton method.

Reagent	Purpose	Spores	Vegetative Cells

21. The Schaeffer-Fulton method is a _____ (type) stain.

22–24. The genus _____ consists of anaerobic sporforming bacteria. Some cause diseases such as _____ and _____ .

25–26. The genus _____ consists of aerobic sporeforming bacteria. Some can cause the disease _____ .

27. Sporeforming bacteria are _____ (morphology).

28–30. Identify the location of the endospore in each of the following drawings.

Location

28. ·_____

29. _____

30. _____

19 Negative Stain

OBJECTIVES

The student will be able to:

1. prepare a negative stain of one or more organisms.

2. describe the theory of the negative stain.

Many eubacteria and cyanobacteria form a **glycocalyx** around the cell variously called slime, a capsule, or a sheath. Usually made of **polysaccharide** polymers, these structures distort and shrink and are very difficult to see in normally stained preparations. They are even more difficult to see in live preparations. A number of methods have been described to stain the capsular material but the best remains a negative stain procedure. This provides a dark background excluded by the glycocalyx allowing it to be seen as a clear area. The cell may or may not be stained. The method of Duguid is the simplest and is widely used. This exercise will introduce the student to the a modification of Duguid's negative stain.

MATERIALS (per person)

1. 5 day old lactose agar slant culture of *Klebsiella pneumoniae*

2. 2 glass slides

3. Dropper bottle of India ink (a suspension of carbon particles)

4. Coverslip

5. Bibulous or blotter paper

PROCEDURE AND OBSERVATIONS (1 day)

1. Place a large drop of India ink near the end of a glass slide (Figure 19-1a).

2. With a sterile loop, emulsify some growth from the slant culture of *K. penumoniae* in the drop of ink (Figure 19-1b).

3. With the second slide held at an angle of about 30° from the horizontal, touch the drop as illustrated in Figures 19-1c and d drawing back slightly to wet the entire edge of the slide.

4. Push the slide away from the drop end, maintaining the 30° angle, at a moderate speed (Figure 19-1e). This provides a smear of gradually decreasing thickness.

5. Drop a coverslip on the slide about halfway from the center to the end where the original drop was placed (Figure 19-1f).

6. Place bibulous paper on the slide over the coverslip and gently press down the *edge of the coverslip nearest the center of the slide* (Figure 19-1f). This will result in a thick preparation on one side of the coverslip and thin on the other.

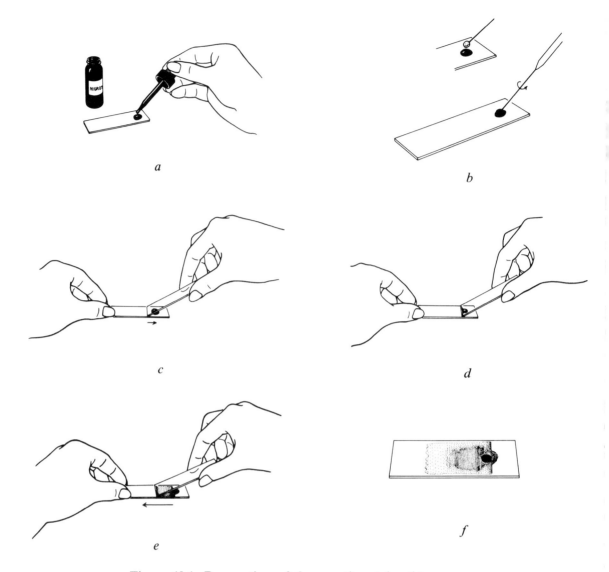

Figure 19-1. Preparation of the negative stain slide

7. Place the slide on the microscope stage, focus under low and high powers and go to oil immersion. Scan the slide from the thin side of the coverslip to the thick side looking for clear areas embedded in a black or dark background. The cell itself will be hard to see since it is not stained. Your diaphragm and condenser must be at optimum positions.

8. If the cells are too difficult to see, prepare a new slide with a loopful or two of safranin added to the India ink.

9. Make a drawing on the report form of what you see.

THOUGHT QUESTIONS

1. What materials *other* than polysaccharides can capsules be composed of?

2. Can you name any widely used products in industry, medicine, foods, or the research laboratory made from capsules or glycocalyx of bacteria?

3. Are glycocalyx materials limited to prokaryotes? In what other organisms are they found?

Name _____ Date _____ Grade _____

19. Negative Stain

RESULTS AND OBSERVATIONS

Make a drawing of your observations and describe what you see.

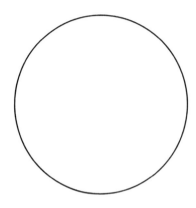

QUESTIONS

Completion:

1. India ink consists of a suspension of _____.

2–4. Glycocalyx is a name given to _____ , _____ ,

   and _____ .

5. In what group of organisms is a sheath a prominent structure? _____

6. The "negative stain" is so-called because the capsule _____
   the India ink particles.

7. Name (genus and species) one important pathogen, other than the one used in this exercise that
   forms a prominent capsule.

   _____

20 Flagella Stain

OBJECTIVES

The student will be able to:

1. perform a flagella stain on one or more bacterial cultures.

2. indicate the type of flagellation for the cultures provided.

3. explain the theory of flagella staining.

The arrangement and shape of flagella on bacterial cells are of considerable taxonomic importance and play an important role in **chemotaxis** or **phototaxis**. Bacterial flagella are normally too small in diameter to be seen in the light microscope, although bunches or tufts can be seen on some of the larger motile cells. While the electron microscope permits study of the details of flagellar structure, the cost and availability of such equipment can be prohibitive. Flagella staining is a technique that allows examination of flagellar morphology in most laboratories. The technique causes a **dye** and a **mordant**, under suitable electrolyte conditions, to build up around the flagellum. This provides color and increases the apparent diameter until the flagellum is large enough to be seen under the microscope. It is not a difficult procedure, although it often requires time and repetition for good results. Scrupulous adherence to slide cleanliness, culture preparation, and gentle handling are essential to the success of this technique.

Flagella are described by location, number, wavelength, amplitude, and overall length (Figure 20-1). Although at one time thought to be an invariant feature of a species, the location and length are often variable under different environmental conditions and from strain to strain. Location may be **polar** (at one or both ends), **lateral**, **peritrichous** (all over), **lophotrichous** (a tuft at both ends), or **multitrichous** (numerous). Length is usually measured on a number of cells and an average calculated. Wavelength and amplitude are also measured on many cells and averaged.

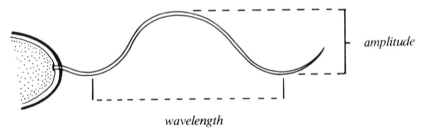

Figure 20-1. Bacterial flagella

MATERIALS (per person)

1. 3 tubes each with 5 ml of bacteriologically filtered, sterile distilled water

2. Wax pencil-best choice Blaisdell Clinical Glass-red 569T

3. 3 slides per organism

4. Flagella stain (pararosaniline, tannic acid, NaCl) sufficient for class

5. 3 Pasteur pipets with bulbs

6. 3 sterile 1 ml pipets

7. 15–18 hour old nutrient agar slants of *Pseudomonas aeruginosa*, *Proteus vulgaris*, and *Aquaspirillum serpens*

PROCEDURE AND OBSERVATIONS (1 day)

1. One of three methods may be used for obtaining scrupulously clean slides:

   a) heat the slide in a Bunsen flame until it shows yellow around the edges, allow to cool; or,

   b) loose-pack slides in a muffle furnace for 20 minutes at 400°C; or,

   c) a slurry of cleanser (e.g., Ajax, Bon Ami) is allowed to dry on the slide in a thin film and removed with a tissue.

2. Warm the slide in the flame and while still hot, make a *heavy* wax line across the center of the slide, then around the outer edge of one end of the slide so that one-half of the slide area is ringed by a heavy wax border (Figure 20-2a). Do not overheat but keep the slide warm enough so that the wax pencil melts while forming the ring. It is important that the wax border be thick, heavy, and without breaks. Prepare all slides in a like manner.

3. If not already mixed and provided for use, mix the dye components in the ratio 1:1:1.

4. With a safety bulb, pipet 1 ml of distilled water to one of the slant cultures provided and agitate by shaking gently. **DO NOT** rub the slant with the pipet as flagella may shear off.

5. With the same pipet transfer, drop by drop, some of the washing to a tube of 5 ml of distilled water until the liquid is somewhat turbid to the eye. Agitate *gently* and allow to sit at 30°C for 5–10 minutes.

6. With a Pasteur pipet and bulb place one drop of the tube (5 above) near the center wax line of one of the prepared slides (Figure 20-2b). Tilt the slide so that the drop runs to the wax line at the opposite end (Figures 20-2c and d). Continue to tilt the slide back and forth so that the drop covers as much of the area within the wax lines as possible. **DO NOT** spread with a loop or other instrument. **DO NOT** fix in any way. Outline the limits of the smear on the *underside* of the slide lightly with the wax pencil. This reduces scanning time. Let the slide air dry.

7. Pipet 1 ml of the complete stain onto the air dried smear, taking care that the entire volume of the dye is within the wax boundary (Figure 20-2e). If dye runs out of the boundary, discard the slide and make another preparation. Let it sit for 10 minutes. If the stain is unsuccessful the time may be increased (usually) (Figure 20-2f). It is often convenient to prepare three slides at the same time, staining one 8 minutes, one 10 minutes, and one 13 minutes.

8. *Float* the stain off of the slide with a large volume of water. Do not pour the stain off (Figure 20-2g).

9. **DO NOT** blot but allow the slide to drain dry (Figure 20-2h). Counterstaining is not necessary.

10. Examine with the oil immersion lens, beginning at the smear origin. Both cells and flagella will appear dark red. Loose flagella should be ignored and only those attached to cells studied. The best areas should have cells separated by some distance so that flagella are not entangled. Searching the slide is time consuming. If available, a binocular microscope can reduce eye strain. If no satisfactory cells are found prepare new slides and increase the stain time.

11. Using the calibrated ocular micrometer (Exercise 2) measure cell length and width, flagella length, amplitude, and wavelength on a number of cells, entering the averages on the record sheet.

THOUGHT QUESTIONS

1. What is the nature of chemotaxis? How does it operate?

2. Which way do flagella rotate?

3. What are smooth runs and tumbles?

Figure 20-2a

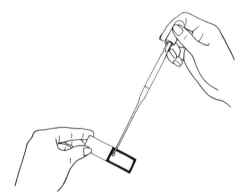

Figure 20-2b

Figure 20-2c

Figure 20-2d

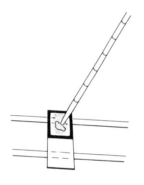

Figure 20-2e

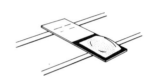

Figure 20-2f

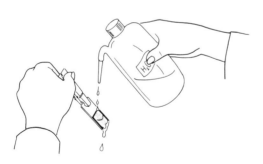

Figure 20-2g

Figure 20-2h

20. Flagella Stain

RESULTS AND OBSERVATIONS

	P. aeruginosa	*P. vulgaris*	*A. serpens*
Best stain time	_____	_____	_____

Drawings

Flagellation

name(s)	_____	_____	_____
length (mm)	_____	_____	_____
amplitude (μm)	_____	_____	_____
wavelength (μm)	_____	_____	_____

QUESTIONS

Completion:

1. Bacterial response to chemicals is called _Chemotaxis_.

2. A tuft of flagella on both ends of the cell is called _lophotrichous_ flagellation.

3. Tannic acid serves as a _mordant_ in this stain procedure.

4. A single flagellum on one end of a cell would be called _polar_ for location and _monotrichous_ for number.

21 Inclusion Granule Stains

OBJECTIVES

The student will be able to:

1. make a lipid stain and/or a polyphosphate stain.

2. describe the nature of the lipid storage material.

3. describe the nature of the polyphosphate storage material and name one disease where the stain plays an important role in identification.

Prokaryotes store a variety of materials intracellularly such as sulfur, calcium carbonate, polyphosphate, poly-beta-hydroxybutyric acid, cyanophycin, and glycogen- or starch-like materials. Eukaryotes also store materials especially glycogen, starch, and oils. Different methods are used to demonstrate the presence of one or the other. This exercise will introduce staining methods for **poly-beta-hydroxybutyric acid** and **polyphosphate**.

Polyphosphate is a linear polymer of ortho-phosphate molecules possibly associated with protein. Originally described as **metachromatic (volutin)** granules because of the appearance of a change in color of the dye used to stain them. Toluidine blue appears red in these granules. The presence of these granules has long been used to distinguish *Corynebacterium diphtheriae* from other similar organisms. Phosphate stored in this form loses some of its osmotic pressure producing characteristics and removes two active bond-forming groups resulting in less stress on the organism.

Poly-beta-hydroxybutyric acid (PHB) is a widely formed polymer of beta-hydroxybutyric acid removing an active bond-forming group and reducing the osmotic stress on the organism. This polymer behaves as a lipid and can be stained with fat stains such as Sudan black. Granules are fairly large and refractory and can be seen without staining using phase contrast microscopy. PHB is formed best under a high carbon to nitrogen ratio. Much of the carbon remaining after complete utilization of the nitrogen goes into PHB.

MATERIALS (per person)

A. Polyphosphate stain

1. 18–24 hour old culture of *Corynebacterium diphtheriae* (avirulent)

2. 1% toluidine blue

3. Slides

B. Poly-beta-hydroxybutyrate stain

1. 24 hour old slant culture of *Bacillus megaterium*

2. 0.3% Sudan black B

3. Xylene

4. 0.5% safranin

PROCEDURE AND OBSERVATIONS (1 day)

A. Polyphosphate

1. Prepare a smear, let air dry, and heat fix it.

2. Add 1% toluidine blue stain for 10–30 seconds.

3. Rinse with tap water and blot dry.

4. Examine under the oil immersion lens for reddish granules in cells stained faintly blue.

5. On the report form, make a drawing and write a description of a representative field.

B. Poly-beta-hydroxybutyrate stain

1. Clean a slide carefully with a final rinse in xylene.

2. Prepare a smear, let air dry, and heat fix.

3. Cover the smear with a *small* amount of 0.3% Sudan black B and let stand for 10 minutes.

4. Remove the dye by blotting with filter or bibulous paper.

5. Dip the slide in xylene until decolorized. Blot dry.

6. Counterstain with 0.5% safranin for 5–10 seconds, rinse in running water, and blot dry.

7. Examine under the oil immersion lens looking for dark or black granules in a pink to red cell.

8. On the report form, make a drawing and write a description of a representative field.

THOUGHT QUESTIONS

1. What is cyanophycin? What group of organisms is it found in and with what cell process is it associated?

2. In what groups of organisms is sulfur found as a storage inclusion? For what is it used?

3. Which of the compounds listed in the opening paragraph (if any) belong uniquely to the prokaryotes?

Name _____ Date _____ Grade _____

21. Inclusion Granule Stains

RESULTS AND OBSERVATIONS

Make a drawing in the space provided and write a description below the drawing.

Polyphosphate   *Poly-beta-hydroxybutyrate*

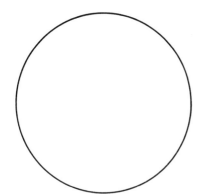 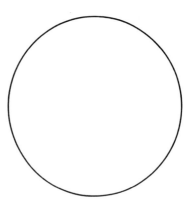

QUESTIONS

Completion:

1–2. Two benefits to the cell of making polymers of phosphate and beta-hydroxybutyric acid is to reduce ___*Osmotic*___ pressure and remove *active bond forming* groups.

3. The stain used for polyphosphate is _____ .

4. The stain used for poly-beta-hydroxybutyrate is _*Sudan black B*_____ .

5–6. Name two non-phosphate inorganic inclusions found in bacteria:
   5. _*Sulfur*_____   6. _*Calcium Carbonate*_

7–8. Name two organic inclusions other than PHB found in bacteria:
   7. _*Cyanophycin*_____   8. _*glycogen ?*_____

9. _____ is a disease in which the causative organism is based in part on polyphosphate granules.

22 Acridine Orange Fluorescent Stain

OBJECTIVES

The student will be able to:

1. perform an acridine orange direct microscopic count (or observation).

2. describe the activity of acridine orange in a cell.

3. explain how the membrane filter is used in this method.

Fluorochromes are dyes which emit visible light when excited by ultraviolet wavelengths. **Fluorescence microscopy** depends on the staining of a cell or its products with a fluorochrome dye and then observing the fluorescence produced with a microscope using ultraviolet light and special lenses. Two types of microscopes are used, the epiluminescent type and the transmission type which are modifications of a standard microscope. Both are described in the introduction to Unit I. The epifluorescent type is preferred. The principle of the method is simple. Filters screen out all visible light between the lamp and the slide giving a black field. If a fluorochrome is excited, then the resultant light is passed through another filter between the slide and the eyepiece so that fluorescence appears as a colored cell against a dark background. If no fluorescence occurs, the field is uniformly black. The most common use of fluorescence microscopy is in the **fluorescent antibody** technique. A fluorochrome is conjugated with an antibody and if the antibody combines with a cell, then the resulting combination can be seen as a visible fluorescence. This technique is described in Exercise 91. A second use is in counting bacteria in water and soil samples using a dye which specifically stains cells. Perhaps the most commonly used dye is **acridine orange** which stains DNA. The color of the fluorescence in cells not treated with solvents has been suggested as indicating whether they are living (active and green) or dead (dormant and red). Much more research needs to be done to demonstrate the validity of this observation. The following exercise illustrates the acridine orange counting procedure. This technique can be modified for use with soil.

PART I. EPIFLUORESCENCE METHOD (preferred method)

MATERIALS (per person or group)

1. Epifluorescence microscope with an exciter filter passing light in the 420–430 nm range; a barrier filter cutting off all wavelengths below 500 nm; a 200 watt mercury vapor lamp (or other suitable UV source); an eyepiece with a Whipple grid or ruled reticule

2. 25 mm or 13 mm diameter membrane filters, pore size 0.2 μm

3. 25 mm or 13 mm membrane filter units or Swinney filters with syringes may be used instead

4. Isopropanol

5. 0.01% acridine orange solution. Must be filtered through a 0.2 μm membrane filter on *each* day used to remove any bacteria growing during the storage period.

6. Glass slides

7. Coverslips

8. Immersion oil

9. Sample of river or lake water low in phytoplankton numbers

PROCEDURE AND OBSERVATIONS (1 day)

1. Place the filter in position in the filter unit as instructed.

2. Filter 10–50 ml of the water sample (1–10 for the 13 mm filter). This will be satisfactory for most natural waters not heavily polluted. Adjust the volume if necessary to give 10–20 bacteria per field of observation.

3. Turn off the vacuum and add 0.5 ml of 0.01% acridine orange (enough to cover the filter surface). Allow this to stand for 1 minute.

4. Vacuum off the stain and again break the vacuum.

5. Add 1 ml of isopropanol and immediately apply the vacuum.
   Note: The isopropanol is necessary to remove background fluorescence from the filter.

6. Without breaking the vacuum, remove the filter, place it on a paper towel and let it dry.

7. Place two drops of oil on a glass slide, and place the filter on top of the oil. (The filter can be cut in half if desired). Then place one drop of oil on the top of the filter and follow it with a coverslip.

8. If the microscope field diameter or Whipple grid has not been calibrated, do this now using the directions in Exercise 2. The barrier and exciter filters will have to be removed for this step.

9. Place the filter-slide preparation on the microscope stage and observe briefly under the high-dry objective. Then place a drop of oil on the coverslip and turn to the oil immersion lens.

10. Count all red, green, orange or yellow cells in the field of view for a total bacterial count. This should be subdivided into rods, cocci, spirals, and other shapes. Count at least ten fields for a total of about 200 bacteria. If there are too few or too many, readjust the water volume at step 2 and repeat.

    Note: A wet mount modification of this procedure can distinguish quantitatively between metabolically active (viable) and inactive or dead cells as discussed in the introduction.

PART II. TRANSMISSION FLUORESCENCE METHOD

MATERIALS (per person or group)

1. Transmission fluorescence microscope equiped as described in Part I Materials
2. 0.01% acridine orange solution
3. 1 dilution bottle with 0.1% peptone water, sterile
4. Tweezers
5. 1 Petri plate
6. 1 Pasteur pipet
7. Slides
8. Coverslips
9. Vaseline
10. Toothpicks
11. Sample of slime collected from a rock in a stream, sewage tricking filter, or other source

PROCEDURE AND OBSERVATIONS

1. Place a few milliliters of acridine orange in the Petri plate cover and a few milliliters of peptone water in the bottom.
2. Tease a very small piece of the slime sample out with the tweezers and place it in the acridine orange for 30 seconds to 1 minute.
3. Transfer the slime to the peptone water and rinse momentarily.
4. Prepare a vaseline edged coverslip as described in Exercise 7.
5. Transfer the rinsed slime to the center of the vaseline ringed coverslip followed by a small drop of the peptone water.
6. Place the coverslip on a slide and press down sealing the edge.
7. Observe under the high-dry objective. Oil immersion is not recommended for this method.
8. Look for red and green cells. Make drawings indicating which cells are red and and which green. The active (green) — inactive (red) distinction does apply to this method but is not quantitative.

THOUGHT QUESTIONS

1. How would this technique be modified to be used on a soil sample?
2. Can you think of a possible explanation for some cells to be green and some red?

Name _____ Date _____ Grade _____

22. Acridine Orange Fluorescent Stain

RESULTS AND OBSERVATIONS

1. Counts of fluorescent cells in water

Field	Total Cells	Counts of			
		Rods	Cocci	Spirals	Other
1					
2					
3					
4					
5					
6					
7					
8					
9					
10					

Average _____ ml filtered _____ total per ml _____

rods _____ cocci _____ spirals _____ other _____

2. Make a drawing of a field of cells. Label the green and red cells.

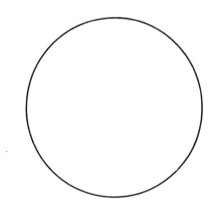

QUESTIONS

Completion:

1. The solvent used to remove fluorescent materials from the membrane filter is _____ .

2. The name of the general type of dye used in this exercise is _____ .

3. The specific dye used here is _____ _____ .

4. One should count about _____ bacteria for an accurate count.

5. A green cell is thought to be one which is _____ .

6-7. The light exciting the dye in this exercise is between _____ and _____ nm.

8. The fluorochrome used here acts with _____ inside the cell.

9. The membrane filter acts to _____ cells.

Determination of Microbial Numbers

Not only is it important to see microbes, it is also often necessary to know the number or mass of cells. To determine how many are present, a number of techniques are available — Most Probable Number (MPN), direct microscopic counts, automated cell counters, plate counts, and many indirect methods as well. In this section the two most commonly used methods of determining numbers will be used, the viable plate count (living cells grow) and an indirect method based on optical density but related to the count on the plates. Also introduced is the method of making dilutions, an integral part of many of the methods. One other, the direct microscopic count, will be used in a later exercise as will the plate count.

23 Quantitative Dilution and Spectrophotometry

OBJECTIVES

The student will be able to:

1. make a quantitative dilution for bacterial counts.

2. perform a plate count of bacteria according to the rules of plate counting.

3. calculate the number of bacteria per milliliter of sample from the dilution and the plate count.

4. use a spectrophotometer to determine the optical density of a bacterial culture and a series of dilutions of a culture.

5. plot the relationship between optical density and bacterial numbers.

6. calculate the number of bacteria per milliliter from his/her own data given an arbitrary optical density.

This exercise is designed to demonstrate a method used to enumerate viable bacteria in a liquid or solid (e.g., food) and a technique for measuring bacterial mass or density by an optical method. The optical method can be made quantitative by relating absorbance (optical density or O.D.) to a number of bacteria per unit volume by the use of the first method.

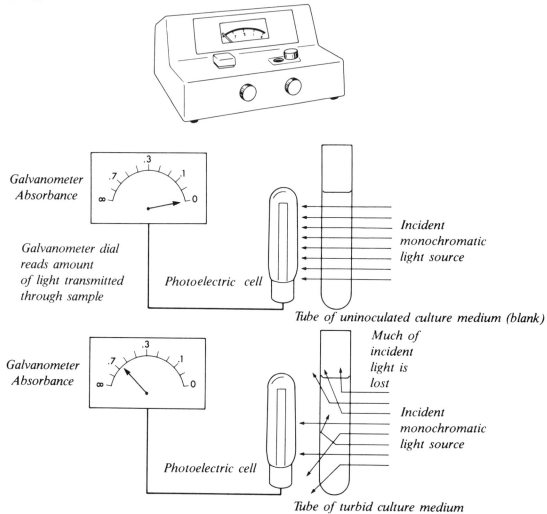

Galvanometer Absorbance

Galvanometer dial reads amount of light transmitted through sample

Photoelectric cell

Incident monochromatic light source

Tube of uninoculated culture medium (blank)

Galvanometer Absorbance

Photoelectric cell

Much of incident light is lost

Incident monochromatic light source

Tube of turbid culture medium

Figure 23-1. Principle of optical method of measuring cell numbers

The optical method of measuring growth depends on the interruption and scattering of a beam of light by the colloidal-size bacterial cells (Figure 23-1). The amount of light lost or scattered is inversely proportional to the cell concentration or directly proportional to the absorbance (optical density). The light loss can be determined by measuring the amount scattered or reflected (nephelometry) or the amount of light transmitted (turbidometry). Scales on galvanometers are measured in % transmission (% T) and/or absorbance. Bacterial numbers are directly proportional to absorbance and inversely proportional to % T. The two scales are related as follows:

$$\text{absorbance} = \log 100 - \log \% \text{ T}$$

The laboratory instructor will provide more detailed information on the instruments used in this exercise.

Unless a given absorbance reading can be quantitatively related to a number of bacteria per milliliter, the density scale must be in arbitrary units. In order to quantify the absorbance reading, a quantitative enumeration must be made of the number of bacteria in a unit volume. The quantitative dilution method is a variation of the pour plate technique of Exercise 12.

A unit volume of sample is usually one milliliter (ml) or one gram (g). One ml (or g) is added to sterile known volumes of water or buffer. While any volume of dilution water can be used, common practice calls for 9 or 99 ml volumes for ease of calculation. Serial dilutions are made (Figure 23-2) and samples plated out from each dilution. After incubation, colonies are counted on plates with 30-300 colonies. Plates with colony numbers outside this range are discarded unless no plates with 30-300 are encountered. The number of colonies is multiplied by the dilution factor, which is the reciprocal of the dilution representing the plate with 30-300 colonies which gives the number of bacteria per ml of original sample. Dilutions are generally expressed as negative exponents (e.g., 10^{-4} rather than 1/10,000).

MATERIALS (per person)

1. 24-48 hour broth culture of *Escherichia coli*
2. 5 tubes containing 5 ml nutrient broth, sterile
3. 6 nutrient agar deeps, sterile
4. 6 Petri plates, sterile
5. 1 sterile 5 ml pipet and safety bulb
6. 5 sterile 1 ml pipets calibrated in tenths
7. 4 sterile 99 ml dilution blanks
8. Spectronic 20 (or other spectrophotometer) with test tube holder
9. Quebec colony counter
10. Hand tally counter

PROCEDURE (2–3 days)

Period 1

A. Determination of Bacterial Count Per Unit Volume

1. You will be provided with one tube of a 24-48 hour old culture of *Escherichia coli.*

2. Prepare a serial dilution of the culture as follows (Figure 23-2):

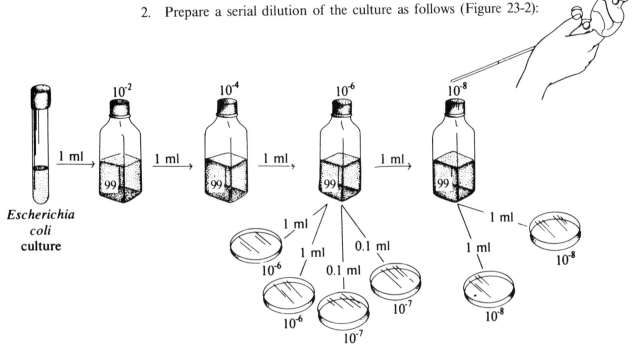

Figure 23-2. Dilution plating procedure

a. Melt 6 nutrient agar deeps and cool to 45°C. Keep them at this temperature until ready for use.

b. With a 1 ml pipet and bulb transfer 1 ml from the culture tube to the first 99 ml dilution blank marked 10^{-2}. Discard the pipet. Shake the dilution blank well (Figure 23-3). *Save the original culture* for part B.

Figure 23-3. Procedure for mixing a sample in a dilution blank

c. With a new sterile pipet, transfer 1 ml from the first dilution blank to a second marked 10^{-4}. Discard the pipet. Shake the dilution blank well.

d. With another sterile pipet, transfer 1 ml from the second dilution blank to a third marked 10^{-6}. Discard the pipet. Shake the dilution blank well.

e. With another sterile pipet, transfer 1 ml from the third dilution blank to a fourth marked 10^{-8}. HOLD the pipet. Shake the dilution blank well.

f. With the same pipet used in step No. 2e., pipet 1 ml from the third dilution blank (10^{-6}) to one plate marked 10^{-6} (Figure 23-4) and 1 ml to a second plate marked 10^{-6}. Then pipet 0.1 ml to one plate marked 10^{-7} and 0.1 ml to a second plate marked 10^{-7}. Discard the pipet.

g. With a new sterile pipet, transfer 1 ml from the fourth dilution bank (10^{-8}) to a plate marked 10^{-8} and 1 ml to a second plate marked 10^{-8}.

h. Pour one nutrient agar deep into each Petri plate and rotate gently in a circle or figure-eight to mix the agar and the sample. Be careful NOT to slop agar on the cover.

i. Allow the agar to solidify, invert, and incubate at 37°C for 24-48 hours.

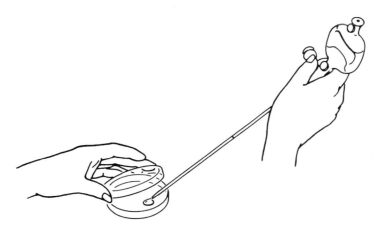

Figure 23-4. Technique for holding a pipet and a Petri plate cover

B. Absorbance vs. Bacterial Count

Period 1

1. With the remainder of the original tube of *Escherichia coli* (after step A.2 above) proceed as follows in Figure 23-5:

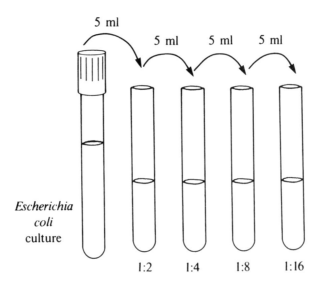

Figure 23-5. Procedure for preparing serial dilutions for optical density determinations

  a. Obtain 5 tubes of nutrient broth, each containing 5 ml, and make serial 1:2 dilutions (use the same 5 ml pipet and bulb throughout):

    i. Transfer 5 ml of the original *Escherichia coli* culture to one of the sterile broth tubes. Mix well. Mark the tube 1:2.

    ii. Transfer 5 ml of the 1:2 tube to another broth tube. Mix well. Mark it 1:4.

    iii. Transfer 5 ml of the 1:4 tube to another broth tube. Mix well. Mark it 1:8.

    iv. Transfer 5 ml of the 1:8 tube to another broth tube. Mix well. Mark it 1:16.

    v. Mark the last broth tube "control".

b. Using the Spectronic 20 (or other instrument) provided, set the wavelength at 525 nm.

    i. Adjust the galvanometer to the 0% T (or ∞ absorbance) mark with the left front knob.

    ii. Insert the "control" broth tube into the holder and replace the cap. Adjust the galvanometer to 0 absorbance using the right front knob (Figure 23-1).

    iii. Beginning with the original *Escherichia coli* tube, insert each dilution tube prepared in B.l.a. into the holder, replace the cap and record the absorbance for each tube in the data sheet provided.

OBSERVATIONS

C. Rules for Counting Colonies

Period 2

1. Following incubation, count colonies on the duplicate plates at the dilution with 30-300 colonies and determine the average. Multiply the average times the dilution factor to get the plate count per g or per ml. Results of counts after multiplying the plate count and the dilution factor should be rounded to two significant figures in order to avoid the idea of fictitious accuracy. The second digit is raised to the next higher number only when the third digit is 5 or more. If the third digit is less than five, it is dropped.

2. In case the condition of step No. 1 cannot be met, act as follows:

    a. If only one of the plates is within the range, count both and average.

    b. If plates from two consecutive decimal dilutions yield 30-300 colonies each, compute the count per ml for each dilution and report the average as the plate count per ml or g unless the higher count is more than two times the lower count in which case use only the lower count.

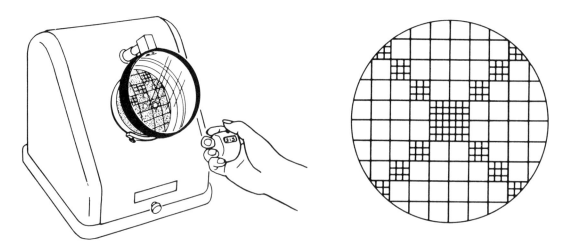

Figure 23-6. Quebec colony counter and grid

c. If no plate has 30-300 colonies but one or more has more than 300, use the dilution with the counts closest to 300. On the colony counter grid (Figure 23-6):

    i. If there are less than 10 per square cm, count the colonies in 11 squares (for plastic plates; 13 if glass) representative of the distribution of the colonies. Multiply by 5 to give the number of colonies per plate. The plastic plate is 56 cm^2 (65 cm^2 if glass). Report as "Estimated Plate Count" per g or ml.

    ii. If there are more than 10 per square cm, count the colonies in 4 squares, average and multiply by 56 (if plastic; 65 if glass) to give the number of colonies per plate.

    iii. If more than 100 colonies per square cm, report as "Estimated >6500" times the dilution factor (e.g., ">65,000,000 Estimated"). Do NOT report as TNTC.

    iv. Always report results from such plates as "Estimated" Aerobic Plate Count per g or ml.

d. If less than 30 colonies are found on each plate, record the actual number, average, multiply by the dilution factor and report as "Estimated" Aerobic Plate Count (e.g., 18 Estimated).

e. If there are no colonies on any dilution, report as "Estimated" less than one times the dilution factor (e.g., "10 Estimated" if no colonies were found on the 10^{-1} plate).

f. Other codes: NC = no colonies; Spr = spreader (if more than half of the plate is covered, do not use for counting); LA = laboratory accident; GI = growth inhibitor (only when growth inhibition is observed; i.e., lower dilutions have lower counts than higher ones. Beware, this may be an error in dilution — LA instead); TNTC = too numerous to count (do not use unless the plate is truly uncountable at the highest dilution).

3. From the count per ml of the original culture tube, now calculate the count per ml of the 1:2 series of dilutions prepared in B.1.a. above. Enter this on the data sheet provided.

4. Using the absorbance and the count per ml of the 1:2 series of dilutions, plot the relationship between absorbance and bacterial count in the graph space provided on the data sheet.

THOUGHT QUESTIONS

1. What effect does shape of the cell have on absorbance?

2. Would you expect absorbance of a culture to be affected by the wavelength of light used? How?

3. Could you use this technique with a mixture cells in a water sample? Why?

4. Counts of bacteria are reported only to two significant figures. What does this tell you about the accuracy of plate counts?

23. Quantitative Dilution and Spectrophotometry

RESULTS AND OBSERVATIONS

A. **Determination of Bacterial Count Per Unit Volume of Culture**

Dilution _____

Count _____

Bacteria _____ per ml of culture

B. **Optical Density vs. Bacterial Count**

Dilution	Absorbance	Bacteria per ml
undiluted	_____	_____
1:2	_____	_____
1:4	_____	_____
1:8	_____	_____
1:16	_____	_____

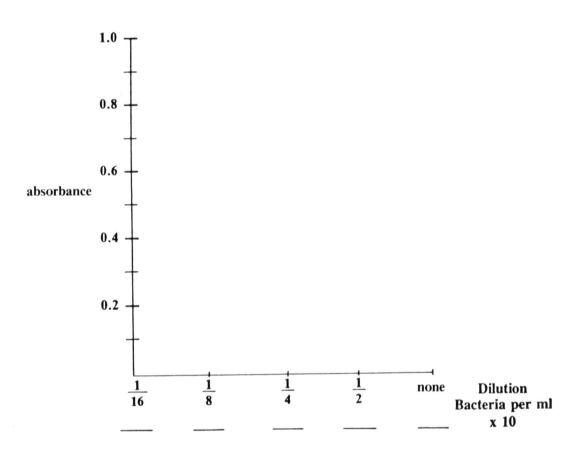

QUESTIONS

A. **True or False Statements:** Circle the correct response.

T F 1. When making your dilutions, it is alright to set all of your pipets on the bench top until you are ready to use them.

T F 2. A 1:2 dilution of a culture has half as many bacteria per ml as the culture itself.

T F 3. A unit volume of a sample is usually one milliliter or one gram.

T F 4. Bacterial numbers are directly proportional to %T.

T F 5. The dilution factor used to multiply a plate count by to obtain the number of bacteria per unit volume is the reciprocal of the dilution on which 30-300 colonies are found.

B. **Completion:**

6. Duplicate plates were counted with an average of 189 colonies present at the 10^{-3} dilution. The bacteria per ml of original sample is _____ .

7. No plates at any dilution had 30–300 colonies but the 10^{-1} dilution had 25. The bacteria per ml is

_____ .

8. A culture had 2×10^9 bacteria per ml. The 1:4 dilution had _____ bacteria per ml.

9–11. From your data graph of absorbance vs. bacteria per ml, what would the following absorbance readings give as bacteria per ml?

Absorbance		Bacteria per ml
0.8	9.	_____
0.5	10.	_____
0.1	11.	_____

24 Bacterial Growth Curve

OBJECTIVES

The student will be able to:

1. determine a bacteria growth curve.

2. explain the various parts of the growth curve: lag, exponential, stationary, and death phases.

3. calculate a generation time from the exponential phase.

Growth can be thought of as an increase in **cell size** or an increase in **cell numbers** leading to an overall increase in biomass. The most widely used measure of bacterial growth is to determine the **number of cells** at any given moment. This can be done by counting cells using the plate count technique or the spectrophotometric method described in Exercise 23. The **plate count technique** is able to measure a very small number of cells per ml; whereas, the **spectrophotometric method** requires >100,000 cells per ml but is easier to use.

Growth begins with a cell adjusting to a new environment, new nutrients and does not immediately result in division. The cell derepresses enzymes, generates ATP, and increases in size which is then followed by division. The next division occurs a little more rapidly and the next faster yet. This phase of growth is called the **lag phase**. Soon, the division rate reaches a constant which is called the **exponential phase**, because it proceeds by each cell dividing in two (i.e., the exponent 2). This is also called the **log** phase, because it is plotted linearly as a logarithm of the number of cells, usually as the base 10. After some time, as the result of the decline of nutrients or the increase of metabolic products, the division rate slows and the cell number reaches a constant. This constant number may be the result of a cessation of division altogether or the number of cell deaths equals the number of new cells formed. This stage is called the **stationary phase**. The cell number may remain stable for a long period of time with only a slow decline or it declines exponentially, in which case it is called the **death phase**. Rarely does the cell number decline to zero. There are always a few unusually resistant cells which survive to begin growth again when conditions are suitable.

Calculation of generation time from the exponential phase.

The rate of increase in bacteria at any given time is proportional to the number (or mass) of bacteria present at that time or

$$\text{rate of increase} = \mu \ (\text{number of cells}) \tag{1}$$

where μ = a constant

or,

$$\log_{10}N_t - \log_{10}N_0 = \frac{\mu}{2.303} \ (t - t_0) \tag{2}$$

where N_0 = number of cells at t = 0
N_t = number of cells at t
t = time in hours
2.303 = conversion of ln to $\log_{10}$

and,

$$g = \frac{\ln 2}{\mu} \quad \text{or} = \frac{.693}{\mu} \tag{3}$$

where g = generation time in hours

Combining equations (2) and (3)

$$g = \frac{0.693\ (t - t_0)}{(\log_{10}N_t - \log_{10}N_0)2.303} \tag{4}$$

Example:

A population of bacteria is measured at the start of an experiment as 10^4 ($\log_{10} = 4.0$) and 10^8 ($\log_{10} = 8.0$) 4 hours later. What is the generation time in hours? minutes?

$$g = \frac{0.693\ (4 - 0)}{(8 - 4)2.303} \qquad g = 0.30 \text{ hour or } .30 \times 60 \text{ minutes/hour} = 18 \text{ minutes}$$

MATERIALS (work in groups of 5 or 6)

1. 18 hour old brain heart infusion (BHI)-2% NaCl broth culture of *Vibrio natriegens*
2. 23 sterile 99 ml 0.1% peptone-2% NaCl dilution blanks
3. 10 sterile 9 ml 0.1% peptone-2% NaCl dilution blanks
4. 31 sterile 1 ml pipets
5. 1 pipet bulb or aid
6. 21 (42 if done in duplicate) prepoured BHI-2% NaCl agar plates, sterile
7. 1 bent glass spreading rod
8. 1 optical glass screw capped tube of BHI-2% NaCl broth, sterile
9. 1 flask of BHI-2% NaCl broth, sterile
10. 95% alcohol
11. Shaking water bath at 37°C
12. Spectrophotometer

PROCEDURE (2 days)

Period 1

1. Adjust the spectrophotometer at 600 nm using the screw-capped BHI-NaCl tube as the blank.
2. Add sufficient *V. natriegens* drop by drop (keep track of the volume) until the absorbancy (OD) is 0.05 to 0.08. Shake the tube periodically during the addition to distribute the cells.
3. Calculate the proportionate amount of culture necessary to add to the 35 ml of broth in the flask (the tube contains 5 ml), add it and shake well.

4. a) As soon as the flask has been inoculated and well shaken, remove 1 ml with a sterile pipet and make the 10^{-2} dilution with a 99 ml blank. Shake well.

   b) With a new sterile pipet, make the 10^{-4} dilution and shake well.

   c) Following the diagram in Figure 24-1, use a new sterile pipet and pipet 1 ml to a 99 ml blank (the 10^{-6}) *and* 1 ml to a 9 ml blank (the 10^{-5}). Discard the pipet and shake each well.

   d) Take a new sterile pipet and pipet 0.1 ml of the 10^{-6} dilution onto the surface of the 10^{-7} plate. Blow the excess liquid back into the blank.

   e) Then, with the same pipet place 0.1 ml of the 10^{-5} blank on the surface of the 10^{-6} plate. Blow the excess back into the blank.

   f) Then, with the same pipet, place 0.1 ml of the 10^{-4} blank on the surface of the 10^{-5} plate.

   g) Alcohol flame the glass spreading rod. Start with the 10^{-7} plate and carefully spread the drop around the agar surface. Without flaming, spread the drop on the 10^{-6} and then the 10^{-5} plate. One member of the group can do this immediately after the pipetting.

5. As soon as the flask has been sampled in step No. 4 above place it in the $37°C$ shaking water bath.

6. At the end of 20 minutes incubation, sample the flask and repeat step No. 4 using the same dilutions (Figure 24-1).

7. At the end of 40, 60, and 80 minutes, remove 1 ml from the flask and prepare the 10^{-2}, 10^{-4}, 10^{-5}, 10^{-6}, and 10^{-7}, and 10^{-8} plates as described previously.

8. At the end of 100 and 120 minutes, remove 1 ml from the flask and prepare dilutions and plates as indicated in Figure 24-3.

9. Incubate all plates at $37°C$ for 18–24 hours.

OBSERVATIONS

Period 2

10. Select those plates with 30–300 colonies and count them as described in Exercise 23. Record the results for each time interval in the results section converting the number to a base 10 logarithm.

11. Plot the log of the number of cells on the Y-axis and time on the X-axis.

12. Calculate the generation time by selecting two well separated points on the exponential part of the growth curve (preferably at the two extremes). Determine the log and the time corresponding to those two points. Then use formula (4) in the introduction and determine the generation time recording the results on the observation page.

THOUGHT QUESTIONS

1. This method assumes that all cells divide and all progency survive. Is this true? What effect might it have on the growth curve if not true?

2. What are some other methods of determining growth?

Dilutions for Exercise 24

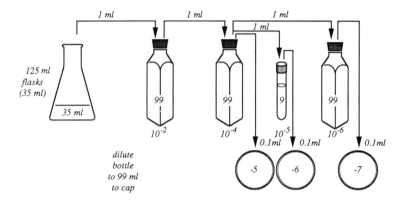

Figure 24-1. t = 0, 20 minutes

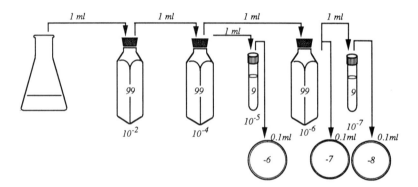

Figure 24-2. t = 40, 60, 80 minutes

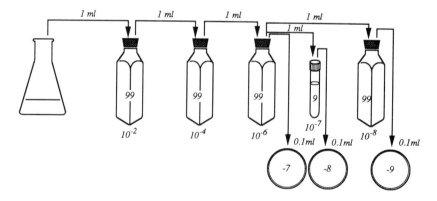

Figure 24-3. t = 100, 120 minutes

Name _____ Date _____ Grade _____

24. Bacterial Growth Curve

RESULTS AND OBSERVATIONS

1. Record the counts and dilutions used in the table below.

Time (minutes)	Count on plate	Dilution used	No. cells per ml	$\log_{10}$ no. cells per ml
0				
20				
40				
60				
80				
100				
120				

2. On the graph paper below, plot the log (Y-axis) vs. time (X-axis).

QUESTIONS (show work equations)

Completion:

1. An organism is inoculated into a broth medium which is determined to be 100 bacteria per ml. Twenty hours later cells are counted and found to be 5×10^8 per ml.

    What is the generation time per hour? _____ , per minute? _____

2. You have an organism with a generation time of 10 minutes. How long would it take for 1 cell to reproduce to a number whose mass equals that of the earth (about 1×10^{25} metric tons)? If one assumes a mass of 10^{-12} g per cell, this cell number amounts to about 1×10^{40}. Hours to reach 10^{40} cells?

3–4.   The mass of cells called for in question No. 2 is obviously an impossibility. Cite two biological reasons it cannot happen.

    3. _____   4. _____

5–6.   In the stationary phase, the viable cell count remains constant ($\mu = 0$). This observation can result from at least two types of behavior of the cells. What are these?

    5. _____   6. _____

7. Since the death phase is also exponential, how would equation (1) or (2) in the introduction change?

    _____

8. You are making a custard-cream pie which is accidentally contaminated after cooking by *Staphylococcus aureus* from a cut on your finger. The result was 10,000 bacteria per gram. This bacterium produces a potent enterotoxin causing typical food poisoning when 400,000 cells are present. How long would you have to leave this custard cream pie at room temperature to cause food poisoning if the generation time were 25 minutes? (*Note:* The organism will not grow in the refrigerator.)

    _____ hours

Metabolic Activities

Microbes are not very interesting as far as morphology is concerned, particularly among the bacteria. The most useful and important aspect of microbes is what they do metabolically: the nature of their metabolic processes and products. In this section a number of widely used metabolic tests are studied. The total examined here is a small fraction of those available, but these are some of the most universally used. If an unknown is to be studied, it might be useful to give it to the student and study it along with these tests. Coordinate this with Exercise 61.

25 Starch Hydrolysis

OBJECTIVES

The student will be able to:

1. name the specific enzyme resulting in the hydrolysis of starch.

2. write a general word equation illustrating a positive starch hydrolysis test.

3. name the chemical reagent used to test for the presence or absence of starch.

4. describe the appearance of a positive starch hydrolysis test.

Starch is a polysaccharide — a complex polymer of glucose found as a storage product in plants and many microbes. Microbes may possess one or more enzymes capable of hydrolyzing the starch molecule. These enzymes are collectively known as **amylases.**

Starch is an excellent source of energy and carbon for microbes but is too large a molecule to pass through the cell membrane. In order to utilize the energy in starch, an organism must excrete an extracellular amylase, an **exoenzyme.** The exoenzyme cleaves the starch outside the cell and the smaller products can then be transported across the membrane. There are a number of kinds of amylases depending on the site of activity in the starch molecule and the organism. Alpha-amylase cleaves starch to oligosaccharides, maltose, and glucose; beta-amylase cleaves starch to dextrins and maltose; and glucoamylase cleaves starch to glucose. These amylases are very important industrially and are harvested commercially from microbes for use in brewing, sizing of linen, and processing of paper among others.

In this exercise amylase activity is detected by the use of iodine to form a blue or brown complex with intact starch molecules. Where starch has been hydrolyzed, no color-complex forms, appearing as a clear zone in a field of color.

MATERIALS (per person)

1. 18-24 hour cultures of *Bacillus subtilis* and *Escherichia coli*
2. 1 starch agar deep, sterile
3. 1 Petri plate, sterile
4. Gram's iodine

PROCEDURE (2 days)

Period 1

1. Pour one Petri plate of starch agar and allow it to solidify.
2. Using a wax pencil, divide the bottom of the plate into three equal segments.

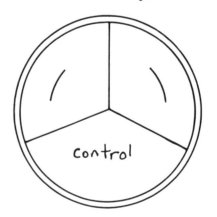

Figure 25-1. Inoculation of a medium

3. Streak inoculate one segment of the plate with *Bacillus subtilis* and another segment with *Escherichia coli*. Leave the third segment as an uninoculated control. (Each streak should be about 1 cm long near the center of the segment.)
4. Incubate at 37°C for 48 hours.

OBSERVATIONS

Period 2

5. Flood the surface of the plate with a thin layer of Gram's iodine and look for a color change of the medium. If the starch has not been hydrolyzed, the iodine reacts with the starch to give a brown, blue, or bluish-black color. When starch is hydrolyzed, the cleavage products no longer give the color reaction and a clear zone of hydrolysis is observed.

6. Sketch the appearance of growth and the surrounding medium for each segment. Also, complete the table provided.

THOUGHT QUESTIONS

1. If starch is hydrolyzed away from the cell producing the amylase, what effect does this have on other microbes in the environment?

2. Can you think of some industrial uses of amylases?

Name _____ Date _____ Grade _____

25. Starch Hydrolysis

RESULTS AND OBSERVATIONS

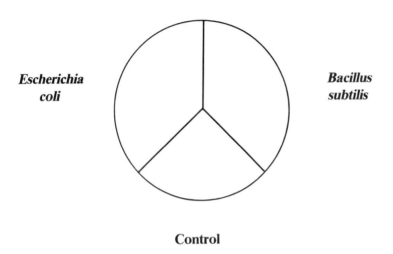

Organism	Starch Hydrolysis	
	+	−
Control		
Bacillus subtilis		
Escherichia coli		

QUESTIONS

A. True or False Statements: Circle the correct response.

T   F   1.   The detection of enzymatic activity on starch is based upon the disappearance of the starch.

T   F   2.   Amylase enzymes hydrolyze proteins.

T   F   3.   A microbe will contain only one enzyme.

T   F   4.   Starch molecules easily pass through the microbial cell membrane.

T   F   5.   Different organisms have different amylases.

B. Completion:

6.   The color of a positive test for starch hydrolysis is _____ .

7.   _____ is the group of enzymes that hydrolyze starch.

8.   _____ is the reagent used to test for starch hydrolysis.

9–10.   The end products of starch hydrolysis include _____ and

_____ .

11.   Starch is a special type of carbohydrate called a _____ .

12.   The color of a negative test for starch hydrolysis is _____ .

13.   What is the purpose of a control? _____

_____

26   Lipid Hydrolysis

OBJECTIVES

The student will be able to:

1. give the general name of the enzyme that hydrolyzes fats and oils.

2. write a general word equation illustrating a positive lipid hydrolysis test.

3. describe the two main ingredients of the medium used to detect lipid hydrolysis.

4. describe the appearance of a positive lipid hydrolysis test.

Lipids are large polymers, generally hydrophobic, and usually containing an alcohol such as glycerol and one or more fatty acids in ester linkage or complex with phosphate, nitrogen, sulfur, and other carbon compounds. A fat, such as olive oil with three fatty acids esterified to glycerol, is a typical lipid as is the membrane lipid of cells (Figure 26-1).

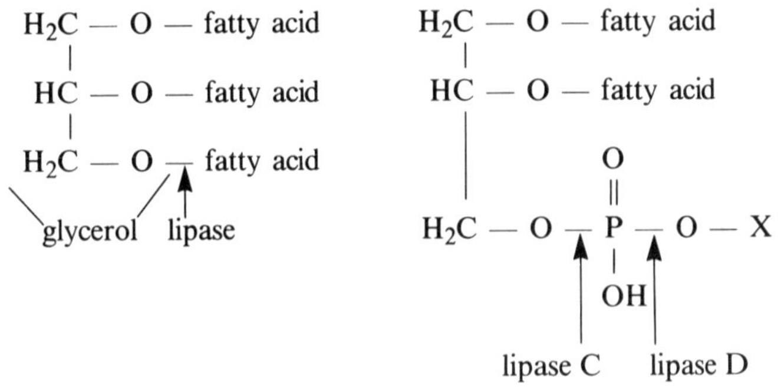

Figure 26-1. (a) A typical fat showing the site of lipase activity. (b) A phospholipid showing the site of activity of phospholipases C and D from *Clostridium perfringens*.

Being a large polymer and unable to penetrate the cell membrane, microbes must secrete exoenzymes, collectively referred to as **lipases** (triacylglycerol acylhydrolases) in order to reduce the size of the molecule. Once inside the cell, fatty acids can be used for energy or as building blocks for biosynthesis. Many lipases are not very specific and attack fats with side chains of various lengths. Some, such as the phospholipases, are more specific and hydrolyze only lipids containing phosphate groups and only at specific sites. One of the phospholipases of *Clostridium perfringens* hydrolyzes the phospholipid found in the blood cell leading to lysis of the cell (hemolysis) and producing some of the symptoms of gas gangrene. The hydrolytic products can then be transported across the membrane of the cell for metabolism.

In this exercise the hydrolytic products of lipase activity are visualized by uptake of a blue dye resulting in an intense blue color.

MATERIALS (per person)

1. 18-24 hour cultures of *Pseudomonas aeruginosa* and *Escherichia coli*

2. 1 Spirit Blue-lipid agar deep, sterile

3. 1 Petri plate. sterile

PROCEDURE (2-3 days)

Period 1

1. Using a wax pencil, divide the bottom of the plate into three equal segments.

2. Pour the melted Spirit-Blue lipid deep into the plate and let it solidify.

3. Streak inoculate one segment of the plate with *Pseudomonas aeruginosa* and another segment with *Escherichia coli*. Leave the third segment as an uninoculated control. (Each streak should be about 1 cm long near the center of the segment as shown in Figure 25-1.)

4. Incubate at 37°C for 48-72 hours.

OBSERVATIONS

Period 2

5. Observe for the presence of a clear, somewhat darker blue color in or around the growth. Organisms which utilize lipid by producing lipase cause an intense blue precipitate to form in or under the growth. This is due to the release of fatty acids and the uptake of Spirit Blue. If no lipase has been produced, no darker color change develops.

6. Record your results in the table provided.

THOUGHT QUESTIONS

1. Lipids mix poorly with water, if at all, and enzymes require water for activity. How do microbes manage to hydrolyze lipids?

2. Is there only one lipase?

26. Lipid Hydrolysis

RESULTS AND OBSERVATIONS

Organism	Lipid Hydrolysis	
	+	−
Control		
Pseudomonas aeruginosa		
Escherichia coli		

QUESTIONS

A. **True or False Statements:** Circle the correct response.

T   F   1.   Lipases hydrolyze very specific lipids.

T   F   2.   Lipases are secreted by microbes to reduce the size of fat cells.

T   F   3.   In this exercise, lipid hydrolysis is tested for by the addition of reagent.

B. **Completion:**

4.   Fats and oils are specifically hydrolyzed by the enzyme _____ .

5–6.   _____ and _____ are the immediate end products of lipid hydrolysis.

7.   The color of a positive test for lipid hydrolysis is _____ .

8.   _____ is another term for lipid hydrolysis.

9.   _____ is a dye which serves as the indicator of lipolytic activity.

27 Gelatin Hydrolysis

OBJECTIVES

The student will be able to:

1. name an enzyme that hydrolyzes gelatin.

2. write a general word equation illustrating a positive gelatin hydrolysis test.

3. name the chemical reagent used to determine gelatin hydrolysis with the overlay method.

4. describe the appearance of a positive overlay method plate.

5. describe the reaction involved in the azocoll method of collagen hydrolysis.

6. describe the appearance of a positive azocoll test.

Many microorganisms produce **proteases (proteolytic exoenzymes)** of a number of different types capable of hydrolyzing proteins of various kinds. This and the following exercise demonstrate several methods of detecting proteolytic activity. In the next exercise, a specific protein, casein, is studied. In this exercise two protein substrates are examined, gelatin and its parent protein collagen. **Collagen** is the material of animal hides and connective tissue which is hydrolyzed to make **gelatin**. They are identical in composition but differ in physical properties. A 12% gelatin solution is a solid at room temperature and melts at 28°-30°C. The collective names for enzymes degrading these proteins are **gelatinases** and **collagenases**, respectively.

Several methods have been developed for detecting gelatinases. The most sensitive is the overlay (Fraser) method. A thin layer of nutrient-gelatin is placed on a nutrient agar base and inoculated. The plate is then developed by adding a protein precipitating agent. If gelatin has been hydrolyzed by the enzyme (a positive test), no precipitation occurs. If no enzyme is present, precipitation of gelatin occurs up to the colony edge (a negative test). This technique can also be used for casein.

The **azocoll** method is a quantitative assay for proteolytic enzyme activity using collagen attached to an azo dye as the starting material. As the enzyme breaks the peptide bonds of the protein, the bright red azo dye is released in a soluble form. Upon separation of the remaining intact azocoll, the soluble dye can be measured spectrophotometrically at 520 nm. When measurements are made over time, rates of enzyme activity can be determined. Conversely, collagenase units can be determined by using differing concentrations of enzyme. This procedure is only described in this exercise and will not be performed.

MATERIALS (per person)

1. 18-24 hour old broth cultures of *Serratia marcescens* and *Escherichia coli*

2. 1 nutrient agar deep, sterile

3. 1 tube nutrient-gelatin agar, sterile

4. 1 Petri plate, sterile

5. Acidified mercuric chloride reagent

PROCEDURE (2–3 days)

Period 1

1. Pour one plate of nutrient agar and allow it to solidify.

2. Overlay the nutrient agar plate with 5 ml of nutrient-gelatin agar and allow it to solidify. Tilt the plate as you pour to ensure complete coverage.

3. Allow the plate to sit about 30 minutes after gelling so that the surface becomes somewhat dry.

4. Using a wax pencil, divide the bottom of the plate into 3 equal segments (Figure 25-1).

5. Streak inoculate one segment of the plate with *S. marcescens* and another segment with *E. coli*. Leave the third segment as the uninoculated control. (Each streak should be 1 cm long near the center of the segment.)

6. Incubate at 32°C for 48-72 hours.

OBSERVATIONS

Period 2

7. Flood the plate with the acidified mercuric chloride reagent and let the plate stand for approximately five minutes.

8. Wherever unhydrolyzed gelatin remains, a white turbidity appears due to the precipitation of the protein. If the gelatin has been hydrolyzed by the action of a gelatinase, no precipitate appears since the hydrolysis products are too small.

9. Sketch the appearance of growth and the surrounding medium for each segment on the report form.

   Note: The plate may be refrigerated for one or more hours instead of using mercuric chloride. The plate is read in the same way but must be read immediately after removal from the refrigerator.

THOUGHT QUESTIONS

1. Design an experiment to test the rate of hydrolysis of azocoll by a bacterial filtrate containing a proteolytic enzyme.

2. Are the terms "gelatinase" and "collagenase" really sufficient names for these enzymes?

Name _____ Date _____ Grade _____

27. Gelatin Hydrolysis

RESULTS AND OBSERVATIONS

Overlay method observations:

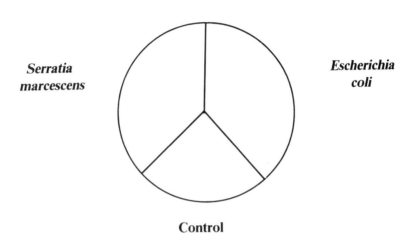

Serratia
marcescens

Escherichia
coli

Control

QUESTIONS

A. **True or False Statements:** Circle the correct response.

     T   F   1.   Gelatin is a liquid at room temperature.

     T   F   2.   Azocoll dye release is measured at 520 nm.

     T   F   3.   The overlay method is the only method for detection of gelatin hydrolysis.

     T   F   4.   Amino acids precipitate with the reagent used in this exercise.

B. **Completion:**

     5.   Gelatin is a hydrolysis product made from _____ .

     6.   Gelatin is a _____ .

     7.   The collective name for the enzymes hydrolyzing gelatin is _____ .

     8.   Gelatin hydrolysis, using the plate overlay method, is detected by using the
_____ reagent.

     9.   Collagen hydrolysis is detected by the release of a _____ .

     10.   If different concentrations of an enzyme preparation are used with the azocoll substrate, enzyme
_____ can be measured.

28 Casein Hydrolysis

OBJECTIVES

The student will be able to:

1. give the group name of enzymes that hydrolyze casein.

2. write a general word equation illustrating a positive casein hydrolysis test.

3. define the terms *peptonization* and *proteolysis*.

4. describe the appearance of a positive casein hydrolysis test.

Casein is an example of a particular protein type found in milk. Some organisms produce **protease** (or proteinase) exoenzymes capable of hydrolyzing casein, a process called **proteolysis** or **peptonization.** Exercise 29 illustrates another method of observing casein hydrolysis. Casein forms an opaque colloidal suspension with calcium in milk preventing the passage of light. If casein is hydrolyzed to peptides and amino acids, the opaque property is lost. Colonies which produce these proteases then appear with clear zones around them. If the milk overlay is dense enough, no special treatment is required to see the zone. Acidified mercuric chloride (Exercise 27) can be used if the overlay is not dense enough.

This exercise demonstrates another method of detecting exoenzymes directed toward large polymers.

MATERIALS (per person)

1. 18-24 hour cultures of *Bacillus cereus* and *Escherichia coli*

2. 1 nutrient agar deep, sterile

3. 1 bottle skim milk-nutrient agar for 15 students

4. 1 sterile Petri plate

PROCEDURE (2-3 days)

Period 1

1. Pour one Petri plate of nutrient agar and allow it to solidify.

2. Overlay the nutrient agar plate with the skim milk-nutrient agar and allow it to solidify.

3. Using a wax pencil, divide the bottom of the plate into three equal segments (Figure 25-1).

4. Streak inoculate one segment of the plate with *Bacillus cereus* and another segment with *Escherichia coli.* Leave the third segment as an uninoculated control. (Each streak should be about 1 cm long near the center of the segment.)

5. Incubate at 37°C for 48-72 hours.

OBSERVATIONS

Period 2

6. After incubation, enzyme activity is read directly. Areas in which the casein has not been attacked will remain opaque due to the colloidal nature of milk. If the enzymes have been produced, a clear zone appears around the area in which the organism has grown. You can usually see the clear zones best against a dark or black background.

7. Record your results in the table provided.

THOUGHT QUESTIONS

1. What is the chemical composition of casein ?

Name _____ Date _____ Grade _____

28. Casein Hydrolysis

RESULTS AND OBSERVATIONS

Organism	Casein Hydrolysis	
	+	−
Control		
Bacillus cereus		
Escherichia coli		

QUESTIONS

A. **True or False Statements:** Circle the correct response.

    T   F   1.   The colloidal nature of milk serves as the basis for interpreting casein hydrolysis.

    T   F   2.   A special chemical reagent must be added to test for casein hydrolysis.

    T   F   3.   Casein is the only protein found in milk.

B. **Completion:**

    4.   The immediate end products of casein hydrolysis include _____ and _____ .

    5.   Casein is a _____ found in milk.

    6.   _____ are the group of enzymes that can hydrolyze casein.

    7–8.   Two terms used to describe casein hydrolysis are _____ and _____ .

29 Litmus Milk Reactions

OBJECTIVES

The student will be able to:

1. list the two main ingredients of litmus milk.

2. write a general word equation illustrating all the possible reactions resulting from microbial action on litmus milk.

3. describe the reactions of litmus dye as a pH indicator and as a reducible molecule.

4. describe the two types of curds formed, gas production, and peptonization.

Litmus milk serves as an excellent culture medium and often is used for biochemical characterization of microorganisms because of the many different reactions that can result when microorganisms are grown in it.

Litmus milk medium consists of 10% powdered **skim milk** and the dye **litmus**. Litmus, when added to rehydrated skim milk, turns the milk suspension from white to lavender and serves as both a pH indicator and as a reducible dye molecule.

If an organism is capable of reducing litmus, the lavender colored milk turns to its normal white color again. When litmus is in the reduced state, it can no longer function as a pH indicator. **Reduction** characteristically begins at the bottom of the tube and progresses in an upward direction.

If lactose (the main carbohydrate in milk) is fermented, then the litmus as a pH indicator turns from lavender to a red or pink color in an **acid** environment. If enough acid is produced, the pH may be lowered to a point where the milk forms a very hard curd. This is called an **acid curd** and may or may not be accompanied by gas production. As the acidity increases, the curd becomes so solid that there is a squeezing out of a clear liquid on top called **whey**.

Gas production occurs only if an organism is capable of fermenting lactose to acid and gas. It is usually detected by the presence of bubbles or a splitting in the acid curd. If an organism produces so much gas that the curd is blown into shreds, it is called **stormy fermentation** of milk.

Some organisms produce a rennin-like enzyme which clots casein, resulting in the formation of a **rennet curd**. The rennet curd, unlike the acid curd, is soft and usually observed at a neutral pH.

Some microorganisms possess proteolytic enzymes capable of hydrolyzing the insoluble casein. This process, called **peptonization**, results in the release of large amounts of peptides and amino acids (also see Exercise 28). Continued incubation results in a clearing of the milk. The transparent liquid supernatant often turns brown. An organism may release ammonia causing a purplish-blue color.

MATERIALS (per person)

1. 18-24 hour cultures of *Escherichia coli, Pseudomonas aeruginosa, Acinetobacter calcoaceticus,* and *Enterococcus (Streptococcus) faecalis*

2. 5 tubes litmus milk, sterile

PROCEDURE (7 days)

Period 1

1. Inoculate each tube of litmus milk with one of the cultures.

2. Keep one tube as an uninoculated control.

3. Incubate all tubes at 37°C. Make your observations at 24 and 48 hours and again at 7 days.

OBSERVATIONS

Periods 2–4

4. After each incubation period, compare each of the inoculated tubes with the control tube.

5. Record your results in the table provided.

THOUGHT QUESTIONS

1. What is the actual cause of the reduction of litmus?

2. Where does ammonia come from in some of these litmus milk reactions?

29. Litmus Milk Reactions

RESULTS AND OBSERVATIONS

Organism	Type of Reaction		
	24 hr	48 hr	7 d
Control			
Escherichia coli			
Pseudomonas aeruginosa			
Acinetobacter calcoaceticus			
Enterococcus faecalis			

NC = no change   P = peptonization
A = acid   R = reduction
AC = acid curd   RC = rennet curd
W = whey   ALK = alkaline
G = gas

QUESTIONS

A. True or False Statements: Circle the correct response.

T   F   1.   Ammonia production very often accompanies peptonization in litmus milk.

T   F   2.   Lactalbumin is the principle protein in milk.

T   F   3.   A rennet curd is firmer than an acid curd.

T   F   4.   When litmus is reduced, hydrogen is added to the molecule and the medium turns pink.

T   F   5.   Stormy fermentation means an extremely rapid acidification has occurred.

T   F   6.   All litmus milk reactions take place within 48 hours.

T   F   7.   Peptonization is a synonym for proteolysis.

T   F   8.   Litmus milk medium is the only medium used to detect peptonization.

B. Completion:

9.   If the lactose in litmus milk is utilized by an organism, then the color of the litmus is

_____ .

10.   When litmus turns white, this indicates that _____ has taken place.

11–12.   Litmus serves as both a _____ and a _____ .

13.   _____ is the main carbohydrate in milk.

14.   _____ results in the clearing of milk.

15.   The principle milk protein is _____ .

16.   When a curd develops in litmus milk, how could you determine whether it was a rennet or acid curd?

_____

_____ .

17.   A _____ color is the normal color of litmus milk.

30 Nuclease Activity

OBJECTIVES

The student will be able to:

1. prepare and interpret a nuclease plate test.

2. describe the use and purpose of the thermonuclease version.

Many bacteria are capable of hydrolyzing RNA or DNA polymers with enzymes collectively called **nucleases**. In some bacteria, *Staphylococcus aureus* in particular, the nuclease is **thermostable** and withstands boiling temperatures. This property is useful in identifying *S. aureus* **food poisoning** organisms either in culture or in foods when heating has destroyed the organism but not the nuclease. The general procedure for DNA or RNA hydrolysis is similar to other large polymers. The nucleic acid is incorporated into an agar medium, an organism applied and incubated for 1-4 hours. The plate is then developed with 4 N HCl which precipitates intact nucleic acid, with hydrolysis appearing as a clear zone. For DNA a colored medium is available with the hydrolysis area appearing as a pink zone in a blue unhydrolyzed background.

Two DNA methods are presented here: 1) a streak plate **overlay**; and, 2) the Food and Drug Administration prescribed **slide** method for thermonuclease in *S. aureus* detection (FDA Bacteriological Analytical Manual, Association of Official Analytical Chemists, Washington, D.C., 1978). An RNA method is also described.

Method 1 for DNA requires the growth of a pure culture on a nutrient agar medium followed by an overlay with **toluidine blue-DNA** (TB-DNA) agar. The overlayed plates are then incubated for 4 hours. DNA hydrolysis is observed by a pink to red color around the colonies producing DNase.

Method 2 for DNA can be used in unheated cultures as well as heated cultures or food slurries. A thin coating of TB-DNA agar is placed on a glass slide. Ten to twelve small 2 mm diameter wells are cut in the agar and several loopfuls of broth cultures or centrifuged food slurries are placed in each well. The slides are incubated for 4 hours and read. A pink to red zone around the well shows DNA hydrolysis.

The RNA method uses the same base agar medium but with RNA instead of DNA (although DNA can be used) and without the toluidine blue. Colonies grown on plates or wells cut in an agar plate are used. After 4 hours incubation, the plates are developed by flooding with 4 N HCl. Intact RNA (or DNA) will precipitate and appear cloudy. Where hydrolysis has occurred, a clear zone is seen.

This exercise is intended to introduce one or more methods of assaying for bacterial nucleases.

MATERIALS (per person or pair)

A. Overlay method

1. 18-24 hour old nutrient broth cultures of *Staphylococcus aureus, Staphylococcus epidermidis,* and *Serratia marcescens*

2. 1 nutrient agar deep, sterile

3. 1 Petri plate, sterile

4. 1 tube toluidine blue-DNA (TB-DNA) agar for overlay, sterile

B. Slide method

1. 18-24 hour old nutrient broth cultures of *Staphylococcus aureus, Staphylococcus epidermidis, Serratia marcescens,* and *Enterobacter aerogenes*

2. A food slurry, centrifuged supernatant

3. Slides

4. 1 tube toluidine blue-DNA (TB-DNA) agar, sterile

5. 1 beaker

6. Plastic straw

7. Cannula

8. Transfer pipet

PROCEDURE AND OBSERVATIONS (1–2 days)

A. Method 1 — Overlay for DNA Hydrolysis

Period 1

1. Divide a nutrient agar plate into 3 sections (Figure 25-1) and label.

2. Streak inoculate each segment with the appropriate organism. Each streak should be about 1 cm long near the center of the segment.

3. Incubate the plate for 24-48 hours at 35°-37°C.

Period 2 or 3

4. Melt 5-10 ml of TB-DNA agar, cool to 50°C, and pour over the growth on the plate. Allow it to solidify.

5. Incubate the overlayed plate at 35°-37°C for 3-4 hours.

6. After incubation, organisms showing DNA hydrolyzing activity will have a pink to red zone around the colony.

7. Record your results on the report form.

B. Method 2 — Slide Method for DNA Hydrolysis

Period 1

1. Clean one or more slides scrupulously with scouring powder and water. Rinse thoroughly with running water. Soak in 95% alcohol. After the slides are dry, mark a symbol on the underside of each for identification.

2. Place the slide on a staining rack over a beaker. Pipet 3–4 ml of melted TB-DNA agar onto the slide and let it solidify uniformly. *Note:* With dirty slides the agar will roll off and not coat uniformly—select another slide. The agar collected in the beaker can be reused.

3. Cut 10-12 2 mm diameter wells in the agar surface with a plastic straw and remove the plug by aspiration with a cannula.

4. Two broth cultures of each organism and a food slurry will be supplied. Heat one broth culture of each pair to boiling very briefly and cool promptly under running water. Mark the tube "heated."

5. On the report form, identify each well with the name of the organism and whether heated or unheated. Mark the food slurry wells also.

6. Using a sterile inoculating loop (3 mm internal diameter), transfer 1-2 loopfuls of a culture to its corresponding well. Sterilize the loop and repeat for each tube and the food slurry provided.

7. Incubate the slide in a moistened Petri plate at 35°-37°C.

8. After 3-4 hours incubation, examine the slide for pink to red zones around the wells indicating hydrolysis. The unhydrolyzed background will be blue.

THOUGHT QUESTIONS

1. The procedures presented here are for extracellular nucleases. How widespread in organisms are endonucleases?

2. Are the nucleases of each of these organisms the same?

3. How do nucleases work?

Name _____ Date _____ Grade _____

30. Nuclease Activity

RESULTS AND OBSERVATIONS

A. Overlay method. Draw the appearance of *one* positive overlay plate.

B. Slide method. Identify each well and draw final slide appearance.

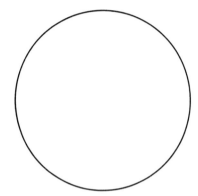

Record which cultures are positive and which negative

	unheated	heated
S. aureus	_____	_____
S. epidermidis	_____	_____
S. marcescens	_____	_____
E. aerogenes	_____	_____
Food slurry	_____	

QUESTIONS

A. **True or False Statements:** Circle the correct response.

T   F   1.   *Staphylococcus aureus* organisms are destroyed by heating.

T   F   2.   Nuclease production is an important characteristic used to identify strains of *S. aureus* causing food poisoning.

T   F   3.   Both DNA methods described in this exercise indicate hydrolysis has occurred when a clear zone appears around the colony.

T   F   4.   Thermostable nucleases are destroyed by heat.

T   F   5.   Hydrolysis of DNA and RNA is very different.

B. **Completion:**

6.   _____ dye is used to demonstrate DNA hydrolysis.

7.   The agent used to precipitate RNA is _____ .

8.   The organism used in this exercise is _____ and causes food poisoning.

9.   Some nucleases, such as the one produced by the organism in question No. 8, are

_____ .

10. The DNA slide method is prescribed by the _____ .

31 Hemolysis of Blood

OBJECTIVES

The student will be able to:

1. name the three types of hemolysis produced by microorganisms.

2. describe the appearance of the three different types of hemolysis.

3. list the two main ingredients of a blood agar plate.

Whole blood, added to a nutrient agar, makes a very rich medium which supports the growth of many of the more nutritionally fastidious microorganisms. Many such organisms produce exoenzymes (**hemolysins**) that have a destructive effect on red blood cells. **Beta (β) hemolysins** completely destroy and decolorize hemoglobin from the red blood cell, resulting in a clear zone around the colony. Some organisms produce **alpha (α) hemolysins** which only partially destroy the hemoglobin, resulting in a greenish area around the colony. Organisms that do not produce hemolysins, and subsequently have no effect on the red blood cells, are sometimes said to demonstrate gamma (γ) hemolysis, or (more accurately) are **non-hemolytic.** The production of these hemolysins is very useful in identifying pathogens.

MATERIALS (per person)

1. 18-24 hour cultures of *Enterobacter aerogenes, Staphylococcus aureus,* and *Enterococcus (Streptococcus) faecalis*

2. 5% sheep blood agar plate, sterile

PROCEDURE (2 days)

Period 1

1. Using a wax pencil, divide the bottom of the blood agar plate into four equal segments (Figure 31-1).

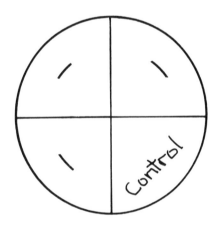

Figure 31-1. Inoculation of a medium

2. Streak inoculate one segment of the plate with *Enterobacter aerogenes*. Repeat the procedure with each of the remaining organisms. Leave the fourth segment as an uninoculated control. (Each streak should be about 1 cm long near the center of the segment.)

3. Incubate at 37°C for 24 hours.

OBSERVATIONS

Period 2

4. Observe for the different types of hemolysis using a lighted Quebec colony counter.

5. Sketch the appearance of growth and the surrounding medium for each segment. Also complete the table provided.

THOUGHT QUESTIONS

1. What possible advantage might a hemolysin give to a bacterial pathogen?

2. Why does alpha hemolysis usually appear greenish?

31. Hemolysis of Blood

RESULTS AND OBSERVATIONS

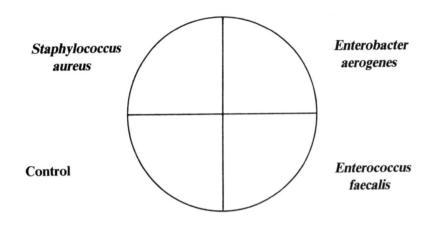

Organism	Type of Hemolysis		
	alpha (α)	beta (β)	non-hemolytic
Control			
Staphylococcus aureus			
Enterobacter aerogenes			
Enterococcus faecalis			

QUESTIONS

A. **True or False Statements:** Circle the correct response.

    T   F   1.   Hemolysis is best observed against a dark or black background.

    T   F   2.   Hemolysins are endoenzymes.

    T   F   3.   The concentration of blood is a determining factor for the length of incubation at 37°C.

B. **Completion:**

    4.   Beta hemolysis is indicated by a _____ zone around a colony.

    5.   The medium used to detect hemolysis production is _____.

    6.   Alpha hemolysis is indicated by a _____ zone around a colony.

    7.   Pathogenic strains of streptococci are usually _____ -hemolytic.

32 Sugar Fermentations

OBJECTIVES

The student will be able to:

1. name the general group of enzymes involved in the fermentation of carbohydrates.

2. define the term *fermentation.*

3. write a general word equation illustrating the major end products of carbohydrate fermentation.

4. list the four ingredients of a fermentation tube and describe the purpose of each.

5. describe all possible reactions that can be obtained from microorganisms growing in fermentation broths.

Fermentation is the term ordinarily applied to the anaerobic breakdown of carbohydrates. The purpose of the fermentation process is to make energy available for utilization by the microorganism, since carbohydrates are quite rich in stored energy.

Whether or not a given carbohydrate is fermented depends upon the **transport proteins** (permeases) and the **endoenzymes** (or carbohydrases) possessed by the organism. The end products of fermentation often will vary from one organism to another depending on the pathways involved. However, the end products are usually acid of various types *or* acid and gas.

Ability to ferment can be determined by inoculating the organism into a fermentation tube containing a nutrient broth to support the growth of the organism, a single chemically-defined carbohydrate, a pH indicator and an inverted Durham tube to collect gas.

pH indicators allow you to determine whether or not an **acid** has been produced as an end product of metabolism. Phenol red (PR) and bromcresol purple (BCP) are the two pH indicators most frequently used in microbiological work. Phenol red appears red in a solution with a pH above 6.9 and is yellow at an acid pH of less than 6.8. Bromcresol purple is purple at a pH of 6.8 and is yellow at an acid pH of 5.2 or lower.

A Durham tube is a small inverted vial placed inside the culture tube. The purpose of the Durham tube is to trap *gas*, if it has been produced as an end product of metabolism (Figure 32-1).

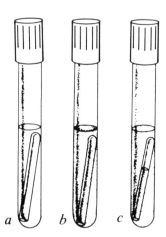

Figure 32-1. Broth culture tubes with Durham tubes to measure gas production. (a) Before inoculation (b) Growth but no gas production (c) Growth resulting in gas production

If the organism is not capable of attacking the specific carbohydrate, growth will occur due to the utilization of the nutrient broth present and either *no change* in pH or a change to a more *basic* pH will be seen.

Some organisms can take amino acids in the broth and convert them to carbohydrate-like molecules called alpha-keto acids. This conversion results in the formation of ammonia (NH_3) which causes the medium to become quite basic or *alkaline*. The bromcresol purple indicator will change to a deeper purple color, while the phenol red indicator turns a deep magenta color.

MATERIALS (per person)

1. 18-24 hour cultures of *Escherichia coli, Staphylococcus aureus, Bacillus subtilis*, and *Alcaligenes faecalis*

2. 5 tubes phenol red-glucose broth, sterile

3. 5 tubes phenol red-sucrose broth, sterile

5. 5 tubes phenol red-lactose broth, sterile

PROCEDURE (7 days)

Period 1

1. Inoculate a series of three different carbohydrate broths with *Escherichia coli*.

2. Repeat this procedure with each of the remaining cultures.

3. Keep one tube of each carbohydrate broth as uninoculated controls.

4. Incubate all tubes at 37°C. Make your observations at 24, 48 and 72 hours and again at 7 days.

OBSERVATIONS

Periods 2–4

5. After each incubation period, compare each of the inoculated tubes with the control tube of the same medium to determine whether growth occurred and whether acid or acid and gas were produced.

   If at any time during the incubation period should a fermentation tube contain both acid and gas, it is not necessary to continue incubation. The tube may be discarded after recording the results.

6. Record your results in the table provided.

THOUGHT QUESTIONS

1. What sequence of events is necessary to get a sugar molecule from outside the cell to the inside where metabolism takes place?

2. How does the mechanism of glucose "fermentation" compare with glucose "oxidation" by some organisms?

3. Is a lack of indicator color change always an indication of lack of ability to utilize a carbohydrate?

Name _____ Date _____ Grade _____

32. Sugar Fermentations

RESULTS AND OBSERVATIONS

Organism	Time	Carbohydrates		
		PR-glucose	PR-sucrose	PR-lactose
Control	24 hr			
	48 hr			
	72 hr			
	7 d			
Escherichia coli	24 hr			
	48 hr			
	72 hr			
	7 d			
Staphylococcus aureus	24 hr			
	48 hr			
	72 hr			
	7 d			
Bacillus subtilis	24 hr			
	48 hr			
	72 hr			
	7 d			
Alcaligenes faecalis	24 hr			
	48 hr			
	72 hr			
	7 d			

NC = no change
AG = acid and gas
A = acid
ALK = alkaline

QUESTIONS

A. **True or False Statements:** Circle the correct response.

T   F   1.   The Durham tube allows you to determine the kind of gas produced during fermentation.

T   F   2.   The formation of alpha-keto acids results in an acid condition.

T   F   3.   Gas production must be preceded by acid production.

T   F   4.   The endoenzymes of fermentation are secreted into the environment.

T   F   5.   If phenol red turns a magenta color, it means ammonia has been produced.

B. **Completion:**

6–7.   The small inverted tube found within a larger tube is called a _____ tube and is used to trap _____ .

8.   When phenol red changes to yellow, this indicates that _____ has been produced.

9–10.   The two pH indicators most often used in a microbiology laboratory are _____ and _____ .

11–12.   The process of fermentation involves 2 groups of enzymes known as _____ and _____ .

13–16.   List the 4 ingredients of a fermentation tube.

13. _____   15. _____

14. _____   16. _____

17–20.   List 4 fermentable carbohydrates other than those used in this exercise.

17. _____   18. _____

19. _____   20. _____

21.   _____ is the term that refers to the anaerobic breakdown of carbohydrates.

22–25.   What is the pH range of the indicator used in this exercise? _____ What colors denote a neutral, acid or alkaline reaction?

neutral _____

acid _____

alkaline _____

26.   If a carbohydrate broth does not change color after it has been inoculated and incubated, how can you tell whether the unchanged color is due to failure of the organism to grow or failure to ferment the carbohydrate?

_____

_____

_____

33 Hydrogen Sulfide Production

OBJECTIVES

The student will be able to:

1. name the component of a substrate that must be present for a microorganism to produce hydrogen sulfide.

2. write a general word equation illustrating a positive hydrogen sulfide test.

3. list four types of media designed to show hydrogen sulfide production.

4. describe the appearance of a positive hydrogen sulfide test using Kligler iron agar.

5. describe all possible reactions that can be observed from the fermentation of carbohydrates in Kligler iron agar.

Hydrogen sulfide (H_2S) is produced by certain microorganisms through **dissimilation** of organic sulfur-containing amino acids (cystine, cysteine, and methionine) or through **reduction** of inorganic sulfur compounds (thiosulfate, sulfite, and sulfate). Such organisms possess the enzymes that reduce the sulfur atom of inorganic sulfur-containing compounds or remove the sulfide group from sulfur-containing amino acids. The growth medium contains ferrous iron salt ($FeSO_4$) that reacts readily with hydrogen sulfide to form a **black** iron sulfide (FeS).

Various types of media have been designed for the purpose of detecting hydrogen sulfide production. Among these are peptone iron agar (PIA), lead acetate agar, Kligler iron agar (KIA), and triple sugar iron agar (TSI).

Both peptone iron agar and lead acetate agar are employed to demonstrate only hydrogen sulfide production. Since lead acetate has been shown to be somewhat less sensitive than peptone iron agar, it is not frequently used to detect hydrogen sulfide production. Both Kligler iron agar and triple sugar iron agar are considered multi-purpose media and are used to demonstrate the fermentation of certain carbohydrates as well as the production of hydrogen sulfide.

MATERIALS (per person)

1. 18-24 hour cultures of *Proteus vulgaris* and *Escherichia coli*

2. 3 Kligler iron agar (KIA) slants, sterile

PROCEDURE (7 days)

Period 1

1. Using an inoculating *needle* and the culture of *Proteus vulgaris*, penetrate the butt of a Kligler iron agar slant about the center of the slant nearly, but not all the way, to the bottom of the tube (Figure 33-1a). Carefully withdraw the needle along the original stab and then streak the culture across the top of the slant (Figure 33-1b).

2. Repeat the procedure with the culture of *Escherichia coli*.

3. Keep one tube as an uninoculated control.

4. Incubate all tubes at 37°C. Make your observations at 24 and 48 hours and again at 4 and 7 days.

OBSERVATIONS

Periods 2–5

5. After the 24 hour incubation period, make observations on carbohydrate fermentation reactions by comparing each inoculated tube with the control. If both the slant and the butt remain red (red due to phenol red indicator), then no change has occurred. In other words, no carbohydrates have been fermented. If the slant is red and the butt is yellow, this indicates that glucose has been fermented to acid. If gas bubbles or splitting appears in the butt, then the glucose has been fermented to acid and gas. If both the slant and butt are yellow, then both glucose and lactose have been fermented. The appearance of gas in the butt indicates that these carbohydrates have been fermented to acid and gas.

    (Note: Fermentation reactions are valid *only* at 37°C and at 24 hours. After 24 hours, the colors are no longer useful since they may have reverted to alkaline colors. Also, a large amount of black precipitate can mask or obscure the yellow or acid condition in the butt.) Record your results in the table provided.

6. After each incubation period, observe for the appearance of a black precipitate along the line of the stab. Such a black precipitate is evidence of hydrogen sulfide production. No change in the medium means that no hydrogen sulfide was produced. Record your results in the table provided.

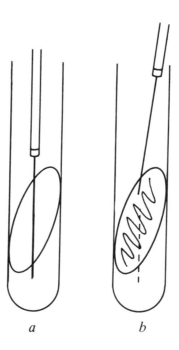

a $\qquad$ b

Figure 22-1. Stabbing (a) and streaking (b) a KIA slant

THOUGHT QUESTIONS

1. Can hydrogen sulfide or FeS be used as an energy source for the growth of microbes? If so, which ones?

33. Hydrogen Sulfide Production

RESULTS AND OBSERVATIONS

Organism	Fermentation Reactions		H₂S Production	
	Glucose	Lactose	+	−
Control				
Proteus vulgaris				
Escherichia coli				

NC = no change
A = acid
AG = acid and gas

QUESTIONS

A. **True or False Statements:** Circle the correct response.

    T   F   1.   Determination of hydrogen sulfide production is useful in the identification of micro-organisms.

    T   F   2.   When hydrogen sulfide is released by microorganisms, it is a gas.

    T   F   3.   An inoculating loop is used to make a stab inoculation.

    T   F   4.   TSI agar and KIA are used solely to detect hydrogen sulfide production.

B. **Completion:**

5. Is the production of hydrogen sulfide an aerobic or anaerobic reaction?

   _____ .

6. Under natural conditions, where might you expect to find hydrogen sulfide production by microorganisms? _____ .

7. _____ is the color of a positive test for hydrogen sulfide.

8. In order to produce hydrogen sulfide, microorganisms must possess the enzymes to attack _____ containing compounds.

9. The formation of the compound _____ provides the basis for the detection of hydrogen sulfide.

10–13. List 4 types of media used to detect hydrogen sulfide production.

   10. _____   12. _____

   11. _____   13. _____

14. _____ is the salt added to the medium to detect hydrogen sulfide production.

15. _____ is the pH indicator used in KIA media.

16–17. The acid colors of carbohydrate fermentation reactions must be read at _____ hours and at _____ °C.

18–19. _____ and _____ are considered to be multipurpose types of media.

20–21. Does protein decomposition result in a shift toward the acid or alkaline side? Explain.

   _____

   _____

   _____

34 IMViC Reactions

OBJECTIVES

The student will be able to:

1. distinguish *Escherichia coli* from *Enterobacter aerogenes* by IMViC tests.

2. explain the biochemical basis for each IMViC test.

3. write down the IMViC reactions for *Escherichia coli* and *Enterobacter aerogenes*.

4. name the chemical reagent(s) used and the appearance of a positive test result for each IMViC test.

The IMViC reactions are four related biochemical tests. The acronym **IMViC** is a mnemonic to aid in remembering the order of the four tests and their reactions. They are **Indole** production, the **Methyl** red test, the **Voges**-Proskauer test and **Citrate** utilization. The small letter "i" is added as an aid in pronouncing the acronym.

The IMViC tests are designed to determine specific physiological properties of microorganisms. As a group they are especially useful in the differentiation of Gram-negative enteric bacilli, especially coliforms of the *Escherichia coli* and the *Enterobacter - Klebsiella* groups. Because enteric organisms have very similar physiological reactions and often cannot be adequately differentiated, the IMViC tests are a considerable aid to identification of organisms within the family *Enterobacteriaceae*.

Indole is a breakdown product of the amino acid tryptophan which is found plentifully in tryptone or trypticase. It is important that the test be read after the 24 hour incubation since continued incubation may lead to a loss of indole by further metabolism. Should this occur, a misleading negative test may result. Typical strains of *Escherichia coli* produce indole, while the *Enterobacter - Klebsiella* groups do not.

The **methyl red** and **Voges-Proskauer** tests are physiologically related and both use the same medium, MR-VP broth. This medium contains peptone, glucose, and a phosphate buffer. The methyl red test depends upon the ability of an organism to produce acid from glucose in sufficient quantity to cause the methyl red indicator to change to its acid color red and hold this low pH of 4.4 for 5 days. Typical strains of *Escherichia coli* are mixed acid fermenters which produce a variety of acid end products which change the methyl red indicator to red. The *Enterobacter - Klebsiella* organisms ferment the same amount of glucose but convert it over several days into neutral products such as acetoin (acetyl methyl carbinol) and 2, 3 butanediol. Consequently, the pH which may initially reach pH 4.4, very quickly rises again and the methyl red no longer displays its acid red color.

The **Voges-Proskauer** reaction is the result of a red color complex formed by the oxidation of 2, 3 butanediol and acetoin in alkali and the presence of creatine and alpha-naphthol. *Escherichia coli* does not produce these end products and is Voges-Proskauer negative. Since the *Enterobacter - Klebsiella* groups produce 2,3 butanediol and acetoin, they produce a positive Voges-Proskauer test.

The last IMViC test determines whether an organism can grow with **citrate** as a sole source of carbon. The test is designed to determine whether or not the bacterium has a cell membrane transport protein to carry citrate into the cell. If the organism has the particular protein, then it grows. If the organism lacks the protein, then it cannot grow. *Escherichia coli* does not utilize citrate, whereas members of the *Enterobacter - Klebsiella* groups do.

MATERIALS (per person)

1. 18-24 hour cultures of *Escherichia coli* and *Enterobacter aerogenes*

2. 3 tubes 1% tryptone broth, sterile

3. 6 tubes MR-VP broth, sterile

4. 3 Simmons citrate agar slants, sterile

5. Kovac's indole reagent

6. Methyl red indicator

7. 5% alpha-naphthol (Barritt's solution A)

8. 40% KOH - creatine reagent (Barritt's solution B)

PROCEDURE AND OBSERVATIONS (5 days)

A. Indole Test

Period 1

1. Inoculate one tube of tryptone broth with a small amount of *Escherichia coli*.

2. Repeat the procedure with the culture of *Enterobacter aerogenes*.

3. Keep one tube as an uninoculated control.

4. Incubate all tubes at 35°C for 24 hours only.

Period 2

5. After incubation, compare each of the inoculated tubes with the control tube.

6. Examine each tube for growth. Add 0.2-0.3 ml (approximately 5 drops) of Kovac's indole reagent to each tube. Shake gently and let stand. Within 10 minutes, the amyl alcohol of the reagent will separate and turn a bright red color, if indole is present. If indole is absent, the amyl alcohol layer will remain as its original color.

7. Record your results in the table provided.

B. Methyl Red Test

Period 1

1. Inoculate one tube of MR-VP broth with *Escherichia coli*.

2. Repeat the procedure with the culture of *Enterobacter aerogenes*.

3. Keep one tube as an uninoculated control.

4. Incubate all tubes at 35°C for 5 days.

Period 2

5. After incubation, compare each of the inoculated tubes with the control tube.

6. Examine each tube for growth. Shake lightly and add 4-5 drops of methyl red indicator. A red color indicates acid below pH 4.4 and is a positive test. A yellow color is a negative test.

7. Record your results in the table provided.

C. Voges-Proskauer Test

Period 1

1. Inoculate one tube of MR-VP broth with *Escherichia coli.*

2. Repeat the procedure with the culture of *Enterobacter aerogenes.*

3. Keep one tube as an uninoculated control.

4. Incubate all tubes at 35°C for 48 hours.

Period 2

5. After incubation, compare each of the inoculated tubes with the control tube.

6. Add 1 ml of Barritt's solution A followed by 0.5 ml of Barritt's solution B. A red positive color will usually develop promptly, but may be delayed up to 2 hours. No change in color constitutes a negative test.

7. Record your results in the table provided.

D. Citrate Utilization

Period 1

1. Using an inoculating needle and the culture of *Escherichia coli*, penetrate the butt of a Simmons citrate agar slant about halfway through the agar. Carefully withdraw the needle along the original stab and then streak the culture across the top of the slant. A *small* amount of inoculum is essential. (See Figure 33-1 for method.)

2. Repeat the procedure with the culture of *Enterobacter aerogenes.*

3. Keep one tube as an uninoculated control tube.

4. Incubate all tubes at 35°C for 48 hours.

Period 2

5. After incubation, compare each of the inoculated tubes with the control tube.

6. Organisms able to transport citrate into the cell grow in the medium. In the Simmons medium, growth is observed on the slant and is usually accompanied by a change of the bromthymol blue indicator from green to a deep blue. This constitutes a positive test. No growth or a green color is a negative test.

7. Record your results in the table provided.

THOUGHT QUESTIONS

1. Can you think of an explanation for all four tests being positive for a single organism? All negative?

2. The VP test is for acetoin and thus 2,3 butanediol. Does the latter compound have any commercial value?

Name _____ Date _____ Grade _____

34. IMViC Reactions

RESULTS AND OBSERVATIONS

Organism	IMViC Reactions			
	I	M	Vi	C
Control				
Escherichia coli				
Enterobacter aerogenes				

+ = positive test

− = negative test

QUESTIONS

A. **True or False Statements:** Circle the correct response.

T F 1. Kovac's reagent must be added to MR-VP medium to detect the results of the Voges-Proskauer test.

T F 2. Indole is a breakdown product of tryptophane.

T F 3. The *Enterobacter - Klebsiella* groups are mixed acid fermenters.

T F 4. The fermentation of lactose is the basis for the methyl red test.

T F 5. 2, 3 butanediol producers can be methyl red positive if measured too early.

B. Completion:

6–7. Name 2 types of media that can be used to detect citrate utilization.

6. _____

7. _____

8. _____ is the medium used to test for indole production.

9. _____ is the chemical reagent used in the indole test.

10. The pH must be below _____ for a positive methyl red test to occur.

11–12. Name the 2 major products produced by Voges-Proskauer positive organisms.

11. _____

12. _____

13–14. _____ and _____ are the reagents used in the Voges-Proskauer test.

15. Members of the *Enterobacteriaceae* are commonly referred to as the enteric bacilli or

_____ .

16. Those enterics that do not fall into the 2 distinctive categories formed by *Escherichia coli* and *Enterobacter aerogenes* are collectively referred to as _____ .

17–24. Indicate the color of positive and negative tests for each of the following:

Reaction	Positive Test		Negative Test	
Indole	17. _____		21. _____	
Methyl red	18. _____		22. _____	
Voges-Proskauer	19. _____		23. _____	
Citrate	20. _____		24. _____	

35 Catalase and Oxidase

OBJECTIVES

The student will be able to:

1. write a general word equation for the catalase reaction.

2. describe the overall oxidase reaction.

3. name the chemical reagents used in the catalase and oxidase tests.

4. name the two major aerobic bacterial groups which are catalase negative.

5. name one family of bacteria most of which are oxidase negative.

Catalase and **oxidase** are **enzymes** playing important roles in the terminal steps of the respiratory electron transport chain. When electrons are transfered to oxygen, hydrogen peroxide (H_2O_2) is formed. Catalase degrades hydrogen peroxide to oxygen and water. The generation of **oxygen** is vigorous enough to be observed and is the basis for the catalase test. Catalase is generally found in all aerobic organisms except the microaerophilic lactic acid bacteria where it is absent. Catalase is not generally found in obligate anaerobes. The lack of catalase in anaerobes in part explains why oxygen is toxic to them. When oxygen is available, aerobic organisms use it as a terminal electron acceptor forming hydrogen peroxide in the process. Hydrogen peroxide is also produced metabolically in other ways. The lactic acid bacteria must still remove hydrogen peroxide and use peroxidases instead. Oxygen is not a product with the peroxidase reaction.

Oxidase is an enzyme formed by most respiring organisms which have **cytochromes** of the c type. This enzyme also oxidizes certain amines to form colored products, an easily observed reaction. Some groups of bacteria do not have this enzyme and its presence or absence is useful taxonomically.

This exercise will introduce you to the catalase and oxidase tests.

MATERIALS (per person)

A. Catalase test

1. 18-24 hour slant cultures of *Enterococcus (Streptococcus) faecalis* and *Staphylococcus aureus*

2. 1 tryptic soy agar deep, sterile

3. 1 Petri plate, sterile

4. 3% H_2O_2 solution

B. Oxidase test

1. 18-24 hour slant cultures of *Pseudomonas aeruginosa* and *Escherichia coli*

2. Filter paper disks 5-10 cm diameter

3. Sterile applicator sticks

4. 1% aqueous tetramethyl-para-phenylenediamine (Kovac's oxidase reagent)

PROCEDURE AND OBSERVATIONS (1 day)

A. Catalase Test

1. With a sterile inoculating loop, place a small amount of growth from the *S. aureus* slant on a clean glass slide.

2. Place the slide on the stage of a microscope and focus the low power lens on the growth.

3. Place a drop of 3% H_2O_2 on the growth and observe for the formation of gas bubbles.

4. The release of gas bubbles is a positive test for the presence of catalase.

5. Record the result in the report form table.

6. Repeat the observation using growth from the *E. faecalis* slant.

7. Record the result in the report form table.

B. Oxidase Test

1. Place a few drops of the oxidase reagent on a piece of filter paper.

2. *Immediately,* using a sterile applicator stick, streak a **HEAVY** mass of cells from the *P. aeruginosa* slant over the moist area. (A nichrome wire loop gives a false positive reaction.)

> **Caution!**
> a. **A massive amount of cell material is necessary. A visible mass on the end of the stick must be present.**
> b. **Pigmented organisms frequently present a problem. Reduce the amount of cells to decrease the amount of pigment.**
> c. **Discard the applicator stick in the to-be-sterilized container.**

3. With a new applicator stick, streak a mass of the *E. coli* culture on another section of the reagent.

4. A change in color of the cells along the streak to a deep purple, almost black color is a positive test for oxidase. No apparent change from the reagent color is a negative test. The change will be almost immediate.

5. Record your results in the report form table.

THOUGHT QUESTIONS

1. What sources of hydrogen peroxide other than direct transfer of electrons to oxygen are there in metabolism?

2. What is superoxide dismutase?

3. What role does cytochrome *c* play in electron transport?

35. Catalase and Oxidase

RESULTS AND OBSERVATIONS

A. **Catalase Test**

Organism	Catalase Production	
	+	−
Control		
Enterococcus faecalis		
Staphylococcus aureus		

B. **Oxidase Test**

Organism	Oxidase Production	
	+	−
Control		
Pseudomonas aeruginosa		
Escherichia coli		

QUESTIONS

A. True or False Statements: Circle the correct response.

T   F   1.   The catalase reaction is the source of hydrogen peroxide.

T   F   2.   Oxidase testing is not useful in taxonomy.

T   F   3.   Catalase is usually not found in anaerobic bacteria.

T   F   4.   Oxidase degrades H_2O_2 to water and oxygen.

T   F   5.   Oxidase and catalase enzymes are found in all aerobic bacteria.

B.   Completion:

6-7.   An enzyme found in most aerobic organisms is _____. It is tested for with the reagent

_____.

8-9.   The catalase test can be used to distinguish between the catalase +, Gram-positive coccus genus

_____ and the catalase -, Gram-positive coccus genus _____.

10-11.   The catalase test can be used to distinguish between the catalase +, Gram-positive, sporeforming rod

genus _____ and the catalase -, Gram-positive, sporeforming rod genus

_____.

12.   _____ organisms do not produce catalase and are poisoned by
the accumulation of hydrogen peroxide.

13.   An obligate anaerobe would be expected to give a _____ test for oxidase.

14.   A positive oxidase test is a _____ color.

15.   The reagent used to test for oxidase is _____.

16.   A positive test for oxidase occurs if the cell has a type of _____.

17.   From your results, name one family of aerobic bacteria, most of which are oxidase negative

_____.

36 Nitrate Respiration

OBJECTIVES

The student will be able to:

1. name the specific enzyme resulting in the reduction of nitrate to nitrite.

2. define *denitrification*.

3. write the general word equations for nitrate reduction and denitrification.

4. name the chemical reagents used to test for nitrate reduction.

5. describe the appearance of a positive test for nitrate reduction.

The nitrogen cycle is of great importance to all living forms (see Exercise 64 and Figure 64-1). Not only does nitrogen serve as an essential nutrient, but many bacteria take part in the nitrogen cycle by utilizing nitrate (NO_3^-) under anaerobic conditions as an alternative to oxygen for receiving electrons generated through metabolism. Nitrate is one of the most commonly available alternate electron acceptors in the absence of oxygen. The nitrogen atom in nitrate is capable of being reduced to a number of other nitrogen compounds, some of which are gaseous and escape the local environment. This may be undesirable in some situations such as agricultural practice and desirable in others, such as nitrate stripping in tertiary sewage treatment. Some of the intermediate gaseous products contribute to atmospheric pollution and to acid rain. The conversion of nitrate to gaseous products is a dissimilatory process referred to as **denitrification** and carried out only by bacteria. Bacteria possessing a membrane bound **nitrate reductase** first reduce the soluble nitrate producing nitrite as part of the assimilatory pathway to ammonia. Because the assimilatory pathway is repressed by ammonia, nitrite is not produced in much greater quantities than needed. In the dissimilatory or respiratory pathway, considerable nitrite is produced only in the absence of oxygen because it is being used as an alternative electron acceptor to oxygen (this pathway is repressed by oxygen). Some bacteria that respire nitrates also have a **nitrite reductase** that reduces the nitrite to gaseous nitric oxide, nitrous oxide, or nitrogen gas depending on the enzymes present.

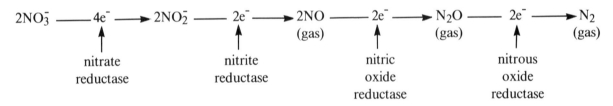

In some organisms, activity may be so vigorous that no nitrate or nitrite remains, because all of it is converted to gaseous forms. Some bacteria do not possess a nitrite reductase and nitrite accumulates, sometimes to toxic levels.

In this exercise, nitrate-respiring organisms will be studied as pure cultures and their presence in the soil demonstrated.

MATERIALS (per person)

1. 18-24 hour cultures of *Pseudomonas aeruginosa*, *Bacillus subtilis*, and *Staphylococcus aureus*

2. Soil sample

3. 5 tubes nitrate broth with gas inserts, sterile

4. Sulfanilic acid reagent (Nitrite A)

5. N, N dimethyl-1-naphthylamine reagent (Nitrite B)

6. Zinc powder

7. 6N HCl

PROCEDURE (4 days)

Period 1

1. Inoculate one tube of nitrate broth with *Pseudomonas aeruginosa*.

2. Repeat the procedure for each organism.

3. Inoculate a fourth tube with a small amount of soil using a wet inoculating loop.

4. Keep one tube as an uninoculated control.

5. Incubate all tubes at 37°C for at least 48 hours.

OBSERVATIONS

Period 2

6. After each incubation period, observe first for the presence of gas in the Durham tube. Then test each tube *and* the control by adding 1 ml of the sulfanilic acid reagent followed by 1 ml of the N, N dimethyl-1-naphthylamine reagent. (*Note:* 20 drops ≅ 1 ml). If nitrites are present, the mixture of the two reagents with the medium will become a red, purple, or a maroon color. Even a transitory color is positive.

7. A negative result requires an additional test since the negative outcome may be due to either the absence of nitrate reductase *or* to the additional presence of a nitrite reductase, in which case all of the nitrate appears as nitrogen gas.

   To determine which of these possibilities is correct, a small amount (trace) of powdered zinc and a few drops of 6N HCl are added to the negative tubes. Zinc, in the presence of H^+, reduces nitrate to nitrite. Therefore, if a red color appears now, it means that the nitrate remained unaltered by the bacterial growth. The red color still indicates a positive test for nitrite, but the nitrate was reduced chemically to nitrite by the zinc. This would not be possible if the nitrate were not present in the broth in its original form. The color change may take 5-10 minutes.

   If no color change occurs upon the addition of zinc, it means that the nitrate has already been reduced by the bacteria beyond the nitrite stage.

8. Record your results in the table provided.

THOUGHT QUESTIONS

1. In what kind of environments would you expect to find nitrate-respiring organisms?

2. What are the intermediates in the pathway from nitrate to nitrogen gas? What metal cofactors are involved?

36. Nitrate Respiration

RESULTS AND OBSERVATIONS

Organism	Nitrite Test			Results of Zinc Test *If* Nitrite Test Negative	Conclusion of Results
	Color	+	−		
Control					
Pseudomonas aeruginosa					
Bacillus subtilis					
Staphylococcus aureus					
Soil Sample					

QUESTIONS

A. **True or False Statements:** Circle the correct response.

    T   F   1.   In testing for nitrate reduction, the zinc is usually added first.

    T   F   2.   Nitrates can only be reduced to nitrites by microbial enzymes.

    T   F   3.   A red color indicates a positive test for nitrite when the correct reagents are added.

    T   F   4.   The addition of zinc to nitrate broth can make changes that some bacteria cannot make.

    T   F   5.   If nitrite is absent and zinc and acid are then added, the development of a red color is a positive test for the presence of nitrate.

B. Completion:

6–7.   List the reagents used to test for nitrite.

  6. _____

  7. _____

8–10.   Give the reaction color for the following when sulfanilic acid and N, N dimethyl-1-naphthylamine reagents are added.

  Reaction   **Reaction Color**

  $NO_3^- \rightarrow NO_2^-$ 8. _____

  NO_3^- 9. _____

  $NO_3^- \rightarrow NH_3^+$ 10. _____

11.   _____ is one enzyme that reduces nitrate to nitrite.

12.   _____ is the enzyme that reduces nitrite.

13.   Is the reduction of nitrate to nitrite favored by aerobic or anaerobic conditions?

  _____

14.   It is preferable to perform this test by periodic testing of some of the culture over a period of several days. Why? _____

  _____

15–17.   Explain each of the following:

  15. Nitrite test negative, no nitrate present _____

  16. Nitrate test negative, nitrite present _____

  17. Nitrite test negative, nitrate present _____

37 Phosphatase Reaction

OBJECTIVES

The student will be able to:

1. describe the function of phosphatases.

2. name the two types of phosphatases based on pH.

3. perform a phosphatase test and describe the theory of the test.

Phosphorous occurs in nature in the form of inorganic and organic compounds. Organic **phosphate esters** are very common and are utilized by organisms through the action of **phosphatase** enzymes which hydrolyze the ester releasing phosphate. Phosphatases fall into two types based on the optimum pH for activity: the **alkaline** phosphatases (around pH 10) and the **acid** phosphatases (around pH 5). Phosphatases are common in organisms, often found in the periplasmic space of Gram-negative bacteria.

The basis of the phosphatase test is to grow the organism in the presence of an organic phosphate, the organic portion being a dye or color compound which is not colored when esterified to phosphate. Phosphatase, if present, will hydrolyze the bond, releasing phosphate and the colored portion assumes its normal color. A general test for both forms of phosphatase is introduced in this exercise using phenolphthalein diphosphate. A test specifically for acid or alkaline forms using para-nitrophenyl phosphate is available.

MATERIALS (per person)

1. 18-24 hour old broth cultures of *Staphylococcus aureus, Micrococcus varians,* and *Escherichia coli*

2. 1 Petri plate, sterile

3. 1 flask of nutrient agar (for 4 people), sterile

4. 1 flask of 1% filter sterilized disodium phenolphthalein diphosphate sufficient for class

5. 1 sterile 1 ml pipet

6. 1 container concentrated ammonium hydroxide with dropper

PROCEDURE (2–5 days)

Period 1

1. Aseptically pipet 1 ml of the phenolphthalein diphosphate solution into the flask of melted nutrient agar tempered to 50°C. Mix by swirling gently. This gives a 0.01% final concentration of the substrate.

2. Pour the agar into four Petri plates with about 20 ml each.

3. After solidifying, divide the bottom of one plate into quadrants as in Figure 31-1. Label with the organism names.

4. Inoculate each quadrant with the appropriate organism, applying a streak of cells about 1 cm long in the middle of each quadrant.

5. Incubate at 30°C for 2-5 days.

Periods 2-5

6. Remove the plate from the incubator and place it on the bench with the cover down.

7. Remove the bottom and place 1–2 drops of concentrated ammonium hydroxide in the cover on the bench.

8. Replace the bottom in the top and let sit for 30-60 minutes after gelling to expose the growth to ammonia fumes.

OBSERVATIONS

9. Examine the color of the growth periodically. If phosphatase is present in the cells, free phenolphthalein will turn the colony red. If the organism does not possess phosphatases, the colonies will remain colorless. Note that both acid and alkaline phosphatases will be detected.

10. Make a drawing of your plate on the report form and indicate which organisms are positive and which negative for phosphatases.

THOUGHT QUESTIONS

1. What is the benefit to the cell of having acid and/or alkaline phosphatases?

2. Is there any evidence from your results as to whether the phosphatases observed are intracellular or extracellular?

Name _____ Date _____ Grade _____

37. Phosphatase Reaction

RESULTS AND OBSERVATIONS

Make a drawing of your plate:

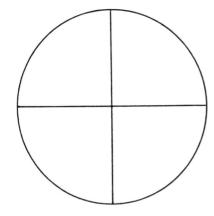

Indicate + or - for each

S. aureus _____

M. varians _____

E. coli _____

QUESTIONS

Completion:

1–2. Phosphatases hydrolyze _____ bonds releasing free _____.

3–6. The two types of phosphatase enzymes are _____ at a pH of _____ and _____ at a pH of _____.

7–8. The substrate used to detect *both* types at once is _____ ; whereas, the substrate for the two types is _____.

9. The detection of phosphatase by phenolphthalein release is really a simple _____ reaction.

10. In Gram-negative bacteria, the phosphatases are often found in the _____ space.

38 Ammonification

OBJECTIVES

The student will be able to:

1. describe the mechanism of ammonification.

2. name the chemical reagent used to test for the presence or absence of ammonia.

3. describe the appearance of a positive test for ammonia.

4. explain under what conditions ammonification occurs.

Ammonification is the release of ammonia from organic nitrogen compounds (usually amino acids). It is an important part of the nitrogen cycle (Exercise 64 and Figure 64-1) and is a widespread ability among microbes.

$$CH_3 - CH - COOH \longrightarrow CH_3 - CH_2 - COOH + NH_3$$
$$|$$
$$NH_2$$

  alanine   propionic acid   ammonia

The release of ammonia results from several needs of the cell. If carbon is in short supply and nitrogen levels are adequate, the carbon skeleton of the organic nitrogen compound is utilized and the ammonia released as unneeded. If nitrogen is in short supply, ammonia is rarely released but instead the amine group is incorporated directly into the new cell mass. The carbon to nitrogen ratio of the medium is thus important for release of ammonia. A C:N ratio of about 20:1 or less usually releases abundant ammonia. Cattle feedlots have a considerable amount of nitrogen rich waste that is especially high in urea which has a very low C:N ratio (0.5:1) (see Exercise 39.) Feedlots usually reek of ammonia. Under anaerobic conditions some of the nitrogen is retained in organic structures as volatile **amines,** a class of very odoriferous compounds. Examples are the fecal odor of indole, skatol, and related compounds. These are usually oxidized to ammonia in the atmosphere. Exercises 34 and 40 have specific examples of amine production.

This exercise demonstrates the production of ammonia with pure cultures and soil organisms using a color reaction between Nessler's reagent and ammonium ion.

MATERIALS (per person)

1. 18-24 hour cultures of *Pseudomonas aeruginosa* and *Bacillus subtilis*

2. Soil sample

3. 4 tubes 4% peptone water, sterile

4. Nessler's reagent

5. Spot plate

6. Glass rod

7. 70% ethyl alcohol

PROCEDURE (7 days)

Period 1

1. Inoculate one tube of peptone water with *Pseudomonas aeruginosa*.

2. Repeat the procedure with the culture of *Bacillus subtilis* and a second tube.

3. Inoculate a third tube with a small amount of soil using a wet inoculating loop.

4. Keep one tube as an uninoculated control.

5. Incubate all tubes at 37°C. Make your observations at 2, 4, and 7 days.

OBSERVATIONS

Periods 2–4

6. After each incubation period, test each culture and the control for ammonia production.

7. Place a drop of Nessler's reagent on a spot plate and add a drop of culture with a flamed glass rod. (A glass rod is flamed by dipping the rod in 70% ethyl alcohol and passing it through the burner flame. Once the alcohol ignites, let it burn off *outside* the flame.) A positive test for ammonia is indicated by the appearance of a yellow, orange, or brownish color. A brown color indicates a greater production of ammonia than does a yellow color. No color change is a negative test for ammonia. Be sure to compare each reaction with the control.

   Cultures exhibiting positive results need not be reincubated. Those cultures giving a negative test should be reincubated and the test repeated after the next incubation period.

8. Record your results in the table provided.

THOUGHT QUESTIONS

1. How does the carbon to nitrogen ratio (C:N) of the nutrients available to the microbes affect the release of ammonia?

2. Under what conditions are amines released instead of ammonia?

Name _____ Date _____ Grade _____

38. Ammonification

RESULTS AND OBSERVATIONS

Organism	Ammonia Production		
	2 d	4 d	7 d
Control			
Pseudomonas aeruginosa			
Bacillus subtilis			
Soil Sample			

+ = ammonia produced
- = no ammonia produced

QUESTIONS

Completion:

1. The _____ reagent is used to test for the production of ammonia.

2. A _____ color indicates a positive test for ammonia when Nessler's reagent is used.

3. Why must this test be performed over a period of several days?

   _____

4. What is the significance of using soil as an inoculum? _____

   _____

5. _____ is the process which involves the release of ammonia.

6. Ammonia is produced when an organism can breakdown _____ .

39 Urea Hydrolysis

OBJECTIVES

The student will be able to:

1. name the specific enzyme resulting in the hydrolysis of urea.

2. write a general word equation illustrating a positive urea hydrolysis test.

3. name the substance that must accumulate to give a positive urea hydrolysis test.

4. describe the appearance of a positive urea hydrolysis test.

5. explain the mechanism of urea hydrolysis and the basis of a positive test.

Urea, $NH_2 - \overset{\overset{\textstyle O}{\|}}{C} - NH_2$, is a common nitrogenous waste product in mammals and a few other animals. Many bacteria, especially enteric bacteria of the family *Enterobacteriaceae,* have evolved the ability to hydrolyze urea and release ammonia. These bacteria produce the enzyme **urease** which releases enough ammonia in the growth medium to produce an alkaline reaction of pH 8.1 or greater. This is detected by a change in color of the phenol red indicator in the medium to a red or cerise color.

Urea hydrolysis is a specific example of ammonification (Exercise 38), but it is studied separately here because of its importance in identifying certain intestinal bacteria in the clinical laboratory.

MATERIALS (per person)

1. 24 hour nutrient broth cultures of *Proteus vulgaris* and *Escherichia coli*

2. 3 tubes urea broth, sterile

PROCEDURE (2 days)

Period 1

1. Inoculate one tube of urea broth with 2 loopfuls of *Proteus vulgaris.*

2. Repeat the procedure with the culture of *Escherichia coli* and a second tube.

3. Keep one tube as an uninoculated control.

4. Incubate all tubes at 37°C. Make your observations at 2 hours and again at 24 hours.

OBSERVATIONS

Period 2

5. Observations of urea hydrolysis are made directly. The appearances of a red or cerise color is a positive test for urea hydrolysis, while a yellow or orange-red (unchanged) color indicates a negative test. Be certain to compare the color with the control tube.

6. Record your results in the table provided.

THOUGHT QUESTIONS

1. What is the source of urea in nature?

2. What applications does urea hydrolysis have in the clinical laboratory? (In what diagnoses might these tests assist?)

Name _____ Date _____ Grade _____

39. Urea Hydrolysis

RESULTS AND OBSERVATIONS

Organism	Urea Hydrolysis	
	+	−
Control		
Proteus vulgaris		
Escherichia coli		

QUESTIONS

Completion:

1–3. The enzyme _____ splits urea into _____ and

_____ .

4. A _____ color appears in urea broth as a result of hydrolysis.

5. _____ is the pH indicator found in urea broth.

6. The pH of urea broth must be at least _____ in order to give a positive urea hydrolysis test.

40 Decarboxylation and Amine Production

OBJECTIVES

The student will be able to:

1. describe a positive reaction for the production of a basic amine from arginine, lysine, and ornithine.

2. explain the biochemistry of amine formation.

3. name amines produced from seven amino acids.

In this exercise three amino acid media will be used to demonstrate the production of basic amines by bacteria of the *Enterobacteriaceae*. The three amino acids used, arginine, lysine, and ornithine, help to distinguish members of this family. The ability to decarboxylate or deaminate amino acids is also found in other groups of bacteria. Initially the enteric bacteria produce acid in the medium; however, under anaerobic conditions some bacteria with decarboxylase or dihydrolase enzymes are able to remove the carboxyl group of these amino acids leaving an amine or other basic products. This results in a basic reaction with the acid-base indicator of the medium. The particular amino acid decarboxylated and the products produced depend on the organism. For example, in *Enterobacteriaceae*, cadaverine is produced from lysine and putrescine from arginine and ornithine. In other groups other products may result. The ability to decarboxylate or deaminate amino acids is common. Other examples in this manual are indole production from tryptophane (Exercise 34) and histamine production from histidine (Exercise 77). Ammonia and tyramine from tyrosine and glutamine from glutamic acid are other examples. These capabilities are found in the lactic acid bacteria, the *Bacilliaceae*, the *Enterobacteriaceae*, and among most obligate and facultative anaerobes.

MATERIALS (pairs)

1. 18-24 hour old nutrient agar slant culture of *Enterobacter cloacae, Serratia marcescens, Enterobacter aerogenes, Escherichia coli*, and *Proteus vulgaris*

2. 5 tubes 1% lysine in Moeller's decarboxylase base broth, sterile

3. 5 tubes 1% ornithine in Moeller's decarboxylase base broth, sterile

4. 5 tubes 1% arginine in Moeller's decarboxylase base broth, sterile

5. 5 tubes Moeller's decarboxylase base broth without amino acid, sterile

6. 1 flask mineral oil, sterile

PROCEDURE (4 days)

Period 1

1. Lightly inoculate one tube of each medium with each organism. *Be sure to sterilize the loop between each medium to destroy any residual amino acid.*

2. Aseptically pour 4-5 ml of sterile mineral oil over the surface of each tube, including the controls, to provide anaerobic conditions. Tighten the caps.

3. Incubate all tubes at 35°–37°C.

OBSERVATIONS

Periods 2-5

4. Read tubes at 24 hour intervals for 4 days. Observe each tube for a change in color from purple to yellow and back to purple again. The change back to purple indicates a positive test. A negative test remains yellow.

5. Record your results in the table provided.

THOUGHT QUESTIONS

1. Can the organisms obtain energy from these reactions?

2. What is the Stickland reaction?

3. What happens if air is present in these tubes?

4. How would you determine if ammonia is a product?

Name _____ Date _____ Grade _____

40. Decarboxylation and Amine Formation

RESULTS AND OBSERVATIONS

Inoculated tube results (+ or –):

	Arginine	Ornithine	Lysine
E. cloacae			
S. marcescens			
E. aerogenes			
E. coli			
P. vulgaris			

QUESTIONS

Completion:

1–7. Name the decarboxylated product of each of the following:

1. lysine _____

2. ornithine _____

3. arginine _____

4. tyrosine _____

5. glutamic acid _____

6. histidine _____

7. tryptophane _____

8. Depending on the organism and the amino acid, what other compound might be produced?

_____

9. The acid produced during the first 24 hours is derived from _____ .

10–11. The indicators in Moeller's base medium used in this exercise are _____

and _____ .

12–13. Name two families of bacteria for which this test is useful in species differentiation.

12. _____   13. _____

41 Miniaturized and Rapid Biochemical Methods

OBJECTIVES

The student will be able to:

1. perform a series of fifteen biochemical tests on an unknown bacterium simultaneously.

2. determine the ID Value from the results and identify the organism.

3. discuss the theory of rapid methods.

The foregoing exercises in Unit VI require a large amount of media and equipment and considerable time to determine only a few characteristics. This has been the traditional approach for identification of clinical specimens. Dichotomous keys have been widely based on these results (Exercise 61A) but suffer from requiring continual updating and do not adequately account for natural variation between strains and the exceptions. A number of commercially available kits have been developed which allow the investigator to inoculate 10-20 different media at a single time, read the results within a short period, and consult a coded data bank which takes into account exceptions and variation based on extensive analysis of thousands of strains. First developed for members of the *Enterobacteriaceae*, perhaps the most commonly encountered clinical group, new kits are available for many different groups. This exercise introduces you to one of these kits, the ENTEROTUBE II with 15 different tests. Exercise 61B utilizes another kit the API 20E consisting of 23 separate tests. In some cases, these tests can be performed in just a few hours, saving considerable time. Most of the kits do require some preliminary information for identification such as growth on a particular isolation medium, isolation from a specific body site, or oxidase testing. In many cases confirmatory tests, such as serology or growth on special media, must be performed.

The ENTEROTUBE II results are determined to be positive or negative for the strain under study and the pattern of these results converted into an ID Value. The ID Value is then looked up in a code book (or a computer can be used) and the name of the organism is found together with a probability if more than one organism has the same ID Value. If the ID Value is not found, it could be an extremely rare variation or some procedure error has arisen.

In this exercise you will be given an unknown organism to inoculate an ENTEROTUBE II and determine its identity.

ENTEROTUBE II instruction booklet, coding forms, and Computer Coding Manual (ID Values) can be obtained from Roche Diagnostic Services, Technical Consultation Services Dept., 11 Franklin Ave., Belleville, NJ 07109.

MATERIALS (per person)

1. 18-24 hour old nutrient agar plate culture of an unknown organism
2. 1 ENTEROTUBE II
3. 1 code form or use the form on the results page
4. ID Code Manual (one for class)
5. 3 plastic syringes and needles for indole and Voges-Proskauer reagents (for class)
6. Indole reagent (Kovac's)
7. Voges-Proskauer reagents
   a. alpha-naphthol solution
   b. KOH solution

PROCEDURE (1 day)

Note: These procedures are color illustrated in the booklet accompanying the kit.

Period 1

1. Remove both caps from the ENTEROTUBE II (Figure 41-1).
2. Touch the tip of the wire to the growth on the plate. Enough cells must be present to make a visible mass on the tip and side of the wire. Avoid touching the agar.
3. Immediately withdraw the wire with a screwing or twisting motion through all 12 compartments (Figure 41-2).
4. Reinsert the wire through all 12 compartments. Then withdraw the wire until the tip is in the H_2S/indole compartment. Now break wire at the notch by bending. Discard the handle and place the caps on the tube loosely. The wire remaining in the tube ensures anaerobic conditions and will not interfere with the reactions (Figure 41-3).
5. Strip off the blue tape after inoculation but before incubation to provide aerobic conditions in certain compartments. *Slide the clear band* over the glucose compartment to keep wax from escaping if gas is produced (Figure 41-4).
6. Incubate at 35°-37°C for 18-24 hours with the tube horizontal on its flat side.

OBSERVATIONS

Period 2

1. If available use the color booklet accompanying the tubes and an uninoculated tube for comparison.
2. **ALL observations must be made before the indole and Voges-Proskauer tests are performed.**

Compartment	substrate	positive test
GLU	glucose	any yellow color
GAS	gas	causes separation of wax, NOT by bubbles in the medium
LYS	lysine	decarboxylation causes a purple color
ORN	ornithine	decarboxylation causes a purple color
H_2S	thiosulfate	H_2S production causes a black color
IND	tryptophane	reagent turns red in 10 sec, MUST be last step
ADON	adonitol	fermentation causes yellow color
LAC	lactose	fermentation causes yellow color
ARAB	arabinose	fermentation causes yellow color
SORB	sorbitol	fermentation causes yellow color
VP	glucose	reagent turns red within 20 min if acetoin is present, orange is negative
DUL	dulcitol	fermentation causes yellow color
PA	phenylalanine	deaminase black to smoky gray is positive
UREA	urea	red-purple is positive
CIT	citrate	growth on citrate turns medium deep blue or light blue-green in some cases

3. After all other observations are made, perform the indole test by placing the tube in a rack with the glucose compartment down then injecting the indole reagent into compartment 4. If positive it will turn red in approximately 10 sec.

4. Finally, inject the Voges Proskauer reagents into compartment 9 with the tube in a rack and the glucose compartment down.

5. Record the results on the ENTEROTUBE II form as + or - for each compartment on the form. If positive circle the number immediately below the compartment.

6. In the hexagon below each arrow, enter the total points circled. If nothing was positive in a bracket, enter zero (0). The five numbers become the ID Value for your unknown.

7. Now go to the Computer Coding book and find the ID Value. The organism's name will be given and any atypical results for your strain. If more than one organism is listed a probability of identification will also be given. The confirmatory test column would provide further aid in identification.

8. Enter the information on the form and other pertinent data on the Reports and Observations form.

THOUGHT QUESTIONS

1. What problems would arise if the ENTEROTUBE II was used on soil or aquatic organisms other than Enterobacteriaceae?

2. How was the "Identification Probability" determined?

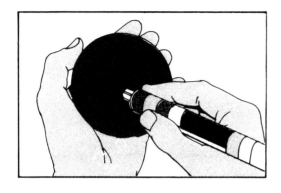

Figure 41-1. Picking a colony

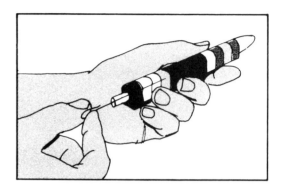

Figure 41-2. Inoculating

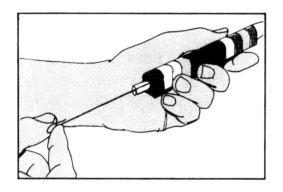

Figure 41-3. Reinserting and breaking wire

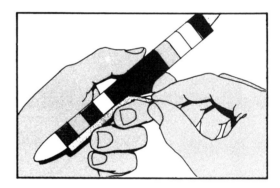

Figure 41-4. Replacing caps and removing blue strip

Name _____ Date _____ Grade _____

41. Miniaturized and Rapid Biochemical Methods

RESULTS AND OBSERVATIONS

Record the results as + or - *in* the box of the test and *circle* the number below the box if the result was positive. Sum the circled numbers within the bracket and enter the number in the hexagon below the arrow. The five numbers reading from left to right make up the ID Value. Go to the Code Book and look up the number. Enter the name of the organism (or organisms) in the space provided and other data as indicated. **If a form was supplied to you, use that instead of the drawing below.** Attach it to this page and submit both to your instructor.

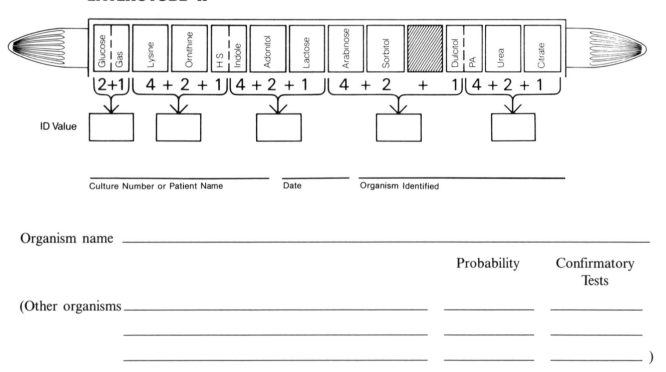

ENTEROTUBE® II

ID Value

Culture Number or Patient Name   Date   Organism Identified

Organism name _____

	Probability	Confirmatory Tests
(Other organisms _____	_____	_____
_____	_____	_____
_____	_____	_____)

QUESTIONS

A. **True or False Statements:** Circle the correct response.

    T   F   1.   Miniaturized kits eliminate testing of traditional media.

    T   F   2.   Dichotomous keys are the most accurate way to analyze the results.

    T   F   3.   An ENTEROTUBE II result can always be converted into an ID value.

B. **Completion:**

    4.   If your organism had an ID value of 00001, what test should you perform? ....

    5.   Name one oxidase negative, glucose non-fermenting organism: ....

    6–7.   Name two tests determined in the API 20E kit not utilized in this Enterotube:

        6. _____

        7. _____

UNIT *VII*

Environmental Stresses

The environmental stresses to which organisms have been exposed since life first evolved cover nearly every aspect of physics, chemistry, and even biology—radiation, temperature, osmolytes, inorganic chemicals, pressure, oxygen, organic compounds, antibiotics, and other organisms. Microorganisms have evolved mechanisms to cope with almost every extreme of each of these. Some archaebacteria have been reported from deep ocean trenches to have an optimum growth temperature in excess of 100°C. Some have adopted an alternate cell type (endospore) in response to certain environmental changes resulting in a problem of food processing for humans. Others have evolved a system of plasmids, often coding for specialized genes which produce enzymes protecting the cell from heavy metals or antibiotics and other functions (studied in Unit IX). Antibiotic resistance is extremely important in human and animal medicine, since the plasmids are transferable to other species or even other genera of bacteria. Plasmids are being exploited in genetic engineering.

The exercises presented in this section are a selection of possible ones to illustrate the range of adaptations organisms have made to extreme and unusual environments.

42 Temperature

OBJECTIVES

The student will be able to:

1. determine the growth temperature range and approximate optimum growth temperature of a bacterial culture.

2. define psychrophile, mesophile, and thermophile.

3. define maximum, minimum, and optimum temperature of growth.

An organism's response to heat in the environment is related to the organism's normal habitat. Generally speaking, cold environment organisms do not grow well or even at all at temperatures above 20°C. These organisms are called **psychrophiles** (psychro (G)-cold/phile (G)-loving). Other organisms grow best at temperatures above 45°C and rarely grow below 40°C. These are called **thermophiles** (thermo (G)-hot). Still other organisms grow best in the range 20°C to 45°C and these are called **mesophiles** (meso (G)-middle). These terms are used to describe the **range** in which the **optimum** growth temperature is found, not necessarily where growth ceases. Many of these organisms grow slowly outside the indicated range and the term **facultative** may be used to indicate that fact. **Minimum** and **maximum** growth temperatures are temperatures below or above which a given organismal strain ceases to reproduce and, in fact, may be killed. Death is commonly the case just above the maximum temperature of growth. Temperatures below the minimum are often not lethal and may be preservative to varying degrees. The optimum temperature of growth is generally the temperature at which division is most rapid. However, the production of some metabolic product may be optimal at a temperature other than the optimum for division. For example, more lactic acid might be produced at a temperature below the growth optimum than at the optimum itself, even though division is slower at the lower temperature. Advantage is taken of this in cheese making.

The extremes of temperature at which microorganisms can grow, especially prokaryotes, is truly amazing: from about –12°C in super-cooled foods to 110°C in undersea thermal vents (e.g., Galapagos trench). An archaebacterium has been reported from a thermal vent with an optimum of 105°C and with maximum and minimum temperatures of 110°C and 90°C, respectively. In most cases it is believed that temperature extremes from the optimum affect enzyme formation or function (by denaturation) resulting in no metabolism or no reproduction. In some cases the cell membrane structure may be altered by either solidifying (freezing) or liquefying (melting), thus resulting in transport or membrane failure.

This exercise illustrates a visual method for determining the range and approximate optimum growth temperature for several organisms. An optical absorbance method using a spectrophotometer can be used for more refined studies.

MATERIALS (groups of four)

1. One 18-24 hour old tryptic soy broth culture tube of each of *Pseudomonas fluorescens*, *Escherichia coli*, and *Bacillus stearothermophilus*

2. One 18-24 hour old marine broth culture of *Vibrio marinus*

3. 19 tryptic soy broth tubes, sterile

4. 7 marine broth tubes, sterile

5. Incubators or water baths at each temperature

PROCEDURE (7 days)

Period 1

1. One student labels 6 tubes of marine broth with the name *V. marinus* and one of six incubation temperatures: 5°, 20°, 30°, 40°, 50°, and 60°C.

2. Each remaining student in the group labels six tryptic soy broth tubes similarly with the name of one of the organisms provided and a temperature of incubation. One tube is reserved as a no growth control for comparison. *Note:* Use an indelible marking pen if water baths are used as incubators.

3. Inoculate the six labeled tubes with *one* loopful of the assigned organism.

4. As quickly as possible, incubate each tube at the appropriate incubation temperature. Don't delay. Even a moderate time at room temperature may permit cell division.

5. Observe after 2 and 7 days of incubation. (Periods 2 and 3 below, respectively.)

OBSERVATIONS

Period 2

6. Handle the tubes carefully looking at each one for a small button of growth. Do this by holding the tube over your head and looking up from below. Record as positive (+) for growth if a button is present.

7. Shake each tube gently and compare the turbidity against the control tube. Record as positive (+) in the results table *only* if growth has occurred. If there is no growth, leave blank.

8. Return tubes to the incubator as quickly as possible.

Period 3

9. Again look for a button on the bottom of the tube. If the button is no larger than on Day 2, record as negative (0) for growth.

10. Shake each tube gently to suspend cells and compare against the uninoculated control tube. Find *the* tube of all the temperatures of incubation which shows the *most* growth (i.e., is most turbid). This tube becomes ++++ (i.e., the maximum growth).

11. Compare each of the other tubes of the same organism with the tube rated ++++, this time recording growth (turbidity) as 0 (no growth), +, ++, +++, or ++++.

INTERPRETATION

The results of this experiment do not lend themselves to an accurate determination of optimum temperature but usually will provide a range. The tube showing 4+ will be near the optimum. In cases where two tubes are 4+, the optimum may lie between them. Temperature gradient bars are commonly used to more accurately determine the optimum. An incubation temperature at which growth does not occur and it does at the next temperature below can be used as an estimate of the maximum growth temperature. Minimum growth temperature is more difficult to determine and requires prolonged incubation. The growth temperature ranges of the psychrophiles, mesophiles, and thermophiles can be seen from these results.

THOUGHT QUESTIONS

1. What are some factors that may account for an organism's ability to grow at 90°C compared to one which can't?

2. Compare the membrane lipids of psychrophiles and thermophiles as to structure and physical properties.

3. What conditions are necessary to permit an organism to grow at –10°C?

42. Temperature

RESULTS AND OBSERVATIONS

Table of Growth Response

	5°C		20°C		30°C		40°C		50°C		60°C		Growth[a] Temperature		
	2d	7d	2d	7d	2d	7d	2d	7d	2d	7d	2d	7d	Max.	Min.	Opt.
V. marinus															
P. fluorescens															
E. coli															
B. stearothermophilus															

[a] If these can be determined from your data, they are approximate only.

This type of recording of growth does not show it very clearly, but was there a difference in amount of growth between 2 and 7 days? Which ones?

QUESTIONS

A. **True or False Statements:** Circle the letter of correct response.

T   F   1.   The optimum growth temperature is also the optimum temperature for all other cellular activities.

T   F   2.   All strains of *Pseudomonas fluorescens* have the same optimum temperature.

T   F   3.   The temperature above which an organism will not grow is said to be the maximum temperature.

T   F   4.   Growth below 0°C requires, among other things, a liquid water phase.

T   F   5.   A mesophile can grow only between 20° and 45°C.

T   F   6.   A button of cells on the bottom of a tube always signifies growth.

B. **Completion:**

7–11.   Give the name of the organism temperature grouping for each of the following:

   7.   Grows at 0°C _____

   8.   Optimum growth at 15°C _____

   9.   Grows at 70°C _____

   10.   Optimum growth at 55° but grows at 37°C _____

   11.   Grows best at 37°C _____

   12.   Growth could be better quantified by using a spectrophotometer and measuring

_____.

43 Heat Stress

OBJECTIVES

The student will be able to:

1. explain the meaning of Thermal Death Time (TDT).

2. define F value.

3. define z value.

4. plot Thermal Death Times and obtain the z and F values.

5. name one industrial use of the z and F values.

Organisms vary widely in ability to survive in the presence of an environmental stress such as pH, chemicals, radiation, or heat. In addition to inherent strain differences, other factors including culture age, the organic environment, minerals, and pH also affect resistance. Heat stress is used in this exercise to illustrate the methodology which is essentially the same for most other stress studies. Only the definitions change somewhat.

Some psychrophiles are killed by temperatures exceeding 20°C, while thermophiles and thermodurics can withstand very high temperatures indeed. **Endospores** of thermophiles are the most heat resistant biological structures known. Some of these survive boiling water for 20 hours or more and are of considerable concern in canned food processing. An organism's response to heat can be quantified and this is often done for studies of adequate cooking or canning processes.

Four commonly used heat measures are the **TDT, z, F,** and **D** values. The **TDT** or Thermal Death Time is the **time** required to kill a specified number of organisms at a particular temperature. The **z value** is defined as the number of **degrees** C (or °F) required to decrease the thermal death *time* by ten-fold. z values range from 1°C or less to about 7°C ($2°–12°$ F) for vegetative cells and from 8° to 12°C ($15°–22°$ F) for endospores. The **F value** is variously defined depending on the purpose. In the canning industry it is defined as the TDT at 121°C, usually expressed as F. If other temperatures (e.g., 80°C or 100°C) are used in cooking, then the F is subscripted with the temperature, thus $F_{80°C}$ or $F_{100°C}$. The **D value,** or decimal reduction time, is defined as the **time** required to reduce the bacterial *population* ten-fold (or 90%) at a specified temperature. It is usually subscripted with the temperature, (e.g., $D_{118°C}$). The z value can be derived from a series of D values at different temperatures. For prevention of botulism, $12D_{121°C}$ heat treatment is given. That is, a processing time of 12 times the D value at 121°C is given to ensure the death of *Clostridium botulinum* spores. That is enough time to destroy 10^{12} spores. D and z values are widely used in dry heat, gaseous, and radiation sterilization by changing the thermal terms to other physical or concentration terms. Determination of the D value is fairly complicated and the TDT method will be used here.

Heat, chemical, or physical resistance of an organism depends on a number of factors such as growth phase, culture medium composition, genetic complement, etc. This exercise is designed to illustrate the principle involved in determination of z and F values. A TDT curve will be determined experimentally and the $F_{80°C}$ and z values determined by plotting.

MATERIALS (per 4 pairs)

No. of items needed for each temperature

60°C	70°C	80°C	90°C	Total items
6	6	6	6	24 1 ml pipets with safety bulb
7	7	7	7	28 lactose broth tubes (5 ml/16 mm tube)
1	1	1	1	4 nutrient broth tubes (10 ml/16 mm tube with loose fitting cap)
1	1	1	1	1 18–24 hour old broth culture of *Escherichia coli* (7 ml/13mm screw-capped tube)
1	1	1	1	4 thermometers
1	1	1	1	1 water bath at each specified temperature
1	1	1	1	4 test tube holders

PROCEDURE (2 days)

Period 1

1. The class is divided into groups of 4 pairs. One pair uses 60°C, one pair 70°C, one pair 80°C, and one pair 90°C as the test condition. The following directions apply to each pair.

2. Prepare a water bath using a container large enough to hold two 16 mm tubes without falling over. Maintain the temperature 1°C above the desired temperature by moving a flame in and out under the bath as illustrated in Figure 43-1. A larger thermostatically controlled bath with racks for the tubes could be used instead for the whole class. Place an uninoculated nutrient broth tube in the water bath assigned.

3. Screw the culture tube cap on tight and shake the *E. coli* culture *vigorously* to suspend cells and break up clumps. One culture is used for the four culture conditions.

4. Place 7 tubes of lactose broth in a rack and label 0 time, 1 minute, 2 minutes, 4 minutes, 8 minutes, 15 minutes, and 30 minutes.

5. Adjust an inoculating loop to 4mm diameter, sterilize it and transfer one loopful of the *culture* to the tube labeled 0 time. This serves as a control to indicate culture viability.

6. Maintain the water bath for 2–3 minutes to ensure that the nutrient broth tube is at the proper temperature.

7. Without removing the nutrient broth tube from the bath, lift off the cap and quickly pipet 0.1 ml of the broth culture into the tube. Be careful not the touch the inside of the tube with the pipet. Replace the cap and lift the tube out of the water bath with a test tube holder or other device and quickly mix by shaking back and forth (**not** up and down). Replace the tube in the bath.

8. Note the time of the addition here ＿＿＿＿＿ . This is **time zero.**

9. Sterilize the same loop and at **exactly 1 minute after time zero** remove a loopful of broth from the heated tube without taking the tube from the bath. Be careful not to touch the walls inside the tube. Transfer the loopful to the lactose broth tube labeled 1 minute. Repeat with the freshly sterilized loop at exactly 2 minutes, then 4 minutes, 8 minutes, 15 minutes, and 30 minutes after time zero.

10. Incubate the lactose broth tubes at 35°C for 24–48 hours.

OBSERVATIONS

Periods 2 and 3

11. Examine the tubes for growth (turbidity) at 24 or 48 hours.

12. Record the presence of growth (+) or no growth (0) in the table on the report form.

13. Collect the data for the other temperatures from the rest of your group so that you have a complete set.

DETERMINATION OF TDT, F, AND z VALUES

1. From the table of observations, calculate the TDT for *each* temperature by finding the adjacent pair of times where growth *occurs* at the shorter time and *no* growth at the longer. Assume the TDT to be the time half-way between the two. For example, growth occurred at 8 minutes and not at 15 minutes. The TDT is assumed to be 11.5 minutes. Enter the midway time in the table as the TDT.

2. On the 3-cycle semi-log graph provided on the report form, plot the four TDTs, one for each temperature. Using a straight edge, draw a line of best fit through the four points as illustrated in Figure 43-2.

3. On the Y-axis of the graph select two time intervals exactly one log cycle apart. Draw a line from the time selected to the plotted curve, then drop a vertical line to the temperature scale on the X-axis, recording the temperature arrived at. Repeat for the second time and record the temperature arrived at. In Figure 43-2, 10 minutes and 1 minute were selected. The corresponding temperatures were 73°C and 90°C. Subtract the smaller from the larger, and that is the z value. In the example, 17°C. Enter the z value on the observation form. The $F_{80°C}$ value is obtained by drawing a line vertically from 80° to the plotted curve, then determine the corresponding time. In Figure 43-2, this is 5 minutes. Determine yours and enter the value on the report form. Using the Q fever organism, this type of curve was used to determine minimum milk pasteurizing times and temperatures.

THOUGHT QUESTIONS

1. What units would be used to report death from gamma radiation? For ultraviolet light radiation? For gaseous sterilization?

2. How are the z, F, and D values used in the canning industry? What impact does their use have on you as a consumer?

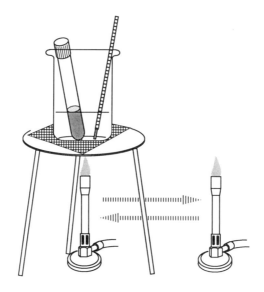

Figure 43-1. Water bath illustration

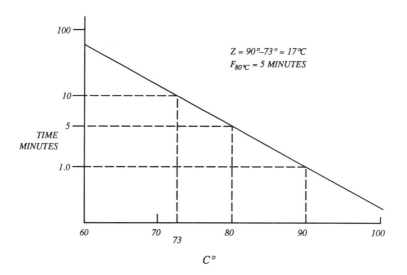

$$Z = 90° - 73° = 17°C$$
$$F_{80°C} = 5\ MINUTES$$

TIME MINUTES

$C°$

Figure 43-2. Example plot and determination of z and F values

Name _____ Date _____ Grade _____

43. Heat Stress

RESULTS AND OBSERVATIONS

Organism Name _____

Thermal Death Time Table

°C	Control time	Minutes of exposure							
	0	1	2	4	8	15	30	TDT
60								
70								
80								
90								

$z =$ _____ °C $F_{80°C}$ _____ min

semi-log graph

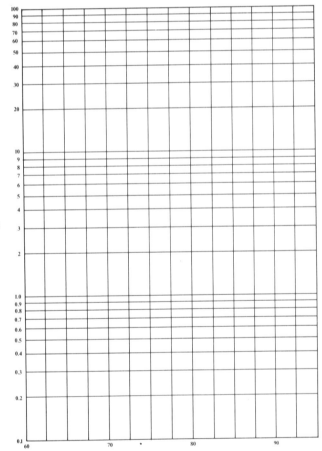

Minutes of exposure

°C

QUESTIONS

A.   **True or False Statements:** Circle the letter of the correct response.

T   F   1.   The F value expresses the same thing as the z value.

T   F   2.   z values are in units of $°C$ (or $°F$).

T   F   3.   Both the z and F values express the slope of a straight line.

T   F   4.   D values are in units of numbers of cells.

T   F   5.   A $121°C$ canned food treatment is achieved in a pan of boiling water on your kitchen stove.

T   F   6.   z values can be plotted on standard graph paper by using the logarithm of time as the y-axis.

T   F   7.   It is possible to determine the D value for an organism exposed to ethylene oxide as a sterilizing agent.

T   F   8.   The units for a D value using radiation as the killing agent are the same as when heat is used.

T   F   9.   The units for a z value using radiation as the killing agent are the same as when heat is used.

B.   **Completion:**

10–11.   A $D_{80°C}$ value means the decimal reduction _____ was determined at _____ .

12–13.   A virus with a $D_{70°C}$ value of 10 minutes is present in a food maintained at $70°C$. If the number of viruses to start with was 10,000, how long would it take to reduce the number to

12.   1 virus particle _____?

13.   0.1 virus particle _____?

14.   How long would a $10D_{70°C}$ heating time of the food in question No. 2 be? _____

15–16.   On either the report graph or the example, Figure 43-2, plot the following data for a suspension of spores and determine the $F_{121°C}$ and the z value. TDTs of 500 minutes at $98°C$ and 5 minutes at $118°C$. The $F_{121°C}$ value is _____ and the z value is _____ .

17.   What is the scientific notation and the logarithm for each of the following?

a. 25   _____ , _____   f. 10,000   _____ , _____

b. 150,000   _____ , _____   g. 43,000,000   _____ , _____

c. 1.0   _____ , _____   h. 2,000,000   _____ , _____

d. 3,200   _____ , _____   i. 4,000,000,000 _____ , _____

e. 0   _____ , _____   j. 2^5 _____ , _____

18.   What is the number (antilog) of the following logarithms? Round to the nearest whole number.

a. 4.123   _____   d. 2.901   _____

b. 1.544   _____   e. 7.552   _____

c. 3.111   _____

44 Osmotic Pressure

OBJECTIVES

The student will be able to:

1. distinguish between hypotonic, isotonic, and hypertonic solutions.

2. define plasmolysis and plasmoptysis.

3. define halophile and name a halophilic bacterial genus belonging to the archaebacterial group.

4. define osmophile and xerophile.

The presence of ions and organic substances in solution binds a certain amount of water and creates an **osmotic pressure** across a semipermeable membrane, such as that around the cytoplasm of a cell. If the amount of "free water" (i.e., not bound to the solute and sometimes called the **aqueous activity** or a_w) differs on each side of the membrane, there is a net movement of water from the side with the more "free water" to the side with the less "free water." That is, from the side with the fewer ions or organic matter to the side with more. This water movement continues until the osmotic pressure is equal on both sides, a condition called **isotonic.** If there is a higher free water concentration outside the cell, the solution is **hypotonic** and water moves into the cell causing it to swell and possibly to burst if the osmotic pressure difference is great enough. This imbibing of water and consequent swelling is called **plasmoptysis.** The reverse process, water leaving the cell to a more concentrated solute or **hypertonic** solution outside the cell, causes the cell membrane to shrivel and shrink, a process called **plasmolysis** (Figure 44-1).

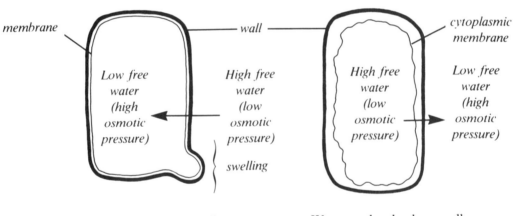

Water molecules moves into cell   Water molecules leave cell

Figure 44-1. Osmotic pressure

Many organisms are able to modify their cell chemistry in such a way as to grow in the presence of solutes, sometimes in rather high concentration, but do not require the solute for growth. An example is sodium chloride (NaCl). Organisms growing in the presence of NaCl but not requiring it are called **halotolerant.** Some organisms have adapted to the presence of high salt concentration in such a way that they require the presence of the solute to grow at all. These organisms are called **halophiles** (halo, (G)-salt). Many marine bacteria require salt at fairly low levels. Such organisms are moderate halophiles. The extreme halophiles, such as the archaebacterial genus *Halobacterium*, require salt in excess of 12% and grow well at NaCl saturation (27% w/w). Sugar and dry conditions also exert a strong osmotic pressure to which organisms have adapted. In sugars and syrups, yeasts often grow and are called **osmophiles** (osmo, (G)-pushing). On dehydrated materials, especially foods, molds can grow and these are called **xerophiles** (xero, (G)-dry).

Osmotic Pressure - 253

MATERIALS (pairs)

1. Cultures of *Escherichia coli*, *Staphylococcus aureus*, *Saccharomyces cerevisiae*, and *Halobacterium salinarium*

2. Five prepoured Petri plates of different concentrations of salt agar, sterile

   a. 0.5% NaCl
   b. 5% NaCl
   c. 10% NaCl
   d. 15% NaCl
   e. 20% NaCl

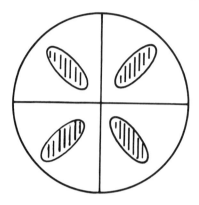

Figure 44-2. Marked and streaked plate

PROCEDURE (7 days)

Period 1

1. With a wax pencil mark the salt concentration on the underside of each Petri plate and divide it into quadrants as illustrated in Figure 44-2. Label each section with the name of one of the organisms.

2. Using a sterile loop, streak one organism on its quadrant beginning near the center and toward the side. Do not get too close to the center or the side (Figure 44-2).

3. Streak the same organism on each plate going back to the stock slant each time.

4. Repeat for the other organisms on the appropriate quadrant.

5. Incubate all plates at 32°C.

OBSERVATIONS

Periods 2 and 3

6. Observe the plates for growth at 48 hours and again at one week.

7. Record the results on the report form as follows:

   Find the plate where a particular species has the greatest amount of growth. That is the control plate for that organism and is scored ++++. Compare each other plate for that organism only and record the amount of growth as 0 (none), +, ++, +++, or ++++. Maximum growth should not occur at the same salt concentration for all the organisms.

THOUGHT QUESTIONS

1. In what kind of environment would you seek a halophile, an osmophile, a xerophile?

2. What do the terms acidophile or alkaliphile mean?

3. What role does aqueous activity play in foods?

44. Osmotic Pressure

RESULTS AND OBSERVATIONS

Table of growth on NaCl agar at

Organism	0.5%		5%		10%		15%		20%	
	48 hr	1 wk	48 hr	1 wk	48 hr	1 wk	48 hr	1 wk	48 hr	1 wk
E. coli										
S. aureus										
S. cerevisiae										
H. salinarium										

Comments:

QUESTIONS

Completion:

1. An organism requiring salt to grow is called a _____ .

2. When it grows, the solution it grows in would be _____ (or nearly so) to the cell cytoplasm.

3. If the organism grown in question No. 2 is suddenly placed in fresh water, it would _____ _____ .

4–5. If the organism grown in question No. 3 is placed in a salt solution, water moves to the _____ of the cell in a process called _____ .

6–7. Movement of water from one side of a membrane to the other depends on _____ water, the amount of which in turn depends on the amount and kind of _____ present.

8. The species of archaebacteria studied in this exercise is _____ .

9–10. An organism growing in syrup would be called an _____ and would most likely be a _____ (organism group).

11–12. An organism growing on a dehydrated food would be called a _____ and would most likely be a _____ (organism group).

13. Where in nature would you go to find a halobacterium?

45   pH

OBJECTIVES

The student will be able to:

1. make a generalization about what kinds of organisms grow at low pH and at high pH.

2. name two species of bacteria, one an archaebacterium, able to grow at pH <2.0.

Among the environmental stresses an organism may encounter, pH is of considerable importance. Each organism has its optimum pH. Most organisms grow well if not best at a pH between 6.5 and 7.5, although many grow well even optimally outside this range. The majority of microbes grow best around a pH of 7.0, but some called **acidophiles** do very well in the 3-4 range (e.g., the lactic acid bacteria). Some members of the bacterial genus *Thiobacillus* and the archaebacterial genus *Sulfolobus* not only grow best at pH <2.0 but generate their own acid and are commonly found in acid mine wastes. *Sulfolobus* additionally grows at very high temperatures. Some of these bacteria will grow at pH 1.0 or less. Yeasts and molds are generally very acid tolerant and grow quite well at pH 3.0 or a little lower. Molds and yeasts generally will grow at lower pH's than bacteria. This is the reason acid foods such as fruit juices are usually spoiled by yeasts and molds rather than bacteria. Media for the selective isolation of yeasts and molds takes advantage of this by lowering the pH and suppressing bacteria. Some algae, but not cyanobacteria, grow at or near pH 2.0.

At higher pH values, a similar situation exists. Organisms grow as high as pH 12 and are called **alkaliphiles.** These include some bacteria, cyanobacteria, algae, protozoa, and a few insects. Alkali lakes are found all over the world in arid climates but have not been studied as extensively as acid environments. It is possible that some organisms may grow at pH values above 12 but such environments do not occur naturally. Many of the alkaliphiles also require Na^+, some in excess of 15%. *Vibrio cholerae*, the causative agent of cholera, will grow readily at pH 9.0–9.6 while most other body organisms do not. Selective media for *V. cholerae* are often adjusted to pH 9.0 for this reason.

MATERIALS (groups of 5)

1. Each student will be assigned one of the following:
    Bacillus sp.
    Saccharomyces cerevisiae
    Staphylococcus aureus
    Escherichia coli
    Enterococcus (Streptococcus) faecalis

2. Each student will have one sterile tube of tryptic soy broth at each pH 4, 5, 6, 7, 8, 9, and 10

PROCEDURE (7 days)

Period 1

1. Label each tube as *you pick it up*. Inoculate a loopful of your assigned organism into each labeled tube of the pH set. Be sure to sterilize the loop between each tube so that no acid or base is transferred to the stock tube and the inoculum size is the same.

2. One uninoculated tube of each pH should be saved for the class as a control.

3. Incubate the tubes and controls at 35°–37° C except for *S. cerevisiae*, which is incubated at 30° C.

OBSERVATIONS

Periods 2 and 3

4. At 48 hours, examine each tube for turbidity comparing it to the control *for that pH*.

5. Record the results on the report form as 0 (no growth), +, ++, +++, or ++++. This last would be the pH of greatest growth.

6. Reincubate the tubes and repeat the observations at 7 days.

7. Collect data for the other organisms from the other members of your group.

THOUGHT QUESTIONS

1. What do you think the pH of the acidophile cytoplasm would be?

2. How do the acidophiles produce the excess protons associated with the acid pH?

3. The acid in acid mine waters comes from what minerals?

45. pH

RESULTS AND OBSERVATIONS

Table of pH results

Organism		pH						
		4.0	5.0	6.0	7.0	8.0	9.0	10.0
Bacillus sp.	48 h							
	7d							
S. cerevisiae	48 h							
	7d							
S. aureus	48 h							
	7d							
E. coli	48 h							
	7d							
E. faecalis	48 h							
	7d							

QUESTIONS

Completion:

1–2. Organisms growing at high pH are generally called _____ and those growing at low pH are called _____.

3. A genus of archaebacteria with a very low optimum pH and a very high optimum temperature is _____.

4. A genus of bacteria found in acid mine wastes is _____.

46 Oxygen

OBJECTIVES

The student will be able to:

1. describe the relationship between organisms and oxygen.

2. define the terms obligate anaerobe, facultative anaerobe, aerobe, and microaerophile.

3. perform an experiment to determine an organism's relationship to oxygen.

Many organisms require oxygen as the final electron acceptor in metabolism. These organisms are **aerobes.** If they cannot metabolize in any other way, they are **obligate aerobes.** An organism which cannot grow in the presence of oxygen is called an **obligate anaerobe.** Within these categories there are degrees of strictness. The inability to grow in the presence of oxygen may be due to a lack of the proper enzymes or the products of oxygen may actively kill the organism. Many organisms can use oxygen when it is available or can grow in its absence if fermentable substrates are present. Such organisms are called **facultative anaerobes.** A few bacteria lack catalase and can grow in the presence of oxygen only if certain organic compounds are available. Some organisms simply do better at low oxygen levels. These are often referred to as **microaerophiles.** The basic responses are illustrated in Figure 46-1.

In this exercise you will do a simple test to demonstrate organism response to oxygen. This method is not useful for all organisms, especially the strict obligate anaerobes but does illustrate the principle.

MATERIALS (per person)

1. 18-24 hour old broth cultures of *Clostridium perfringens, Escherichia coli, Enterococcus (Streptococcus) faecalis,* and *Bacillus megaterium*

2. 4 sterile 1 ml pipets and safety bulb

3. 5 yeast extract-tryptone agar tubes, sterile

PROCEDURE (2 days)

Period 1

1. Melt five yeast extract-tryptone agar tubes in a boiling water bath and temper them to 45°-50°C.

2. With a sterile pipet, transfer 1 ml of a broth culture to a tempered agar tube by inserting the pipet tip to the bottom of the tube. Release the pipet contents slowly *as you withdraw* the pipet. Discard the pipet. Label the tube with the culture name and let it solidify.

3. Repeat step No. 2 with the remaining three cultures.

4. Incubate all the tubes at 32°C for 48 hours.

OBSERVATIONS

Period 3

5. Using the fifth tube as a control, compare the growth pattern of each organism in the tube.

6. Draw your observations on the report form.

7. Name the response each organism exhibits to oxygen.

THOUGHT QUESTIONS

1. What is superoxide dismutase and how does it fit into the oxygen response picture?

2. What is the biochemistry of the lactic acid bacteria response to oxygen considering they do not possess catalase? How do they grow in the presence of oxygen?

3. What stress does sunlight and oxygen together put on bacteria? How do microbes combat this problem?

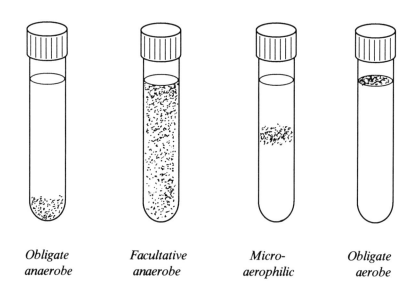

| Obligate anaerobe | Facultative anaerobe | Micro-aerophilic | Obligate aerobe |

Figure 46-1. Growth responses to oxygen

46. Oxygen

RESULTS AND OBSERVATIONS

Draw the growth pattern for each organism and give a name to the oxygen relationship (e.g., obligate aerobe, etc.).

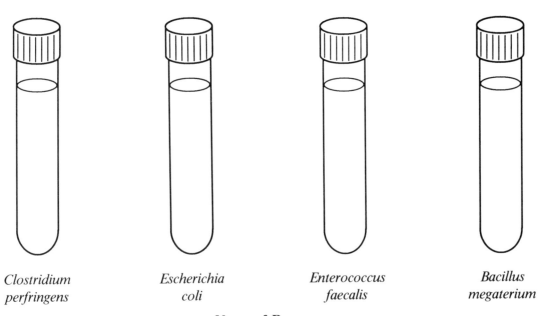

| *Clostridium perfringens* | *Escherichia coli* | *Enterococcus faecalis* | *Bacillus megaterium* |

Name of Response

_____   _____   _____   _____

QUESTIONS

True or False Statements: Circle the correct response.

T F 1. All bacteria are aerobes.

T F 2. Lactic acid bacteria have catalase.

T F 3. Some bacteria are killed by oxygen even at low levels.

T F 4. An anaerobe grows better in the absence of oxygen.

T F 5. A microaerophile grows best at 20% oxygen.

T F 6. The method used in this exercise will work for even strict obligate anaerobes.

T F 7. The medium used here is a soft agar (<1% agar).

T F 8. *Saccharomyces cerevisiae* is a facultative anaerobe.

47 Ultraviolet Light

OBJECTIVES

The student will be able to:

1. perform a simple demonstration of the effects of ultraviolet light.

2. define photoreactivation, light repair, and dark repair.

3. explain how ultraviolet light causes mutation.

4. explain why the height of the ultraviolet lamps in this exercise is important.

Ultraviolet light is widely used to disinfect or sterilize air in hospital air circulation systems and surgical tools, and has a number of applications in the food industry for control of airborne mold spores, bacteria, and bacteriophages around packaging equipment, fermentation vats, and other places. Ultraviolet light is highly germicidal between 130 and 400 nm but is most effective at 256 nm. Double bonds in the purines and pyrimidines absorb strongly near this wavelength, resulting in rupture and reformation in unusual configurations. Adjacent thymines in particular form a thymine dimer which prevents DNA duplication thus causing the death of the cell. Many microbes have enzyme systems which can repair such damage in some cases. One system requires the presence of visible light in the 420-540 nm range. This is sometimes called **photoreactivation** or the **light repair** system. Some organisms possess a **dark repair** enzyme system which operates in the absence of light. Out of all of the cells affected, only a few can perform these repairs and allow growth. Some of the cells surviving may carry mutations as a result of changes in the DNA codons of the cell. These express themselves in different ways.

Ultraviolet light has a number of drawbacks as a germicidal agent. It has very poor penetrating power, being effectively blocked out (absorbed) by clear glass, plastics, thin films of water, and any opaque material. Thus it is useful only where the organisms are directly exposed to the light waves. Ultraviolet also can cause severe eye and skin damage to workers, even when reflected from surfaces. Direct exposure to the skin and eyes must be limited. Reflected light is also dangerous.

This exercise is intended to illustrate the lethal and mutational effects of ultraviolet light and some of its limitations.

MATERIALS (per pair)

1. 18-24 hour old broth culture of *Staphylococcus aureus* or *Serratia marcescens*

2. 1 sterile cotton swab

3. 5 Petri plates, sterile

4. Nutrient agar, sterile

5. 3 x 5 file cards (3)

6. 3 ultraviolet lamps (may be one set for whole class) (Universal Illuminator, Fisher Scientific Co., Sylvania Germicidal lamp G15T8)

7. Aluminum foil wrap

PROCEDURE (1 day)

Period 1

1. Place three germicidal lamps well separated from each other with the bulbs at 15, 30, and 60 cm respectively above the bench top. Allow the lamps to warm 15 minutes before use.

2. Work in a group of three pairs for each organism. Each pair in the group uses a different lamp height.

3. Each pair should prepare 5 Petri plates of nutrient agar.

4. Wet a large sterile cotton swab in a broth culture of the assigned organism. Press out the excess fluid on the inside wall of the tube and spread the swab evenly over the entire surface of one of the plates. Repeat this step for each plate.

5. Each pair sets one plate aside as a growth control.

6. On the underside of three plates, divide the bottom in half with a wax pencil line and place a mark on the to-be-covered side for identification.

7. Four Petri plates (excluding the control) are placed cover up under the assigned germicidal lamp. Remove the covers of the three previously marked plates and quickly place a 3 x 5 card over the marked half of the plate and note the exact time. Leave the covers off. The fourth plate is exposed with the cover in place (Figure 47-1).

CAUTION: Expose your hands to the light only briefly and be cautious of reflecting light into the eyes.

---

8. Expose one card covered plate for 30 seconds, one for 1 minute, and one for 3 minutes. The covered plate is exposed for 3 minutes. Remove the paper masks aseptically and replace the cover. Label the plate covers with your name, lamp height, and exposure time.

9. Discard the paper shields in an autoclave bag, NOT the trash.

10. Place all of the plates bottom up in a dark light-proof box or wrap them with aluminum foil to exclude all light.

11. Incubate all plates at room temperature for 24-48 hours.

OBSERVATIONS

Period 2

12. After 24-48 hours incubation, make drawings of each plate in the space provided on the Results and Observations form showing the relative amount of growth as compared to the masked half of the plate.

13. Count the total number of colonies in the exposed area of each plate and enter the number in the table on the report form.

14. Count all colonies which are white, and all colonies which are sectored with red or white. Enter the number in the appropriate columns on the table. These colonies represent pigmentation mutations which occur as a result of the ultraviolet radiation or spontaneously. To determine the rate due to ultraviolet light, the spontaneous mutation rate must be known. This exercise will not provide the spontaneous rate. *S. marcescens* is much more likely to show mutation than *S. aureus.*

15. Obtain the complete data for the other two lamp heights from the other members of your group. Each person should have a complete table on the results form.

16. An apparent mutation rate can be determined using the data and formulas on the results form.

THOUGHT QUESTIONS

1. What are the biochemical steps in the modification of DNA by ultraviolet light?

2. How does ultraviolet light induce mutations?

3. Distinguish between light and dark repair.

Figure 47-1. Exposure times.

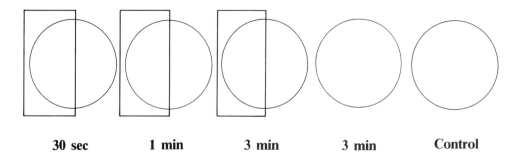

| 30 sec | 1 min | 3 min | 3 min | Control |

Name _____ Date _____ Grade _____

47. Ultraviolet Light

RESULTS AND OBSERVATIONS

Draw your results and those of the other two lamps.

Organism _____

Relative growth on control plate _____

Amount of growth on covered plate _____

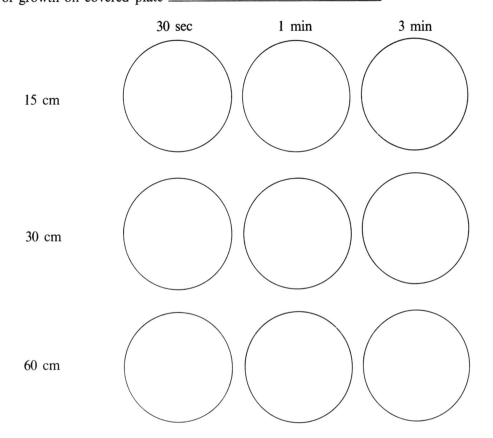

Colony counts

Lamp height and exposure time

	15 cm			30 cm			60 cm		
	30 sec	1 min	3 min	30 sec	1 min	3 min	30 sec	1 min	3 min
Total white colonies									
Total sectored colonies									
Total number colonies									

Survival rate:

$$\frac{\text{Total colonies on exposed side}}{\text{Total number of colonies on exposed side at 60 cm or 3 min}} \times 100 = \text{relative \% survival}$$

Apparent UV mutation rate:

$$\frac{\text{Number white colonies on exposed side}}{\text{Total number colonies on exposed side}} \times 100 = \text{\% mutations}$$

Apparent spontaneous mutation rate:

$$\frac{\text{Number sectored colonies on exposed side}}{\text{Total number of colonies on exposed side}} \times 100 = \text{\% spontaneous mutations}$$

Note: These are apparent mutation rates since the spontaneous rate was not actually determined.

Rates table
Lamp height and time of exposure

	15 cm			30 cm			60 cm		
	30 sec	1 min	3 min	30 sec	1 min	3 min	30 sec	1 min	3 min
% survival									
Apparent % mutation									
Apparent % spontaneous									

QUESTIONS

Completion:

1-3.   Name three factors which limit the use of ultraviolet light as a sterilizing agent.

1. _____

2. _____

3. _____

4.   Ultraviolet light primarily affects the _____ .

5.   The wavelengths of light effective in light repair mechanisms are in the range _____ nm.

6-8.   Name three places where ultraviolet light is used for its germicidal properties.

6. _____

7. _____

8. _____

9. The most effective germicidal wavelength of ultraviolet light is approximately _____ nm.

10. One cause of failure of DNA to replicate when irradiated with ultraviolet light is the formation of dimers between adjacent _____ molecules.

11. By adjusting the height of the lamps as done in this exercise, a simple physical law of radiation is used. Write the formula for this law (consult a physics text).

12. Define photoreactivation.

48 Oligodynamic Action

OBJECTIVES

The student will be able to:

1. describe the effect of heavy metals on bacteria.

2. describe the role of plasmids in resistance to heavy metals.

The term **heavy metal** is ill-defined and includes some elements which are not true metals, such as mercury, arsenic, selenium, and tellurium. Heavy metals include silver, copper, chromium, cadmium, lead, and zinc among others. Some of these metals are toxic to bacteria, even in very small amounts, an effect called **oligodynamic action** (oligo (Gr.) = small, dynam (Gr.) = power). Enough of the element dissolves from a piece of metal to affect the growth of bacterial. Heavy metals are used in many industries, in pesticides and paints and are, therefore, quite common in industrial wastes, sewage, and sewage sludge. If the wastes contaminate soils or water, the heavy metals have a marked effect on bacterial processes of various kinds.

Some bacteria become relatively resistant, as much as 100 times, to fairly high concentrations of these heavy metals. The resistance factor is carried on a plasmid in many bacteria. Antibiotic resistance is often carried on the same plasmid. These resistance plasmids are further discussed in Exercise 60.

Resistance to heavy metals is probably not the result of a single mechanism but involves special surface proteins to inactivate the metal, special enzymes which reduce or oxidize the metal to some innocuous form, or attach methyl groups making a gas which escapes from the cells' environment.

This exercise illustrates the action of heavy metals by comparing the effects of copper, silver, nickel, and aluminum.

MATERIALS (per pair or person)

1. Metals. Members of the class will be asked to supply coins (two of each) and silver jewelry for the experiment; pennies, nickels, and a silver piece (ring or other silver jewelry); copper, nickel and silver metals. An aluminum disk about the size of a coin may be cut from the bottom of a beverage can or from aluminum foil.

2. 2 nutrient agar deeps, sterile

3. 2 Petri plates, sterile

4. 2 sterile cotton swabs with large ball

5. 18-24 hour old nutrient broth cultures of *Staphylococcus aureus* and *Escherichia coli*

6. Alcohol 95%

7. Forceps

PROCEDURE (2 days)

Period 1

1. Prepare two nutrient agar plates by pouring 20 ml of medium into each plate and allowing them to solidify.

2. Invert the plates and mark the bottom into quadrants with a wax pencil.

3. Dip one of the sterile cotton swabs into one of the cultures and swab the surface of one of the plates, back and forth in one direction covering the entire plate. Rewet the swab in the same culture and swab the plate again, this time swabbing in a direction 90° to the first. It is important that the surface is heavily inoculated. Discard the swab as instructed.

4. Take the coins and the aluminum piece and wash them thoroughly with scouring powder and water. Rinse well.

5. With a forceps, dip one coin into the alcohol and flame in the Bunsen burner. Hold in the air until cool, then place the disk in the middle of one of the quadrants on the plate, carefully tapping it down with the forceps to ensure contact (Figure 48-1).

6. Repeat with each of the disks. Be careful not to overheat the aluminum disk.

7. Prepare the other plate with the culture in a similar manner; place the flamed disks in position.

8. Incubate the two plates at 37°C for 24 hours.

OBSERVATIONS

Period 2

9. Observe the plates and measure any zones of inhibition around the disks. Enter the data on the report form. If there is a second zone, make a note of it and measure the diameter also. Although there is not a satisfactory explanation for it, sometimes a ring of heavy growth will be seen around the zone of inhibition. If present, make a note of the ring of growth.

10. Salvage the coins or metal by removing them from the plates with forceps and flaming each one (quite hot) in the Bunsen burner until all organic material is combusted. Do **not** dip them into alcohol first.

THOUGHT QUESTIONS

1. Of what use is the plasmid for metal resistance to the bacterial cell in nature?

2. What result would you predict if you were to use a present day dime in this exercise?

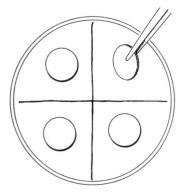

Figure 48-1. Place coins in quadrants with forceps

48. Oligodynamic Action

RESULTS AND OBSERVATIONS

Metal	Zone of inhibition (mm dia)	
	E. coli	S. aureus
copper notes		
nickel notes		
silver notes		
aluminum notes		
     notes		
     notes		

QUESTIONS

Completion:

1–2. Which metal had the greatest inhibition on *E. coli*? _____ on *S. aureus*? _____

3–5. Resistance to heavy metals is often carried on a _____ which is composed of _____ and carrying a code for certain _____ .

6. The effect on bacteria of a small amount of heavy metal is called _____ .

7–8. Despite their toxicity to bacteria, are any of the metals listed in the introduction necessary for nutrition? _____ If so, which one(s)? _____ .

9. What are some other "heavy metals" not used in this exercise?

_____

49 Antibiotic Resistance

OBJECTIVES

The student will be able to:

1. describe the gradient plate technique for isolation of resistant organisms.

2. isolate a streptomycin resistant bacterium.

3. describe some of the mechanisms of resistance.

Many microorganisms in nature produce **antibiotics,** presumably to compete more successfully with other organisms. These substances would be expected to affect the producing cell as well; a so-called **suicide effect.** Since the object is to inhibit or kill competitors and not oneself, antibiotic producers have generally developed **defenses** against the agents. The mechanisms involved are highly variable depending in part on the antibiotic and in part on the organism. Such defenses include degrading or inactivating enzymes, cell wall or membrane alterations to prevent the substance from reentering the cell, and configuration changes in some cell structures. In many bacteria the genes which code for these defensive mechanisms are located on **plasmids.** Plasmids often find their way into related or unrelated bacteria thus transferring the resistance. Resistance may often be due to a mutation causing changes in the cell surface or other structures.

In this exercise, you will use the **gradient plate technique** to isolate a streptomycin resistant organism resulting from a spontaneous mutation of the wild-type or **prototroph.** (See Exercise 59 for a method to increase the mutation rate.) The gradient plate (Figure 49-1) is made by pouring a nutrient medium into a Petri plate with one side elevated. After the agar is solidified, the plate is leveled and a streptomycin agar is poured over the surface of the base medium. After it is solidified a gradient of streptomycin concentration is established from low to high. A culture (or other source for naturally resistant organisms) is then spread on the surface and colonies growing on the high side are resistant, although the degree of resistance is unknown. A colony can be isolated and tested for level of resistance or the process repeated with a higher streptomycin level. This technique also can be used for selecting mutants to other substances.

MATERIALS (per pair)

1. 18-24 hour old nutrient broth culture of *Escherichia coli*

2. 2 nutrient agar deeps, sterile

3. 2 streptomycin sulfate (100 μg/ml) nutrient agar deeps, sterile

4. 2 Petri plates, sterile

5. 1 sterile 1 ml pipet and safety bulb

6. 1 glass spreading rod (4 mm diameter glass rod approximately 27 cm long, bent into "hockey stick" shape)

PROCEDURE (6 days)

Period 1

1. Place one edge of a Petri plate on a standard wooden pencil as in Figure 49-1. Pour the plain nutrient agar into the Petri plate until the deep side is near the rim and the shallow side is just at the plate edge. Adjust the pencil position as necessary to achieve this. Let it solidify.

2. Remove the pencil and mark an arrow on the bottom of the dish with a wax pencil identifying the shallow side where the agar just touches the plate side. Now pour the streptomycin agar on the surface until it just covers the base layer (Figure 49-1) and let it solidify. The established gradient is from 0 μg/ml on the one side to 100 μg/ml on the other.

3. Pipet 0.1 ml of the culture of *E. coli* on the surface of the plate.

4. Dip the glass spreading rod in alcohol, flame, cool, and spread the culture over the plate surface.

5. Incubate the plate at 35°–37°C for 48 hours.

OBSERVATIONS

Period 2

6. Prepare a second gradient plate as above. (*Note:* Must be prepared at the time of use.)

7. Make a drawing of the original plate on the report form showing the location of the resistant colonies.

8. Select a colony growing at the higher concentrations of streptomycin and with a sterile inoculating loop, streak the colony on the second plate from the low concentration in the direction of the gradient.

9. Incubate the plate at 35°–37°C for 48 hours.

Period 3

10. Make a drawing of the second plate on the report form and estimate the resistance at the point where growth stops. The gradient established is 0 μg/ml on one side to 100 μg/ml on the other. The middle of the gradient would be 50 μg/ml.

THOUGHT QUESTIONS

1. In this exercise, what would cause the resistance mutation?

2. How would you design an experiment to isolate a streptomycin resistant organism from soil? Would it necessarily be a mutant?

3. How would you determine if a plasmid was the cause of the resistance observed in question No. 2?

(a) The base layer   (b) The streptomycin layer

Figure 49-1. Making the gradient plate. NA = nutrient agar; SNA = streptomycin nutrient agar; 0 = low streptomycin concentration; 100 = high streptomycin concentration

Name _____ Date _____ Grade _____

49. Antibiotic Resistance

RESULTS AND OBSERVATIONS

1. Drawing of the first plate

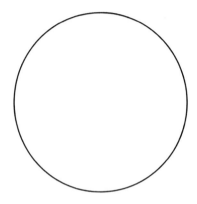

2. Drawing of the second plate

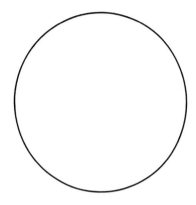

3. Resistance is approximately _____ μg/ml.

QUESTIONS

Completion:

1. A wild type organism is called a _____.

2. Resistance genes are often located on a _____.

3. The technique used in this exercise is called the _____
   _____.

4. When an organism is killed by its own antibiotic, it is said to be a _____ effect.

5. Plasmids can often transfer _____ resistance to other kinds of cells.

6. In this exercise you are attempting to isolate a _____.

7–8. Name two mechanisms which organisms have used to protect themselves against their own or others' products.

   7. _____

   8. _____

50 Protoplast Formation

OBJECTIVES

The student will be able to:

1. prepare a suspension of protoplasts.
2. describe the protoplast.
3. indicate why osmotic pressure is important in protoplast formation.
4. cite one example of the importance of protoplasts in medicine.

A **protoplast** is a bacterial cell which has lost its cell wall, either as a result of continued growth in the presence of a cell wall inhibitor such as penicillin, or by exposure to an enzyme which digests the wall such as lysozyme. Protoplasts may continue to metabolize or reproduce provided the osmotic pressure outside the cell membrane is approximately that inside the cell. Extreme differences cause the cell to rupture. Osmotic stabilizers include blood serum or sucrose solutions. Protoplasts are important in studying cell structure and metabolism, and sometimes cause chronic infections in man or animals when under prolonged antibiotic therapy. Members of the **mycoplasma** group, which never form a cell wall, are sometimes described as naturally occurring protoplasts; however, the term is usually reserved for cells from which the cell wall has been physically removed.

MATERIALS (per person or other grouping of students)

1. 18–20 hour old trypticase soy broth culture of *Bacillus megaterium*
2. 1 tube of 15% sucrose-trypticase soy broth, sterile
3. Lysozyme solution (400 μg or 4800 units per 0.1 ml) sufficient for class
4. 1 sterile 13 mm diameter test tube
5. 2 sterile 1 ml pipets and safety bulb
6. Formaldehyde
7. Slides
8. Vaseline
9. Gram stain reagents

PROCEDURE AND OBSERVATIONS (1 day)

(Sterility is not required aside from the primary culture.)

1. Add 1.0 ml of the culture of *B. megaterium* to 1.0 ml of the 15% sucrose-trypticase soy broth in a 13 mm diameter test tube. A flow diagram is presented in Figure 50-1.
2. Add 0.1 ml of lysozyme to the mixture and mix thoroughly.
3. Make a wet mount (see Exercise 7) with one drop of the preparation.

4. Observe with a phase contrast microscope using the oil immersion objective. Motility ceases in 10 minutes or less. Transition from rods to spheres occurs shortly after with protoplast formation within 30 minutes. Protoplasts will appear spherical. Either constant observation or observation every few minutes is required. Make drawings at intervals.

5. After protoplasts have formed, add 0.5 ml of formaldehyde to the lysozyme-culture mixture in the tube. Make a smear for staining by mixing two loopfuls of the stock culture with two loopfuls of the protoplast culture on a glass slide. Gram stain and observe the results.

THOUGHT QUESTIONS

1. Protoplasts are often seen in what kind of disease?

2. What can be done to treat these cases or to prevent the bacteria from forming protoplasts?

3. How do protoplasts of Gram-positive and Gram-negative bacteria differ?

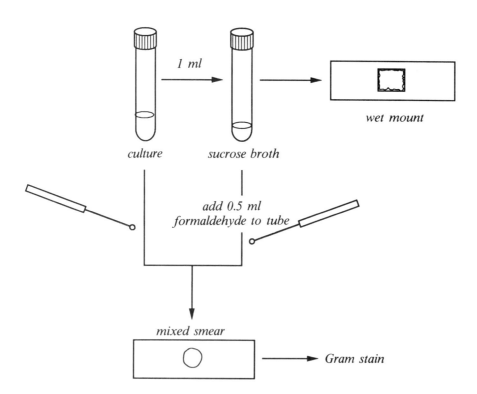

Figure 50-1. Flow diagram for protoplast formation

Name _____ Date _____ Grade _____

50. Protoplast Formation

RESULTS AND OBSERVATIONS

Drawings at time intervals:

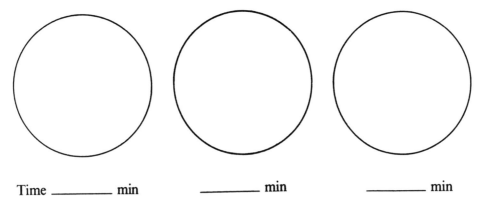

Time _____ min   _____ min   _____ min

Gram stain results:

Comments:

QUESTIONS

Completion:

1-2. Name two natural sources of the enzyme lysozyme.

     1. _____

     2. _____

3. _____ is the antibiotic which most frequently produces protoplasts in animal therapy.

4. An alternate to sucrose as an osmotic pressure equalizer is _____.

5. The group name of naturally cell wall-less prokaryotes is _____.

6. *Bacillus megaterium* also forms an endospore. Lysozyme would/would not (cross out incorrect term) be likely to remove the wall from the endospore.

7. In this exercise, aseptic technique is not necessary except to grow the primary culture. Why?

51 Bacterial Motility

OBJECTIVES

The student will be able to:

1. determine whether a bacterial culture is motile or non-motile.

2. recognize Brownian movement.

3. prepare a wet mount for determining motility.

4. inoculate a motility medium and interpret the results.

An important characteristic of some microorganisms is the ability to move, thus enhancing an organism's opportunity to acquire food from areas of fresh supply (i.e., **chemotaxis**).

Eukaryotic cells have complex **flagella** or **cilia** which are large enough to be seen through the microscope or move by **amoeboid** or **gliding** types of motility. Prokaryotes move by **gliding** or with **flagella** of a type too small to be seen through the microscope.

Motility of all types can be determined by directly observing live cells in a **wet mount** preparation under the microscope, or, in the case of bacteria, by inoculating a very soft agar medium and looking for growth beyond the stab line.

The location and number of flagella on a cell also provide useful information, especially in identification and taxonomy. Because bacterial flagella are so small, they must be specially stained to make them visible or observed with the aid of an electron microscope.

MATERIALS (per person)

1. 12-18 hour slant culture of *Pseudomonas aeruginosa*, *Bacillus subtilis*, and *Staphylococcus aureus*

2. Depression or plain microscope slides

3. Coverslips (22 × 22 mm)

4. Vaseline

5. Toothpicks

6. 4 tubes motility test medium, sterile (may be omitted)

PROCEDURE AND OBSERVATIONS (1 day or 3 days)

A. Wet Mount Preparation

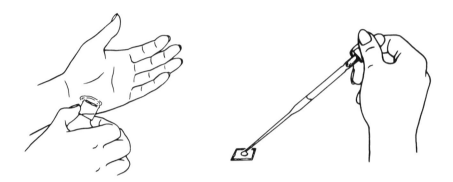

Figure 51-1. Preparing a wet mount

Period 1

1. Obtain a depression slide (or a plain slide for phase microscopy).

2. Using your hand or a toothpick, ridge each edge of a 22 × 22 mm coverslip with a *small* amount of Vaseline. Do NOT make the ridge too thick (Figure 51-1).

3. With a 3-5 mm diameter loop, place a drop of freshly boiled distilled water on the center of the coverslip with the Vaseline side up.

4. Emulsify a small amount of a young culture in the drop. It should be *faintly* turbid. (Note: Use 12-18 hour old cultures since older cultures may lose their motility.)

5. Invert the depression slide and place it over the coverslip, pressing down lightly to make a seal. Quickly turn the entire preparation right side up.

6. Place the slide on the microscope stage and reduce the light. Using the low power objective, locate the edge of the drop and center it across the field of the microscope.

7. Place a drop of oil on the coverslip, *carefully* switch to the oil immersion objective and refocus on the edge of the drop. Adjust condenser and diaphragm for optimum contrast and move over the drop.

8. Look for cells and motility or Brownian movement. Cells are often hard to see because of their low contrast.

9. In young motile cultures, most cells will be motile. Generally, a cell which moves 3 or 4 times its own length in one direction is considered motile. If none of the cells move this distance, it is probably Brownian movement due to bombardment by water molecules. In Brownian movement, a random movement is imparted to the cells, rarely moving them more than once their own length in one direction. Patience is cautioned in observation! Examine a field for some time before moving on.

10. Record your observations on the table provided. Describe the type of motility using such terms as darting, sedate, undulate, corkscrew, rapid, slow, only a few, most move, etc.

11. Repeat steps No. 1-10 for each culture provided.

B. Soft Agar Method

Period 1

1. Using a straight inoculating needle, stab a tube of motility test medium with *Pseudomonas aeruginosa*. Care should be taken to withdraw the needle along the line of the stab.

2. Repeat the procedure for each of the remaining cultures.

3. Leave one tube as an uninoculated control.

4. Incubate for 24-48 hours at the appropriate temperature for each organism.

Period 2

5. Using the control tube for comparison, observe for growth restricted to the stab line (non-motile) or diffused into the medium (motile). Some motile organisms may spread throughout the tube and across the surface (Figure 51-2).

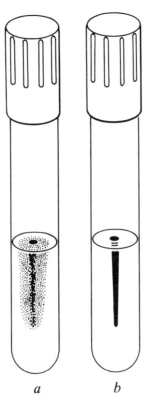

a   *b*

Figure 51-2. Motility test medium. (a) Motile organisms (b) Non-motile organisms

6. Record your results in the table provided. Describe how far into the agar growth has occurred and whether it is heavy or light.

THOUGHT QUESTIONS

1. What are some of the differences and similarities between the flagella of eukaryotes and those of prokaryotes?

2. What kinds of motility occur in the prokaryotic group? The eukaryotic group?

3. In general terms, how is the bacterial flagellum constructed and how does it work?

51. Bacterial Motility

RESULTS AND OBSERVATIONS

A. Wet Mount Preparation

Organism	Motility		Description of Motility
	+	–	
Pseudomonas aeruginosa			
Bacillus subtilis			
Staphylococcus aureus			

B. Soft Agar Method

Organism	Motility		Extent of Growth	Amount of Growth
	+	–		
Control				
Pseudomonas aeruginosa				
Bacillus subtilis				
Staphylococcus aureus				

QUESTIONS

A. **True or False Statements:** Circle the correct response.

T   F   1.   Wet mounts are used more often than stained smears in the study of microorganisms.

T   F   2.   The numbers and location of flagella can be utilized for classification purposes.

T   F   3.   A motile organism migrates through the agar gel in a motility medium.

B. **Completion:** Underline the correct response(s).

4.   Prokaryotic flagella usually can (be seen, not be seen) on live cells.

5.   An obligate anaerobe would be best observed using a (depression, plain) slide preparation.

6.   Bacteria as a group may show the following: (gliding movement, flagella motility, amoeboid movement, Brownian movement, cilia).

7.   Brownian movement results when a cell is bombarded by (bacteria, water molecules).

52 Chemotaxis

OBJECTIVES

The student will be able to:

1. perform a chemotaxis experiment.

2. describe the bacterial response to a chemotactic attractant and to a repellent.

3. discuss the conditions necessary for chemotaxis.

Bacterial motility is a mechanism whereby the organism is able to direct its net movement toward environments favorable to growth or away from some environments. In *Escherichia coli* counterclockwise rotation of the flagella (looking from the end of the flagellum toward the cell) causes the formation of a stable bundle of synchronously rotating flagella resulting in smooth, forward swimming. Clockwise rotation causes the flagella to lose synchrony, fly apart, and the cell tumbles or fibrillates aimlessly with no forward motion. After a while, counterclockwise rotation again begins and smooth forward motion resumes—but in a different direction, depending on the orientation of the cell when forward motion begins. Smooth and tumble motions alternate on a fairly regular basis if no chemical gradient exists.

| Smooth run | Tumble | Smooth |

In the presence of a chemical **attractant,** counterclockwise rotation of the flagella is stimulated by chemical receptors in the cell membrane which cause methylation of certain proteins using a substrate of S-adenylmethionine. Methylation sends a signal to the flagellar 'motor' causing counterclockwise rotation. If the cell is in a chemical gradient, the methylation process is stimulated and smooth swimming results up the gradient toward the attractant. If it swims down the gradient, methylation decreases and tumbling occurs more frequently. The net movement of the cell is toward an attractant. A **repellent** operates in the opposite fashion with net movement down the gradient. The bacterium senses the chemical gradient by a sort of memory and responds accordingly.

This exercise illustrates attraction and repulsion in *E. coli.*

MATERIALS (per pair)

1. 1 tube of GC agar, sterile

2. 1 tube of G1C agar, sterile

3. Suspension of *Escherichia coli*, very heavy

4. 6 Petri plates, sterile

5. 4 tubes of AC agar, sterile

6. Spatula

7. 1 agar plug each of 0M (control), 0.01M, 0.1M and 1M acetate, sterile

8. 2 sterile 1 ml pipets and safety bulb

PROCEDURE AND OBSERVATIONS (1 day)

A. Repulsion or Avoidance. See Figure 52-1 for flow chart.

1. Cool 4 tubes of avoidance chemotaxis (AC) agar to 50°C.

2. Pipet 1 ml of the *E. coli* suspension into each of 4 Petri plates and pour one tube of the AC agar into each. Mix well by rotating in a figure-8. Allow them to cool. The plates should be visibly cloudy.

   Note: This medium is only 0.2% agar and very fluid. DO NOT even tip the plate. Handle with care.

3. Label the covers of the plates: control, 0.01M, 0.1M, and 1M acetate, respectively.

4. Flame a spatula and after it is cool, place one 0M acetate agar plug in the center of the control plate and gently push it down in the agar.

5. Place the 0.01M acetate agar plug in place on its plate, followed by the 0.1M and 1M acetate plugs on their plates. Place the plugs in the order indicated to avoid washing and resterilizing the spatula each time.

6. Set the plates aside and observe them beginning at about 30 minutes. Cells should be moving away from the acetate plug in a band leaving a clear or less dense area around the plug as seen in Figure 52-3. Observe on a colony counter tilted to be level, or against a black background with reflected light.

7. Measure the diameter of each zone periodically for comparison and enter the measurements on the report form.

B. Attraction. See Figure 52-2 for flow chart.

1. Once the plugs have been placed on the plates in part A, pour one plate of glucose chemotaxis (GC) agar and one plate of glycerol chemotaxis (G1C) agar plate and allow them to solidify for about 30 minutes.

   Note: As noted above, this is 0.2% agar. DO NOT invert the plate.

2. Add 0.1 ml of the *E. coli* suspension to the center of each plate.

3. Carry the plates carefully to the 37°C incubator and incubate them for 3 hours or longer.

4. Observe as in A.6 and A.7 above, looking for a wave or a band of cells migrating toward the edge of the plate as in Figure 52-4.

THOUGHT QUESTIONS

1. Why is methionine is used in the media?

2. If an organism is attracted to a compound, must the organism use or metabolize it?

3. If avoidance is the result, does it mean that chemical is toxic?

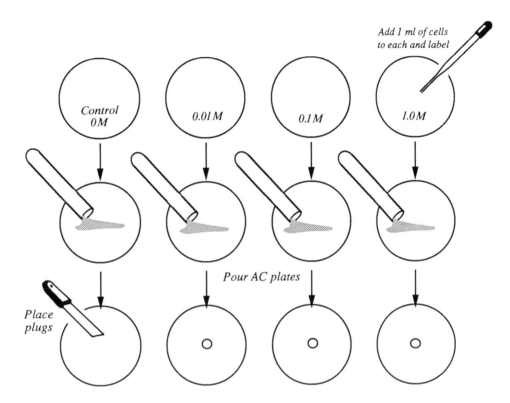

Figure 52-1. Flow diagram for avoidance.

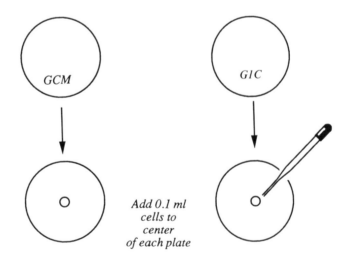

Figure 52-2. Flow diagram for attraction

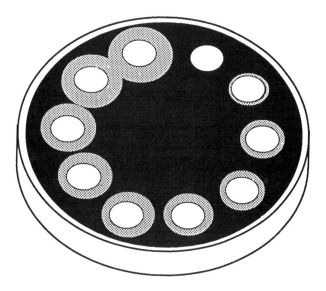

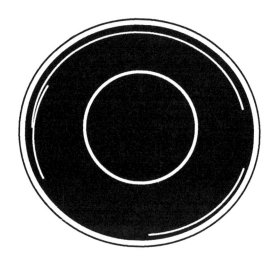

Figure 52-3. Avoidance. Negative chemotaxis is demonstrated by visualizing the ring of bacteria fleeing from a repellent. Plugs of concentrated agar (*bright disks*) containing the repellent acetate were placed in a dish of dilute agar containing a suspension of *E. coli.*

Figure 52-4. Attraction. Rings of bacteria in pursuit of attractant demonstrate positive chemotaxis. Bacteria are put at the center of an agar plate containing attractant, proliferate, and follow the gradient they create, forming an expanding ring.

52. Chemotaxis

RESULTS AND OBSERVATIONS

Make a drawing of each plate and the zones of cells:

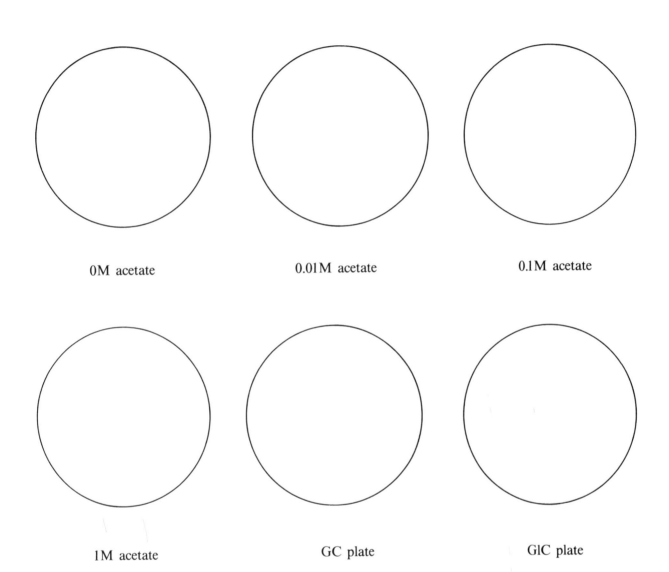

0M acetate

0.01M acetate

0.1M acetate

1M acetate

GC plate

GlC plate

QUESTIONS

Completion:

1. _____ is the substrate involved in membrane protein methylation for motility.

2. Counterclockwise (observed from the flagellated end) rotation of the flagella results in _____ motility.

3. Clockwise (from flagellated end) rotation of the flagella results in _____ motility.

4. How do you explain the movement of an expanding ring of *E. coli* across the medium if glucose is uniform through the medium?

5. Why was glycerol inactive?

53 Microbial Syntrophism

OBJECTIVES

The student will be able to:

1. perform an experiment demonstrating bacterial synergism.

2. discuss the type of symbiosis represented by the synergistic relationship of this exercise.

3. describe biochemically the relationship between these organisms.

Symbiosis is defined as the close living together of two organisms without regard to the nature of the relationship. Microbial **syntrophism** or **synergism** is a symbiotic association between organisms, wherein one prepares a substrate or other conditions by which another can produce a product neither can produce alone. This non-obligatory type of symbiosis is called **protocooperation** when both benefit (it is called **mutualism** if it is obligatory) or **commensalism** if one benefits and the other is unaffected. An example of protocooperation would be a vitamin produced by one organism and required by a second organism which in turn produces a necessary metabolite required by the first. Neither organism grows without the other. An example of commensalism is an organism which can split lactose into glucose and galactose and ferment these into lactic acid. An organism which cannot split lactose can then use the lactic acid or the glucose producing carbon dioxide and hydrogen gas, a result neither could do alone. In this exercise, *Staphylococcus aureus* and *Proteus vulgaris* will be used to illustrate this. Both organisms will grow in the medium used here and the ability to use lactose by one and subsequent use of the lactic acid by the other is demonstrated by gas formation which it cannot produce from lactose directly.

MATERIALS (per person)

1. Nutrient agar slant cultures of *Proteus vulgaris* and *Staphylococcus aureus*

2. 3 tubes of lactose broth + 0.006% bromthymol blue indicator and gas insert, sterile

PROCEDURE (2-3 days)

Period 1

1. Label one lactose broth tube *S. aureus* and inoculate with a loopful of that organism.

2. Label a second tube *P. vulgaris* and inoculate with a loopful of that organism.

3. Label the third tube "mixed" and inoculate with both organisms.

   Note: Make sure the inoculating loop is sterilized after each of these inoculations to ensure the pure culture status of the stock tubes.

4. Incubate the 3 tubes at 35°-37°C for 24-48 hours.

OBSERVATIONS

Period 2

5.   Observe the tubes for acid (yellow) and gas production recording your observations on the report form.

6.   Determine which organism did what on the lactose.

THOUGHT QUESTIONS

1.   How does protocooperation differ from mutualism?

2.   If the lactose were the *sole* carbon source, which of the two organisms would *not* show any growth? Why?

3.   Do such symbioses as illustrated here occur under natural conditions?

53. Microbial Syntrophism

RESULTS AND OBSERVATIONS

1. Record your results in the table below:

	Lactose broth		
	growth	**acid**	**gas**
S. aureus alone			
P. vulgaris alone			
Mixed organisms			

2. In your own words, describe what has happened biochemically to the lactose in each tube.

    S. aureus alone

    P. vulgaris alone

    Mixed culture

3. How do you explain that growth is observed for each organism when grown alone?

QUESTIONS

Completion:

1. The general term for interactions between organisms without regard for the nature of the interaction is _____.

2-3. When both organisms benefit but it is not an obligatory association, then the association is called _____ ; if it is an obligatory association, then it is called _____.

4-5. When one organism benefits and the other is unaffected, it is called _____ or _____.

6-7. Lactose is split into the two carbohydrates _____ and _____.

8-10. The gas in the insert is composed of _____ and _____ which comes directly from _____.

54 Microbial Antagonism

OBJECTIVES

The student will be able to:

1. explain in general terms the nature of microbial antagonism.

2. name one bacterial product producing antagonism.

3. perform an experiment demonstrating microbial antagonism.

Antagonism is a negative symbiotic activity between microbes and can take many forms. It can involve toxins, colicins, and antibiotics, causing one organism to grow poorly or be actively killed while the producing organism remains unaffected. A simple system to demonstrate antagonism is to grow an organism producing an antibiotic in the presence of one that is sensitive to it. In some ways this is similar to the antimicrobial susceptibility test (Exercise 81) except that a living organism is used instead of an inert disk soaked in the antibiotic.

MATERIALS (sufficient for 4 students)

1. Nutrient agar slants of *Bacillus subtilis* and *Sarcina subflava* (a strain of *Micrococcus luteus*)

2. 1 tube nutrient broth, sterile

3. 100 ml nutrient agar, sterile

4. 5 Petri plates, sterile

5. 1 sterile 1 ml pipet and safety bulb

PROCEDURE (2 days)

Period 1

1. Pipet 2-3 ml of nutrient broth onto the slant culture of *S. subflava*. Gently rub the growth off of the slant with the pipet tip. Be careful not to gouge the agar. Remove as many cells into the broth as possible and discard the pipet.

2. Flame the lip of the *S. subflava* tube *lightly* and pour the cells into the tempered (45°-50°C) flask of nutrient agar.

3. Mix well by rotating the flask in a circle, first clockwise, then counterclockwise. DO NOT swirl so vigorously that the agar entrains bubbles or foams.

4. Pour the agar equally into 5 Petri plates and let solidify.

5. Flame a loop and transfer a small amount of the *B. subtilis* culture to two or three spots on the solidified agar plate surface as in Figure 54-1.

   Note: Each student does one plate and one plate serves as a control for the group.

6. Incubate the plates at 30°-32°C for 24-48 hours.

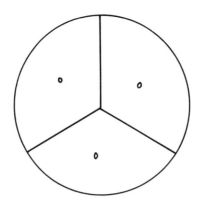

Figure 54-1. Inoculation of *B. subtilis*

OBSERVATIONS

Period 2

7. Measure the diameter of the *B. subtilis* colony and the diameter of the zone of inhibition. Record your results on the report form.

THOUGHT QUESTIONS

1. What are some of the arguments for the ecological function of these antagonistic substances?

2. This exercise involves an antibiotic produced by *B. subtilis*. What other substances are produced by sporeforming bacteria which are antagonistic to to other life forms (e.g., *Clostridium botulinum*)?

3. How would you design an experiment to test an unknown organism for antagonistic activity to another organism?

4. Discuss the statement "The botulism toxin is an antibiotic."

Name ———————————————— Date ——————— Grade ———————

54. Microbial Antagonism

RESULTS AND OBSERVATIONS

1. Draw your plate appearance

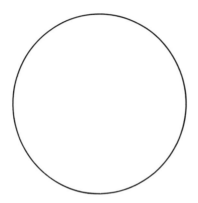

2. Table

Observation	diameter in mm
B. subtilis colony	
Inhibitory zone	

3. Explain your results to someone who has not had a course in microbiology.

QUESTIONS

A. True or False Statements: Circle the letter of the correct response.

T   F   1.   A toxin such as that produced by *C. botulinum* is an antagonistic substance.

T   F   2.   Colicins are antagonistic compounds.

T   F   3.   All bacteria are susceptible to the *B. subtilis* antagonistic substance.

B. Completion:

4–6.   Name an antibiotic produced by:

4.   *Bacillus*

5.   actinomycetes

6.   fungi

55 Bacterial Morphogenesis

OBJECTIVES

The student will be able to:

1. produce a morphogenic change in a bacterial species.
2. list the conditions bringing about this change.
3. list at least three other morphogenic changes among prokaryotes.

Morphogenic changes involve a drastic change in morphology in response to environment and/or genetic influences. Examples of morphogenic changes among prokaryotes include heterocyst formation in the cyanobacteria, endospore formation in the eubacteria, fruiting body formation among the myxobacteria, and complex life cycle changes among the higher actinomycetes. Morphogenesis among prokaryotes is difficult to study in the laboratory because the conditions for change are not known in many cases or the time involved is too lengthy.

Myxococcus xanthus, a soil myxobacterium, undergoes a drastic cellular metamorphosis under certain environmental stresses. In this transformation, labile, active, rod-shaped cell forms (termed **vegetative** cells) change into resistant, spherical-shaped, resting bodies (termed **myxospores** to distinguish them from endospores). Accompanying this cellular change is an aggregation of the once independent vegetative cells into a visible, multicellular and often times very beautiful **fruiting body.** In nature these changes are brought about by a hostile environment (e.g., lack of proper nutrients), but in the laboratory, myxospore formation can be brought about artificially by exposing vegetative cells to 0.5M glycerol. A rapid and almost synchronous transformation of large populations of vegetative cells to myxospores can be brought about by this method. This technique has proven very useful in experimental analysis of myxospore formation.

MATERIALS (per person)

1. 18 hour old CT broth culture of *Myxococcus xanthus* FBa
2. 2 conical centrifuge tubes, sterile
3. Centrifuge
4. 1 flask of morphogenesis solution, sterile
5. Shaking water bath at 30°C
6. 1 sterile 13 mm empty test tube
7. 1 sterile 10 ml pipet and safety bulb

PROCEDURE AND OBSERVATIONS (1 day)

1. Remove about 1 ml of *M. xanthus* vegetative cells from the CT broth tube and refrigerate for later comparison with the myxospores.

2. Pour the remainder of the vegetative culture into a centrifuge vessel and sediment the cells by centrifugation for 5-10 minutes at 5-10,000 rpm.

3. Discard the supernatant.

4. Resuspend the vegetative cells in 20 ml of of the morphogenesis solution by drawing cells back and forth with a clean 10 ml pipet.

5. Transfer the suspended cells to the flask and place the flask in a 30°C shaking water bath at slow speed.

6. At half hour intervals (for 2-3 hours), remove a drop from the flask and make a wet mount. Make a wet mount of the refrigerated vegetative cells also. Compare the treated cells with the refrigerated vegetative cells under the microscope. A phase contrast microscope is best suited for this.

THOUGHT QUESTIONS

1. What kind of biochemical properties do the myxobacteria possess?

2. How do members of the myxobacteria move?

3. Where would you go to isolate members of this group?

Name _____ Date _____ Grade _____

55. Bacterial Morphogenesis

RESULTS AND OBSERVATIONS

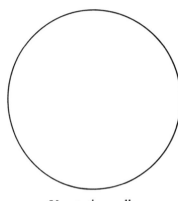
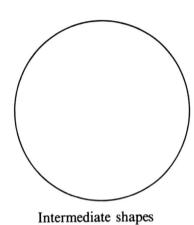
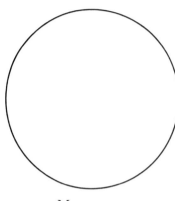

Vegetative cells   Intermediate shapes   Myxospores

Time 0   _____ hr   _____ hr

Draw a representative group of cells to show the range of morphologies present. Measure a few of the the vegetative cells to get an average and a few of the mature myxospores, also to get an average.

average length x width of vegetative cells _____

average diameter of myxospores _____

As an exercise in calculation, determine the volume of the

vegetative cell ($V = \pi r^2 l$) _____

myxospore ($V = 4/3\pi r^3$) _____

QUESTIONS

A. True or False Statements: Circle the correct response.

T F 1. The myxospores are the vegetative cells that aggregate to form the fruiting body.

T F 2. Different environmental stresses can induce morphogenic changes in an organism.

T F 3. A Gram stained smear of the cells in the morphogenesis solution provided the best technique for observing morphogenic changes.

T F 4. Endospore formation in the myxobacteria is an example of morphogenesis.

B. Completion:

5-7. List three prokaryotic groups exhibiting some form of morphogenesis.

5. _____

6. _____

7. _____

8. The inducer of morphogenesis in this exercise is _____ .

9. In nature, the myxospore is induced by a lack of _____ .

10. From a textbook of microbiology, find an inducer for the transformation of *Bacillus* sp. into endospores. One inducer is _____ .

11. A structure formed by the gathering together and cooperation of myxobacterial vegetative cells is called a _____ .

56 Microbiological Assay — Niacin

OBJECTIVES

The student will be able to:

1. perform a titrimetric assay for the vitamin niacin using *Lactobacillus plantarum.*

2. plot a standard titrimetric growth curve for niacin content.

3. calculate the niacin content of an unknown solution using the standard curve.

4. name the organism used in this exercise and several others used for vitamin assay.

Nutrient supply is always a problem for free-living microbes. Competition leaves many essential nutrients in short supply. Some microbes are so specific for a particular nutrient that they stop growing when it is gone. The syntrophism exercise illustrated one way organisms benefit one another. In this exercise the need for a specific nutrient is exploited in a microbiological assay procedure to determine the concentration of the nutrient. This assay for the vitamin niacin is an example of the very important field of analytical microbiology. Vitamins, amino acids, and antibiotics are among the biochemicals for which potentcy can be assayed.

Vitamin assay is widely used particularly in nutritional studies, although other methods of analysis are available. Vitamins are generally required in such small amounts that scrupulous cleanliness of glassware is necessary to avoid interference. One advantage of the microbial assay is the ability of the organisms to use several forms of the vitamin and not just one. Most of the microbial assays involve the B-complex vitamins which are used in cellular coenzyme structures. The vitamin selected for this exercise is niacin or niacinamide (nicotinic acid or nicotinamide) which is a **functional group** in nicotinamide adenine dinucleotide (NAD) and NADphosphate (NADP). These **cofactors** are vital to cellular oxidation-reduction reactions by transferring electrons from one substrate to another. The structure of nicotinic acid and its amide is given below.

nicotinic acid   nicotinamide

A test organism requiring niacin, *Lactobacillus plantarum* ATCC 8014, is provided a nutrient medium complete in all respects except for the necessary vitamin. The test substance is placed in this medium and the growth response taken as a measure of the amount of the vitamin present in the material. Growth can be measured either as increase in cell mass (**turbidimetry**) or production of lactic acid from glucose in the medium (**titrimetry**). The titrimetric method will be used here. As in all microbial assays, the establishment of a standard response curve is an important part of the procedure.

In addition to *L. plantarum* ATCC 8014, *Lactobacillus leishmannii* ATCC 7830, *Enterococcus (Streptococcus) faecium* ATCC 8043, *Lactobacillus casei* subsp. *rhamnosus* ATCC 7469, and several other bacteria, yeasts, and fungi are used for vitamin assay. The Difco Manual (see Procedure for complete reference) is an excellent general procedures reference.

MATERIALS (group of 2–3)

1. 18–24 hour old micro inoculum broth culture of *Lactobacillus plantarum* ATCC 8014
2. 3–5 sterile 1 ml pipets
3. 5–8 sterile 10 ml pipets
4. 1 1 L volumetric flask
5. 1 sterile 100 ml beaker
6. 14 sterile 50 ml Erlenmeyer flasks
7. 2 sterile 15 ml centrifuge tubes
8. 2 sterile 99 ml 0.85% saline dilution blanks
9. Bromthymol blue indicator
10. 200 ml 0.1N NaOH
11. 50 ml burette

PROCEDURE AND OBSERVATIONS (4 days)

(Reference: Difco Manual, Difco Laboratories, Inc., Detroit, MI, 10th Edition, 1984 pp. 1055-1114.)

Period 1

A. Preparation of niacin standard solution

    1. A niacin stock solution will be prepared for you by weighing 50 mg of niacin into a volumetric flask and making the volume up to 1 L with distilled water.

    2. Make a niacin standard solution by adding 1 ml of the stock solution to a volumetric flask and making the volume up to 1 L with distilled water.

B. Preparation of the sample

    1. A sample will be provided by your instructor and dilution instructions, if required, will be given along with it.

C. Preparation of media

    1. Suspend 5.6 g of niacin assay medium in 70 ml of distilled water, sufficient to make 14 flasks.

    2. Heat the suspension to boiling for 2-3 minutes with agitation to disperse the slight precipitate that forms. Cool in cold water.

    3. Place 5 ml in each of the 14 50 ml flasks to be used.

    4. Label six flasks with the volume of the niacin standard solution to be used as follows: 0.5, 1, 2, 3, 4, and 5. Label the seventh flask 0 as the control. Add the ml amount of the niacin standard solution to each flask as indicated by the number. Bring the volume of each flask to 10 ml with distilled water.

5. Label seven flasks with the sample dilution and the same volume numbers as in step No. 4 above including a control flask. The control flask serves as an uninoculated blank. To each of these flasks add the appropriate volume of the sample dilution according to the label. Make the volume of each flask up to 10 ml with distilled water.

6. Sterilize all 14 flasks at the same time for 10 minutes at 121°C. DO NOT OVER STERILIZE. *Note:* All standard curve and sample flasks must be sterilized at the same time under the same conditions.

D. Preparation of inoculum

1. Centrifuge a **fresh** 18-24 hour old 10 ml micro inoculum broth culture at 10,000 rpm for 5 min.

2. Discard the supernatant and resuspend the cells in 10 ml of sterile 0.85% saline.

3. Centrifuge once more as in step No. 1, discard the supernatant, and suspend the cells in 10 ml of sterile 0.85% saline.

4. Add 1 ml of the saline suspension to 99 ml of sterile 0.85% saline. Mix well. This serves as the inoculum.

E. Assay

1. Each of the standard curve and sample flasks, except the 0 flasks, is inoculated with one drop of the inoculum suspension. The same pipet must be used for all the flasks.

2. Incubate the flasks at 35°C for 72 hours.

Period 2

3. Remove the flasks from the incubator and add several drops of bromthymol blue indicator to each.

4. Titrate each flask with 0.1N NaOH from a burette. Record the volume in the Results and Observations form.

F. Calculations

1. Plot the ml of 0.1N NaOH used to titrate the niacin standard series of tubes on standard graph paper with the concentration of niacin in ml of standard as the X-axis. Note that 1 ml of the standard contains 0.05 μg of niacin (i.e., the tube labeled 1 ml contains 0.05 μg of niacin). The curve should be similar to that in Figure 56-1.

2. Plot the sample assay results on the same graph.

3. Determine the niacin concentration in the sample as follows:

   a. Determine the equivalent volume of standard for each of three assay volumes as nearly in a straight line as possible.

   b. From Figure 56-1, 0.5 ml of standard is equivalent to 1 ml of assay, 0.5/1.0. Multiply this ratio by the concentration of niacin per ml and by the dilution to give the concentration of niacin in the assay volume. Do this for at least three points and take the average. *Note:* Figure 56-1 uses %T instead of ml NaOH.

   Report the average as the niacin concentration per ml of the sample. Example:

   $$0.5/1.0 \times 50 \times 10 = 300\ \mu g/ml$$
   $$1.0/2.0 \times 50 \times 10 = 300\ \mu g/ml$$
   $$1.55/3.0 \times 50 \times 10 = \underline{258.3\ \mu g/ml}$$
   $$858.3/3 = 286\ \mu g/ml$$

THOUGHT QUESTIONS

1. Although cells no longer increase in number when a nutrient is exhausted, do they stop dividing? What conditions are necessary for continued division without increase in numbers?

2. The standard curve in Figure 56-1 appears to flatten at higher concentrations of niacin. What would cause this?

3. Why would microbiological assay of vitamins, amino acids, or antibiotics be more useful in some cases that chemical analysis?

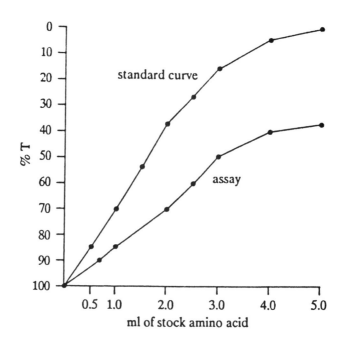

Figure 56-1. Example of a standard curve and sample assay

(Data: 0.05 $\mu g/ml$ of niacin in standard solution; 1:10 dilution of the assay sample)

56. Microbiological Assay — Niacin

RESULTS AND OBSERVATIONS

Titration data

		ml 0.1N NaOH per flask						
		0	0.5	1.0	2.0	3.0	4.0	5.0
Standard	end	———	———	———	———	———	———	———
	start	———	———	———	———	———	———	———
	ml	———	———	———	———	———	———	———
Sample	end	———	———	———	———	———	———	———
	start	———	———	———	———	———	———	———
	ml	———	———	———	———	———	———	———

From standard curve

	std point/assay point	x	μg niacin/ml	x	dilution		
1.	/	x		x		= ——— μg/ml	
2.	/	x		x		= ——— μg/ml	Sum ___/3
3.	/	x		x		= ——— μg/ml	Avg. ———

QUESTIONS

A. **True or False Statements:** Circle the correct response.

    T   F   1.   Cleanliness of glassware is an essential requirement for performing vitamin assays.

    T   F   2.   This assay measures growth as an increase in cell mass.

    T   F   3.   Niacin is a functional group in NAD and NADP.

    T   F   4.   Lactobacilli produce lactic acid from glucose.

B. **Completion:**

    5.   _____ is the organism used in this exercise.

    6-7.   From the Difco Manual, name one bacterium (not listed in the introduction to this exercise) and one fungus used for vitamin assay.

        6. _____

        7. _____

    8-9.   Two methods used to assay vitamins are _____ and

    _____ .

    10-12.   List three biologically active substances which can be assayed microbiologically.

        10. _____

        11. _____

        12. _____

Bacterial Viruses

Viruses differ from cells by consisting only of one nucleic acid type, either RNA *or* DNA but not both. They can be thought of as parasitic nucleic acid coated with proteins (although viroids lack even that) and occasionally other substances. No group of living organisms has been found free of infecting viruses. Because viruses all require a living cell or organism in which to reproduce, they are rather difficult and expensive to cultivate. Bacteriophages are perhaps the easiest to work with in the teaching laboratory. Although only one exercise is presented in Unit VIII, viruses are an extremely important part of medicine and public health and are at the forefront as a genetic engineering tool.

57 Isolation of a Bacteriophage

OBJECTIVES

The student will be able to:

1. isolate a bacteriophage for a specific host.

2. describe a phage plaque on a lawn of bacteria.

Bacterial viruses, commonly called **bacteriophages** or **phages,** can be isolated from most environments where bacteria are found. Since bacterial viruses are not common even where their hosts are found, it is necessary to **enrich** for them, a procedure allowing the virus numbers to increase making isolation easier and more likely. Since phages are fairly host specific, incubation with a known host culture causes an increase in any phages specific for that host. Removal of cells results in separation of the viruses which can then be isolated by solid plating techniques. Since any given material may not always have present a phage specific for the host used, an exercise such as this one is not always successful.

After enrichment, phage and host cells are separated first by centrifugation and finally by filtration. The filtrate containing the phage is then added in small amounts along with a standard inoculum of host cells to a **soft agar** which is then layered in a thin film over a standard agar base. The cells grow and some are infected with phage which lyse infecting neighboring cells which also lyse leaving a visibly clear area called a **plaque** in an otherwise confluent **lawn** of growth. A soft agar overlay is used to enhance the physical spread of the viruses between cells. Standard agar is so confining, a plaque may not be seen at all. A plaque may contain 10^8 to 10^{12} phage particles and can be transfered to new host cells in much the same way as a bacterial colony.

One of the problems with this procedure is the high likelihood of contamination due to the considerable handling required. Detailed attention to aseptic technique is essential. Always ask yourself in each step the question, "Is this item I am using sterile or has it been contaminated by handling?" If in doubt, do not proceed until you are certain. A flow diagram will be found in Figure 57-1.

MATERIALS (per group)

1. 18-24 hour nutrient broth culture of *Escherichia coli* B
2. 12 nutrient broth tubes, sterile
3. 1 deca broth tube, sterile
4. 1 sterile 100 ml beaker with aluminum foil cover
5. Container for collecting 50 ml of sewage
6. Clinical centrifuge for 13 x 100 mm test tubes
7. 2 sterile 10 ml pipets and safety bulbs
8. 6 sterile 13 x 100 mm empty test tubes
9. 2 sterile 10 ml syringes with 35-40 mm long needles
10. 2 sterile 12 mm diameter Swinney filter units, each containing a 0.45 μm membrane filter
11. 6 Petri plates, sterile
12. 6 nutrient agar deeps, sterile
13. 6 soft agar overlays, sterile
14. 2 sterile 1 ml pipets
15. Plastic bags, if required

PROCEDURE AND OBSERVATIONS (4–5 days)

Period 1

1. Subculture the *E. coli* culture in nutrient broth one day before starting work. Repeat each day so that an 18–24 hour old culture is always available on the next day.
2. In preparation for later, melt 6 nutrient agar deeps, cool to 45–50°C, and pour into 6 Petri plates. Allow them to solidify and set aside in a protected place to dry for one day at 37°C, cover down.
3. To 45 ml of raw sewage (or other supplied sample) in a 100 ml beaker, add 5 ml of deca broth.

4. Inoculate the sewage-broth with 5 ml of an 18–24 hour old culture of *E. coli* and incubate at 37°C for 24 hours. If present, phage specific for the host bacterium will increase greatly in numbers.

Period 2

5. Stir the incubated sewage-broth–*E. coli* mixture briefly with a pipet and divide 12–15 ml of the mixture equally between two sterile 13 x 100 mm test tubes. **Warning:** DO NOT mouth pipet.

6. Centrifuge the two tubes at 2,500 rpm for 10 minutes.

7. Remove 5–10 ml of supernatant from one tube with a sterile 10 ml syringe and needle.

8. Carefully remove the needle from the syringe and aseptically replace with a sterile 12 mm diameter Swinney filter unit. Be very careful not to contaminate the outlet end.

9. *Slowly* push the syringe plunger in forcing the supernatant through the filter into a sterile 13 x 100 mm test tube. Only 2–3 ml of filtrate is needed. Too much force in pushing the plunger will rupture the filter.

10. Melt 3 soft agar tubes. Cool to 45-50°C and add 0.1 ml of an 18–24 hour old broth culture of *E. coli*.

11. Three of the previously prepared and dried agar plates are set out and labeled, one drop, 5 drops, and control respectively.

12. Add one drop of the sewage-broth filtrate from step No. 9 to one cooled soft agar tube and immediately pour it on the surface of the agar plate labeled one drop. Tilt the plate back and forth to ensure complete coverage of the overlay.

13. Add five drops of the filtrate to a second soft agar tube and pour it on the plate labeled five drops.

14. Pour the third soft agar tube onto the plate labeled control. This is a growth control for the host organism.

15. After solidification, incubate the plates inverted in plastic bags at 37°C until clear areas (plaques) are visible (6-24 hours). These may be very small depending on the virus present.

    Note: You will need two young (10-12 hour old) broth cultures of *E. coli* on the next day (see step No. 17 below).

Period 3

16. Draw the appearance of the plates on the report form. Measure the diameter of a number of isolated plaques and determine an average. Enter this on the results form. Also describe the edge of the plaque in terms of whether sharp or fuzzy since this sometimes assumes some importance.

17. Have ready two young (10-12 hour old) very lightly turbid broth cultures of *E. coli*.

    Note: The age of these cultures is critical to the success of this step.

18. Using a sterile inoculating loop, touch an isolated plaque as nearly in the center as possible and then inoculate one of the broth tubes. Use the second tube as a non-virus growth control. Incubate both for 24 hours at 37°C.

Period 4

19. The control tube should be turbid while the phage tube will be much less turbid or even clear. Draw the appearance of these tubes on the report form.

20. Another filtering, plating, and reisolation beginning at step No. 19 should be done using the cleared tube in order to ensure purity.

THOUGHT QUESTIONS

1. What are some of the factors determining the plaque size?

2. How can phages be used to type strains of bacteria such as *Staphylococcus aureus*?

3. How does the use of tissue culture with animal viruses compare to this procedure? How is it similar? How is it different?

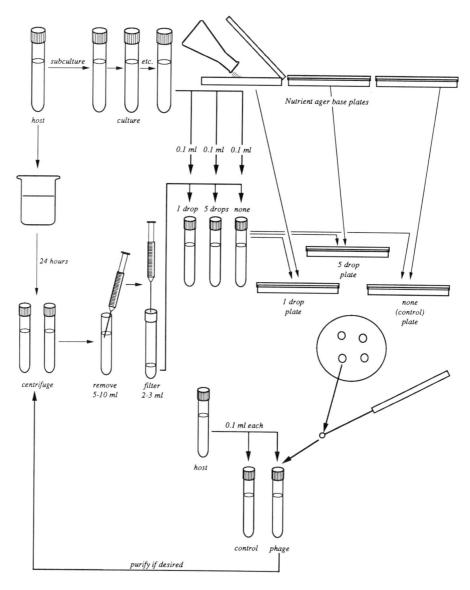

Figure 57-1. Flow diagram of the bacteriophage isolation procedure

57. Isolation of a Bacteriophage

RESULTS AND OBSERVATIONS

Drawings of plates with plaques

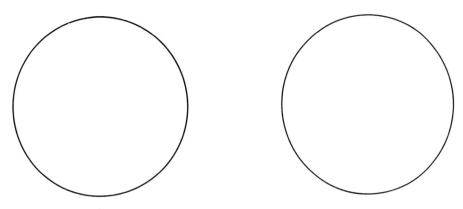

Average plaque diameter _____

Describe the plaque border

Tube appearance

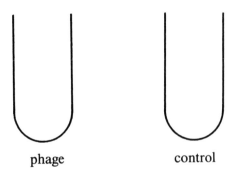

phage   control

QUESTIONS

A. True or False Statements: Circle the correct response.

T   F   1.   After incubation, the sewage-deca broth-virus suspension should be pipetted to the centrifuge tubes with a mouth pipet.

T   F   2.   If phage is added to host cells which are in late exponential or early stationary phase, lysis will probably not be observed.

T   F   3.   Plaques will continue to enlarge in size even after the host cells stop reproducing.

T   F   4.   Too much surface moisture will cause confluent plaques due to spreading of the virus in the fluid layer.

T   F   5.   If excessive drying of the overlay occurs during incubation, plaques may be too small due to lack of spreading to new host cells.

T   F   6.   Care in aseptic technique is of little importance in this exercise, since viruses are so host specific.

B. Completion:

7.   Confluent growth of the host on a control plate is called a _____.

8-9.   A virus infecting bacteria is called a _____ or for short a _____.

10.   Soft agar is made by reducing the agar content to _____ %.

11.   A tube of host cells in the early exponential phase of growth when phage is added will usually appear _____ at 24 hours compared to the control.

12.   Explain why plaques reach a certain size at about 24 hours and then do not grow any larger.

UNIT *IX*

Bacterial Genetics

The study of bacterial genetics has had a profound influence on our understanding of many of the fundamental properties of enzymes, the nature of enzymes, the nature of the genetic material itself, and how genes function. Manipulation of bacterial genes lies at the foundation of genetic engineering, and this tool has a brilliant future in biology, medicine, and biotechnology. The work on bacterial genes has also pointed the way for research on eukaryotic genes despite the many differences between them. Part IX consists of three exercises illustrating aspects of bacterial genetics.

58 Enzyme Induction

OBJECTIVES

The student will be able to:

1. define constitutive and inducible enzymes.

2. perform an assay for beta-galactosidase.

3. relate enzyme activity to cell mass and substrate.

In a cell, enzyme production and activity are usually regulated in some manner. Some enzymes are produced under all conditions of growth, and these are called **constitutive** while others are produced only in the presence of a particular substrate (i.e., **induced** by the substrate). One of the earliest studied inducible enzymes was **beta-galactosidase,** the lactose splitting enzyme of *Escherichia coli.* Studies on the genetics of this enzyme have led to much of our understanding of bacterial genetics and enzyme regulation. The beta-galactosidase gene is part of a gene complex called the lactose **operon.** The genes of this operon are transcribed only when lactose or some related **inducer** is present. Even then, other growth substrates suppress the transcription of the operon if present in large amounts until the substrate has been metabolized.

In this exercise the non-metabolizable inducer methyl beta-D-thiogalactoside (thiomethyl-beta-galactoside, TMG) is used in the presence of various carbon sources.

MATERIALS (per group of 10 students in 5 pairs)

1. 5 capped 125 ml graduated flasks, sterile
2. 1 flask of methyl beta-D-thiogalactoside (TMG) sufficient for entire class
3. 1 flask for entire class with sterile 1M glucose
4. 1 flask for entire class with sterile 1M glycerol
5. 1 flask for entire class with sterile 1M Na succinate
6. 1 dropper bottle with toluene
7. Cuvettes for Spectronic 20, 13 mm diameter optically matched tubes
8. Spectronic 20
9. 1 flask of 500 ml of *E. coli* (lac+) in early exponential growth phase
10. 1 beaker or flask for disposal of cells to be later autoclaved
11. 1 flask with 60 ml of 0.1M Na phosphate buffer, pH 7.5, sterile
12. 1 flask with 60 ml of 5mM o-nitrophenyl-beta-galactoside (ONPG), sterile
13. 1 flask with 60 ml of 1M Na_2CO_3, sterile
14. 1 flask with uninoculated broth for the absorbance blank, sterile

PROCEDURE AND OBSERVATIONS (1 day) See flow chart in Figure 58-1.

1. Obtain the *E. coli* culture and prepare 5 flasks by pouring 50 ml into each.
2. Each pair will be responsible for preparing and analyzing one flask. Set them up as follows:

Flask 1	0.5 ml 10mM TMG	+ 0.1 ml M glucose
Flask 2	"	+ 0.5 ml M glucose
Flask 3	"	+ 0.5 ml M glycerol
Flask 4	"	+ 0.5 ml M succinate
Flask 5	none	+ none

3. Incubate the 5 flasks at 37°C with vigorous shaking. This would be best done in a shaking water bath.
4. From the remainder of the culture in the large flask, the group determines the initial optical density (OD) and the initial beta-galactosidase activity once. All 5 pairs share this as the starting point.
5. With a sterile 10 ml pipet, withdraw 7 ml of culture from the flask. Place 2.0 ml into a 13 mm diameter test tube and the remainder into a cuvette for the spectrophotometer.
6. Immediately add 2 drops of toluene to the 2.0 ml in the test tube only, shake well, and place the tube in a water bath at 37°C. The toluene stops any further enzyme activity and makes the cells "leaky."

Cell mass measurement

7. Read the absorbance of the cuvette at 540 nm using uninoculated broth as the blank. Record the result in the results section Table 1.

8. Discard the cuvette contents into a container for later sterilization and rinse the cuvette with distilled water *into* the discard container. **DO NOT** discard into a sink.

Enzyme assay

9. Remove the toluenized cells from the water bath after 10 minutes.

10. Add 1.5 ml of pH 7.5 phosphate buffer and 1.5 ml of ONPG.

11. Incubate for 10 minutes (initial readings or low activity samples may be incubated 15 or 20 minutes) at 37°C.

12. Stop the reaction by adding 1 ml of Na_2CO_3.

13. Centrifuge the tubes at 3,000 rpm for 5 minutes to sediment cells.

14. Transfer the supernatant to a clean cuvette and read the absorbance at 420 nm using a reaction mixture without cells as the blank. If the color is too intense, dilute the supernatant with distilled water to give an absorbance between 0.1 and 0.8. Multiply the reading by the dilution factor if this is done. Record the reading as absorbance in the results section Table 2.

15. Dispose of cells and cuvette contents in the disposal container.

16. Each pair samples their assigned flask every 20 minutes and repeats steps No. 5–16.

THOUGHT QUESTIONS

1. What is the structure of the lactose operon? How many enzymes does it code for?

2. How does the inducer work?

3. What effects do the growth substrates, glucose, succinate, and glycerol have on enzyme induction?

ACKNOWLEDGEMENT

We would like to thank Dr. J.Y. Takemoto, Dept. of Biology, Utah State University, for permission to use this exercise.

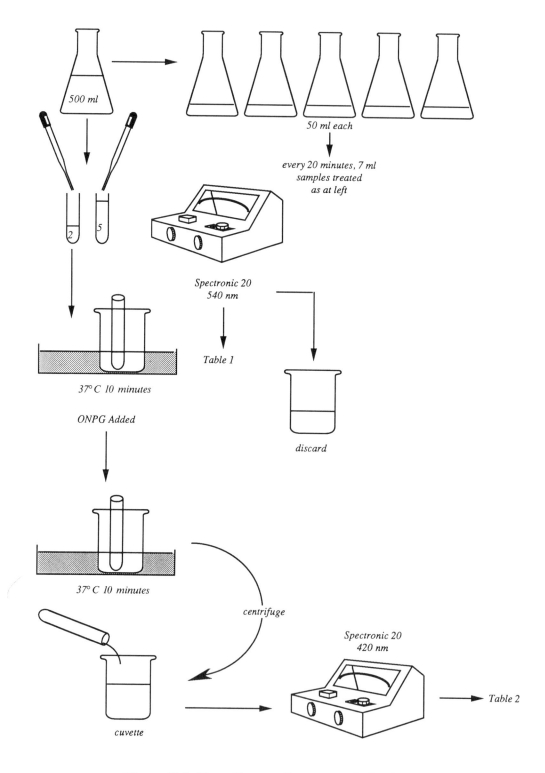

Figure 58-1. Flow diagram for enzyme induction

58. Enzyme Induction

RESULTS AND OBSERVATIONS

Table 1. Cell mass (absorbance)
Absorbance at 540 nm at time (minutes)

Flask No.	0	20	40	60	80	100	120	140	160
1									
2									
3									
4									
5									

Table 2. Enzyme units (absorbance)
ONPG absorbance at 420 nm at time (minutes[a])

Flask No.	0	20	40	60	80	100	120	140	160
1									
2									
3									
4									
5									

[a] Note any variation in time of incubation or dilution since these will have to be accounted for to create Table 3.

Table 3. Enzyme activity
Units of enzyme (absorbance)/cell mass (absorbance)/10 minutes at time (minutes)

Flask No.	0	20	40	60	80	100	120	140	160
1									
2									
3									
4									
5									

Table 3 is completed by converting the readings (modified by any time and dilution changes) of Tables 1 and 2 into units of enzyme (absorbance) per cell mass (absorbance) per 10 minutes incubation of the ONPG tube (not the flask).

On separate pieces of graph paper plot your data as follows:

1. Growth absorbance (Table 1) as Y axis vs. time as the X axis.

2. Enzyme activity absorbance (Table 3) as Y axis vs. time as the X axis.

3. Enzyme activity absorbance as Y axis vs. growth as X axis from Tables 3 and 1, respectively.

QUESTIONS

Completion:

1-2. When an enzyme is produced all of the time by an organism, the enzyme is said to be _____. If it is repressed, except when a substrate is present, it is called an _____ enzyme.

3. The enzyme beta-galactosidase is a member of a gene complex called an _____.

4. If a mutation occurs in the operator section of the *lac* operon so that the repressor cannot function, the resulting clone phenotype would show beta-galactosidase as a _____ enzyme.

5. What makes the TMG non-metabolizable while ONPG is?

6. Explain why glucose is a repressor.

7. Many bacterial species possess a beta-galactosidase. Is it always an inducible enzyme?

59 Replica Plating for a Nutritional Mutant

OBJECTIVES

The student will be able to:

1. define auxotroph.

2. explain the purpose of mutating a bacterium to produce a desired auxotroph.

3. perform an experiment to produce an auxotroph requiring an amino acid.

Wild type organisms are those which are isolated from nature and grow on a complete or minimal medium. Mutations often occur in nutritional pathways, and the progeny of these cells are unable to grow on the complete medium without supplementing with the newly required nutrient. These mutations often cause changes in the control mechanisms for metabolic pathways, not only leading to new nutrient requirements but resulting in increased production of some end product of a pathway. These nutritional mutants are called **auxotrophs.** Auxotrophs have been extensively used to study metabolic pathways, enzyme structure and function, and are exploited in industry to produce metabolic products.

Simple selection of strains for a desired trait or suppression of an undesired one from among those spontaneous mutants occuring in cultures has been used to obtain modified microbes as illustrated in Exercise 49. Deliberate genetic mutation for loss of one or more characters is done using ultraviolet light or chemical mutagens as the modifying agents.

This exercise illustrates the principle of **replica plating** and the use of a potent chemical mutagen to produce a nutritional mutant. The chemical N-methyl-N'-nitro-N-nitrosoguanidine (MNNG) generally causes mutations by the replacement of GC bases with AT bases although the reverse change may sometimes occur as well as transitions, transversions, and frameshifts at low frequencies. **CAUTION: MNNG is also a carcinogen and should be handled with great care.** Using the replica plating technique described below, thousands of colonies can be tested for auxotrophic mutations, these auxotrophs will grow on a complete medium but not on a medium deficient in some nutrient. MNNG may yield up to 20% total auxotrophs or 1-2% of a particular nutrient-requiring mutant.

The replica plating technique allows the transfer of a large number of colonies simultaneously to many different media to test nutritional requirements (Figure 59-1). A piece of sterile velveteen is attached to a wooden block the shape and size of a Petri plate bottom. The velveteen is placed on the surface of a Master plate with many colonies and the fibers act as inoculators. The block is then transferred to another plate and touched to the surface transferring some cells in the process. It is then removed and touched to another plate, and so on. Each plate contains a different assortment of nutrients. Because both the block and the plate are marked, a plate showing a no growth for a particular colony can be traced back to the Master plate and the organism isolated for further study.

The bacterium used in this exercise (*Escherichia coli* K12 ATCC 25404) is capable of growing on a minimal salts medium. You will attempt to isolate an auxotrophic mutant requiring one of several amino acids to grow.

Reference: Gerhardt, P. et al. Manual of Methods for General Bacteriology. American Society for Microbiology, Washington, D.C., 1981, pp. 232-242.

MATERIALS (per pair)

1. 1 peptone broth centrifuge tube, sterile
2. 2 peptone broth tubes, sterile
3. 1 tube tris-maleic acid buffer, sterile
4. 1 pair of latex or rubber gloves
5. Solution of MNNG, sterile
6. 7 sterile 1ml pipets and safety bulb
7. 2 sterile 99 ml phosphate buffer dilution blanks
8. 3 sterile 9 ml phosphate buffer dilution blanks
9. 1 glass spreading rod
10. 1 flask peptone agar, sterile
11. 8 Petri plates, sterile
12. 2 pre-dried plates each of minimal salts agar + the amino acid combinations in II.1 below (10 plates), sterile
13. Replica plating block with rubber band or other restraining device
14. Sterile velveteen
15. Indelible marking pen, narrow point
16. 18-24 hour old peptone broth culture of *Escherichia coli* K12

PROCEDURE AND OBSERVATIONS (about 6 days)

I. Mutagenesis

Period 1

1. Inoculate a centrifuge tube containing 10 ml of peptone broth with *E. coli* K12.

2. Incubate at 35°-37°C on a rotary shaker to the logarithmic stage of growth (absorbance will be about 0.3). The cell concentration will be about 5×10^8 cells/ml.

Period 2

3. Centrifuge the culture for 5 minutes at 5000 x g and remove the supernatant.

4. Resuspend the cells by aseptically pouring in 9 ml of tris-maleic acid buffer at pH 6.0.

5. **CAUTION: Put on protective latex or rubber gloves** and add 1 ml of freshly prepared (1 mg/L) N-methyl-N'-nitro-N-nitrosoguanidine (MNNG) giving a final concentration of 100 μg/L. Incubate at 35°-37°C for 30 minutes without shaking.

6. Centrifuge the cells as before. **NOTE: Dispose of the MNNG supernatant in the special container provided for that purpose.** This will be disposed of later as a hazardous waste.

7. Resuspend the cells by aseptically pouring in 10 ml of peptone broth.

8. Recentrifuge again. **NOTE: Dispose of the supernatant in the special container as in the step No. 6.** Resuspend the cells by aseptically pouring in 10 ml of peptone broth.

9. Incubate the medium and cells at 35°-37°C for 24-48 hours to allow the mutagenized cells to grow and express any mutations present.

10. Pour 8 plates of peptone agar and allow them to dry thoroughly, inverted, overnight at 35°-37°C.

Period 3

11. Prepare a serial dilution of the incubated culture from the last step to include the 10^{-5}, 10^{-6}, 10^{-7}, and 10^{-8} dilutions as illustrated in Figure 59-2.

12. With a sterile 1 ml pipet, pipet 0.1 ml of the 10^{-8} dilution onto the surface of each of duplicate, pre-dried peptone agar plates.

13. Repeat with the 10^{-7}, 10^{-6}, and 10^{-5} dilutions onto separate duplicate plates.

14. Spread the volume on the plates with an alcohol flamed bent glass rod beginning with the highest dilution plates. Allow the liquid to absorb into the medium.

15. Incubate the plates inverted at 35°-37°C for about 24 hours until the colonies are >1 mm in diameter.

II. Replica Plating

Period 4

1. Five minimal salts agar plates will be provided with the following compositions:

No.	Composition
1	+ thr + met + leu + ala
2	+ met + thr
3	+ leu + ala
4	+ met + leu
5	+ thr + ala

2. Prepare the replica plating block by placing a square of velveteen on the block and stretching it taut. Be careful not to touch the face of the cloth with your fingers. Hold the cloth in place with a rubber band or other retaining device.

3. Make a mark on the **edge** of the velveteen with an indelible pen (Figure 59-1). This mark will serve to orient the block.

4. Make a corresponding mark on the side of the **bottom** of each Petri plate (Figure 59-1). Next to the mark, put the number of the medium from the table above.

5. Replica plate one of the dilution plates containing the closest to 20–50 colonies onto the five amino acid plates according to Figure 59-1. Be sure the orientation marks are lined up. This ensures each plate will be oriented exactly the same.

6. Incubate the five plates at 35°-37°C until colonies appear.

Period 5

7. Interpret colony growth or non-growth as follows:

Medium with amino acid pairs

Type Colony	2 met^+thr^+	3 leu^+ala^+	4 met^+leu^+	5 thr^+ala^+
met^-	+	-	+	-
thr^-	+	-	-	+
leu^-	-	+	+	-
ala^-	-	-	-	+

An example of intrerpretation: met auxotroph will grow on media 2 and 4 but not 3 and 5, thr^- auxothroph will grow on media 2 and 5 but not 3 and 4.

8. Plate 1 serves as a Master plate. Make a drawing of this plate on the Results and Observations form showing the location of each colony. Do the same for each remaining plate drawing each colony. If a colony did not grow on a medium, use a light dashed line around the spot it should have been. Note the orientation marks on the form.

III. Isolation and Verification

Period 6

1. Select a colony from plate 1 which does not show growth on one of the amino acid plates. Streak the colony for isolation on plates of medium number 1 and the four amino acid media.

2. Incubate the plates at 35°-37°C for 24 hours or until colonies are well developed. Growth should occur on medium number 1 and not on at least one other.

Period 7

3. Record your results on the Report and Observations form.

THOUGHT QUESTIONS

1. Why is the mutation rate so low?

2. Could you have plated directly onto medium 1 instead of peptone agar?

3. Design an experiment to find a double auxotroph.

4. What could you do with the isolate of Part III to find out what the lesion might be?

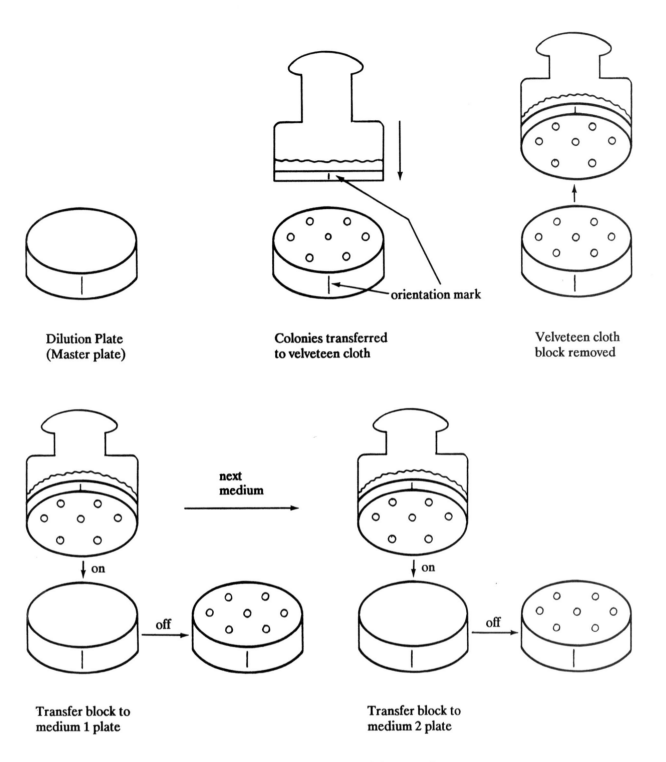

Dilution Plate
(Master plate)

Colonies transferred
to velveteen cloth

orientation mark

Velveteen cloth
block removed

next
medium

on

on

off

off

Transfer block to
medium 1 plate

Transfer block to
medium 2 plate

Repeat for each of the remaining 3 media

Figure 59-1. Replica plating procedure

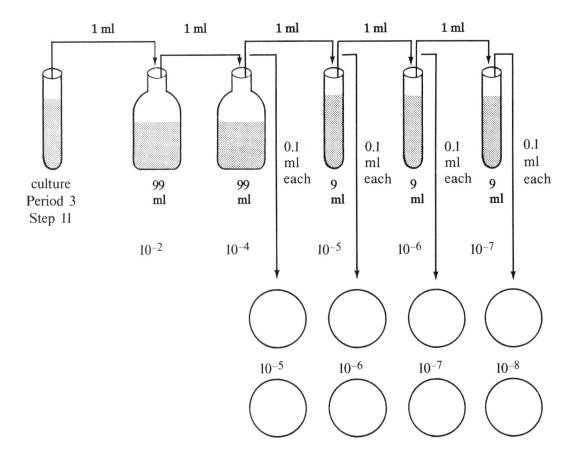

Figure 59-2. Dilution sequence for replica plating

59. Replica Plating for a Nutritional Mutant

RESULTS AND OBSERVATIONS

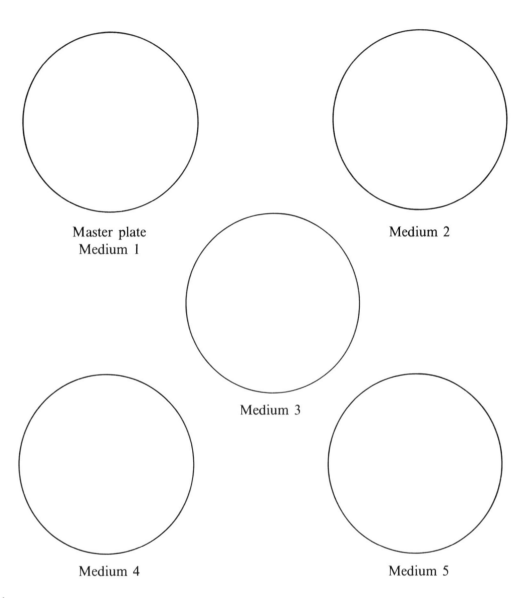

Master plate
Medium 1

Medium 2

Medium 3

Medium 4

Medium 5

Verification:

On the form above, mark the colony selected for verification with the letter S.

Growth on medium 1 _____ (use + or -)

Growth on medium 2 _____ 3 _____ 4 _____ 5 _____

Conclusions:

QUESTIONS

A. **True or False Statements:** Circle the correct response.

T F 1. The most likely mutation to have occurred in this exercise is the replacement of GC by AT in the DNA.

T F 2. An auxotroph is a mutant lacking a specific nutritional characteristic.

T F 3. Mutants are widely used to study metabolic pathways.

T F 4. MNNG is capable of causing cancer.

T F 5. MNNG use may result in 1-2% yield of a particular mutant.

T F 6. The replica plate technique can usually be done successfully without marking the plates or the velveteen.

T F 7. Colonies growing on the replica plates but not on the Master plate are probably auxotrophs.

T F 8. The MNNG must be disposed of as a toxic waste.

T F 9. Aseptic technique is not important in this procedure.

T F 10. Auxotrophic mutants occur naturally.

B. **Completion:**

11. The name given to an organism just isolated from a soil sample relative to its nutritional requirements is _____ .

12. A strain of the above organism requiring a nutrient that the original organism did not require is called an _____ .

13-14. Name two agents to produce nutritional mutants

13. _____

14. _____

15. The technique used to test nutritional requirements of a large number of strains is the

_____ .

16. In working with MNNG you should wear _____ .

60 Plasmid Mediated Transformation

OBJECTIVES

The student will be able to:

1. describe the meaning of vector, competent cell, cloning, and gene or plasmid amplification.

2. clone a plasmid having an antibiotic resistance factor.

Plasmids are double-stranded, closed, circular DNA molecules occurring extrachromosomally in a variety of bacteria. These genetic elements carry a number of phenotypic characters often advantageous to the host organism, such as resistance to antibiotics and heavy metals (see Exercise 49), degradation of polymers and other complex organic molecules, production of toxins, colicins, and antibiotics. Transfer of plasmids to new hosts can be accomplished in nature by a process similar to **conjugation** and in the laboratory by **transformation** to **competent** host cells—cells that are temporarily permeable and able to receive the plasmid DNA.

Plasmids are now widely used as **cloning vectors** for production of proteins. A vector is created by ligating a gene onto an enzymatically opened plasmid DNA strand and closing it again (a process called **splicing**). The **recombinant** plasmid is then inserted into a competent host cell and the host cell replicated, **amplifying** the vector. The amplification of the plasmid, or the gene it contains, is called cloning of the gene.

This exercise will demonstrate the cloning of a plasmid and the above concepts. No new genes will be spliced into the plasmid (a complicated process), but the method of cloning the plasmid is the same as used in modern **genetic engineering.** The plasmid used in this exercise has a gene (cat) specifying resistance to the antibiotic chloramphenicol which interferes with peptide bond formation at the 50S ribosome subunit. The gene specifies an acetyltransferase enzyme acetylating the chloramphenicol thereby inactivating the antibiotic.

MATERIALS (per pair or other group)

1. 2 13 mm diameter tubes with 0.2 ml of competent *E. coli* host strain, chilled to 4°C. (See Figure 60-1 for preparation method.)

2. 1 container of plasmid concentrate sufficient for class. (See Figure 60-2 for preparation method.)

3. 3 plates of L agar with 10 μg/ml of chloramphenicol, sterile

4. 1 sterile 13 mm diameter tube

5. 3 sterile 0.1 ml pipets and safety bulb

6. 3 sterile 1 ml pipets

7. 1 glass spreading rod (4 mm diameter glass rod approximately 27 cm long, bent into "hockey stick" shape)

8. 1 tube with 10 ml of L broth, sterile

PROCEDURE (2 days) Figure 60-3 shows a flow diagram.

Period 1

1. Label one tube of *E. coli* "plasmid-host" and add 0.01 ml of the plasmid preparation to it and 0.01 ml to the empty sterile tube (labeled "plasmid control"). The second tube of host cells is labeled "host-control."

2. Place all three tubes into a preheated water bath at 42°C for 2 minutes.

3. Add 1.0 ml of sterile L broth first to the plasmid control tube, then 1.0 ml to the host control tube, and finally 1.0 ml to to the plasmid-host tube. Discard the pipet.

4. Incubate all three tubes at 37°C for 30 minutes to 1 hour which allows the bacteria to recover.

5. Pipet 0.1 ml of the plasmid control tube onto the surface of one L-10 μg/ml chloramphenicol plate and discard the pipet. Spread the drop with an alcohol dipped, flamed glass spreading rod. Label the plate "plasmid-control."

6. Pipet 0.1 ml of the *E. coli* host control tube onto the surface of one L-10 μg/ml chloramphenicol plate with the freshly flamed glass spreading rod. Label the plate "host-control."

7. In a like manner spread 0.1 ml of the host-plasmid tube on a third plate of the same medium. Label the plate "host-plasmid."

8. Let all three plates sit at room temperature until the liquid has absorbed.

9. Incubate inverted at 37°C for 24 hours.

OBSERVATIONS

Period 2

10. Observe the three plates for colonies. The presence of colonies means resistance to the antibiotic is present on a plasmid carried by cells of the colony. Susceptible cells will not grow. Expected results are: *E. coli* host control, no colonies; plasmid control, no colonies; host-plasmid treated culture should show colonies, the number related to efficiency of transformation of the competent cells.

11. Record the results on the report form.

THOUGHT QUESTIONS

1. Find out from your instructor how the plasmid preparation is made.

2. What additional steps are necessary to purify the plasmids?

3. How is a host cell made competent?

4. How are plasmids used in genetic engineering?

5. Are plasmids limited to prokaryotes?

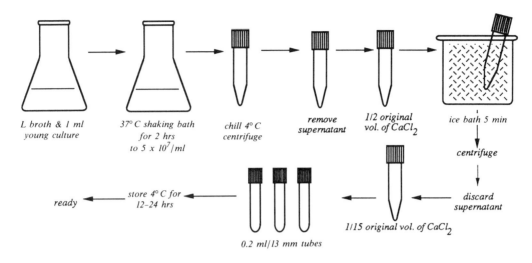

Figure 60-1. Preparation of competent host cells

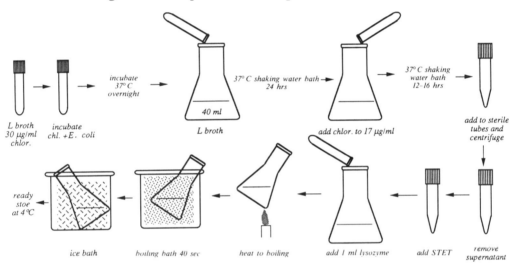

Figure 60-2. Plasmid amplification

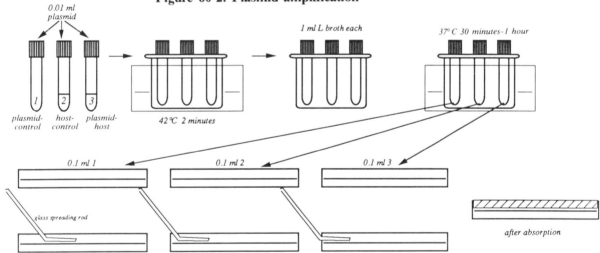

Figure 60-3. Flow diagram for transformation of *E. coli*

Name _____ Date _____ Grade _____

60. Plasmid Mediated Transformation

RESULTS AND OBSERVATIONS

Record the number of colonies on each of the plates.

	Host-control	Plasmid-control	Host + plasmid
No. of colonies			

1.   What would it mean if you were to find colonies on the

   a) plasmid-control plate?

   b) host-control plate?

2.   Would any other transformations occur? How would you determine if they did?

QUESTIONS

Completion:

1-2.   Two terms are used in genetic engineering to mean an increase in number or amount of a plasmid or gene. These two terms are _____ and _____.

3-5.   Chloramphenicol resistance is specified by a plasmid gene called _____ and works by producing an _____ which _____ the chloramphenicol molecule.

6.   The plasmid into which a gene has been inserted in the laboratory is called a _____.

7.   A host cell is called competent if it can _____ a plasmid.

8.   A small number of host cells in a culture can be made competent by treatment with

    _____.

9.   The uptake of plasmid DNA by a competent cell in the laboratory is called _____.

10.   In the case of amplification of this particular plasmid, what is a necessary ingredient of the medium?

    _____.

11-12.   Name two other resistance factors on the particular plasmid used in ths experiment

    11. _____

    12. _____

Identification of Unknown Bacteria

One of the more interesting aspects of microbiology to most students is puzzling out the identity of an unknown organism. Characterization is a necessary part of taxonomy, clinical microbiology, and many of the applied areas of microbiology. Unit X is divided into several approaches for the study of an unknown. One approach is taxonomic through the use of a computer for which a large number of tests (50) are performed on an organism. The data is then entered on a computer and compared character by character to an organism data bank resulting finally in a similarity coefficient with no weighting of any feature. In case a computer is not available, a dichotomous key may be used in which the characters are weighted. The unknown for either of these approaches may be given out at the beginning of the exercises on biochemical testing. The second approach is a probabilistic method using one of the commercially available rapid procedures consisting of a large number of tests performed simultaneously. If this procedure is used, one or more unknowns will be given at the time of the test. Good detecting!

61 Identification of an Unknown Organism

This exercise consists of two independent parts which may be used separately. Exercise 61A uses a computer similarity coefficient or a dichotomus key; 61B uses one of the rapid miniaturized methods of identification. Your instructor will determine which of these you will do.

Taxonomy concerns the arranging of organisms into groups based on common characteristics. This process is also referred to as **classification.** A group of organisms so arranged is called a **taxon. Identification** is the placing of an unknown organism into an established taxon on the basis of shared characters. This exercise is designed to acquaint you with the identification of unknowns in the microbiology laboratory using computers with a numerical approach. (Note: This exercise can be done without recourse to computers by using the dichotomous key or 61B.)

In clinical microbiology, microbes must be identified quickly and accurately with a minimum of cost. It is not necessary to know how the organism fits in the taxonomy of all other organisms but only which one it is. To do this, tests are often weighted; the possession of a single character has great importance in recognizing what it might be. Dichotomous keys and probablistic models are derived from taxonomic characters and used as aids in identification. Traditionally this has involved inoculation of many media as exemplified in 61A and the physiological tests done earlier. This is expensive and time consuming and recent developments in clinical laboratory practice has centered around reducing the time and cost involved.

61A Similarity Coefficient— Dichotomous Key Method

OBJECTIVES

The student will be able to:

1. identify an unknown organism using *Bergey's Manual* and other diagnostic keys.

2. use the collected data with a computer program, if available.

3. explain the meaning of a similarity coefficient.

4. use a numerical method involving a rapid diagnostic method.

The basic approach of 61A is to make a number of observations, inoculate a battery of diagnostic media with an unknown organism, read and record the results on the Data Collection Sheet provided for this exercise. Using the data on the collection sheet, your instructor will select one of several methods (see the Instructor's Manual) for identifying the unknown: a similarity coefficient method using the computer program TIDENT; a computer generated dichotomous key with weighted characters; or a printed form of the key. Once your organism is identified, you must then consult *Bergey's Manual of Systematic Bacteriology* (Vol. 1, 2, 3, or 4), compare your data, and decide whether the identification is correct or not. The Data Collection Sheet and your analysis are then submitted to the instructor.

The **similarity coefficient** method requires that as many characters as possible be determined for an organism, usually more than 100 is suggested. This exercise uses only 50, a bare minimum when very similar organisms are included in the data base. The similarity coefficient program compares the characters determined for your unknown with a set of known organisms, one character at a time, and sums the number of similarities (S) and the number of differences (N), ignoring comparisons where either organism has missing data, and calculates a simple matching coefficient as a percent similarity ($\%S_{sm}$) as follows:

$$\%S_{sm} = \frac{S}{S + N} \times 100$$

While this program is a simple matching coefficient, the same method of calculation and matching is also used in more sophisticated taxonomy methods. After comparison with all the organisms in the data bank, the computer prints the name of the organism or organisms most closely resembling your unknown, the percent similarity, and the complete coded data. If your data is not sufficiently close to one or has the same $\%S_{sm}$ with more than one organism, then a suggestion is printed for you to check your coding or re-evaluate your data.

A **dichotomous key** does not utilize all characters of an organism but only a subset of those characters which distinguish between the various organisms. The problem with keys of this sort is that each character used must be held by 100% of the strains, otherwise the key becomes extremely complex and unwieldy. Since not all the characters on your Data Collection Sheet are used, your instructor may limit the tests used to only a portion of those available. A dichotomous key is available for this exercise as a computer program or as a printed form. A question is posed about a particular characteristic for your unknown. Respond with a yes or no from the Data Collection Sheet. You will then be directed to another question and so on until your organism has been identified. You must then verify this with *Bergey's Manual of Systematic Bacteriology* as described above.

MATERIALS (per person)

1. An 18-24 hour slant culture of an unknown will be provided.

2. Your instructor may choose to provide the unknown at the time the metabolic studies are begun (Exercise 25) which will permit you compare your results with positive and negative cultures for a particular test. The media list under Procedure is presented with this in mind.

3. Your instructor will designate the incubation temperature to be used for your unknown.

4. If the similarity coefficient program is used, all 50 characteristics on the Data Collection Sheet should be determined. This is a minimum for reasonable similarities.

5. If the dichotomous key is used (computer or printed form), your instructor may designate the minimum set of tests and media necessary.

PROCEDURE (1-3 weeks)

A. When given your unknown

1. Record the number of your unknown on the Data Collection Sheet.

2. Inoculate one tryptic soy agar slant, incubate it at your designated temperature for 24-48 hours, and then move it to room temperature for storage. This will serve as your reserve culture in case contamination occurs.

3. Use your original culture for inoculations.

4. If the unknown is given with Exercise 25, stop here; otherwise proceed with B.

B. Period 1 (Parentheses refer to Data Collection Sheet characters)

5. Inoculate 4 tubes of tryptic soy broth. Incubate one tube each at 25°C, 37°C, 45°C, and 55°C for 48 hours to determine the maximum temperature at which growth occurs (21).

6. Make preliminary observations of Gram reaction (8), acid fastness (10), cell shape (1), end of cell (4), and arrangement (5). If micrometers are available, measure Gram stained cell dimensions of length and width (2, 3).

C. Period 2—After 48 hours

7. If your unknown organism is a Gram-positive rod, inoculate a manganese agar slant and incubate at the designated temperature for 18 hours. Then perform the endospore stain (6).

8. Inoculate all media below not already provided to perform the following biochemical tests. Incubate the media at the designated temperature for your organism for the time period indicated in the relevant exercises.

Not previously supplied

a. Colony size, elevation, and margin (11, 12, 13), density (17), pigmentation (14), pigment (15) and fluorescence under ultraviolet light (16)—streak for isolation on a plate of plate count agar and incubate for 48 hours.

b. Growth characteristics in tryptic soy broth (18, 19, 20).

c. Oxygen requirements—pipet 1 ml of a broth culture grown at the designated growth temperature into a melted but cooled yeast extract–tryptone 0.75% agar shake, mix, and allow to solidify. Incubate for 48 hours (7) Exercise 46.

d. Motility—from slant using wet mount or soft agar method (9) Exercise 51

e. Sugars—fructose (23), galactose (24), maltose (27), mannitol (28), sorbitol (29), arabinose (30), and xylose (31) Exercise 32.

May have been supplied with Exercises 25-40

f. Sugars—glucose (22), lactose (25), and sucrose (26) Exercise 32

g. Litmus milk reactions (32, 33, 34) Exercise 29

h. Hemolysis—5% sheep blood (35) Exercise 31

i. Starch hydrolysis—starch agar (36) Exercise 25

j. Gelatin hydrolysis—Fraser's overlay method (37) Exercise 27

k. Casein hydrolysis—skim milk overlay method (38) Exercise 28

l. Lipid hydrolysis—Spirit blue-lipid agar (39) Exercise 26

m. Nitrate respiration and/or gas—nitrate broth (40, 41) Exercise 36

n. Ammonia production—4% peptone broth (42) Exercise 38

o. Catalase and oxidase—tryptic soy agar (43, 44) Exercise 35

p. Hydrogen sulfide production—Kligler iron agar (45) Exercise 33

q. IMViC reactions—tryptone broth, MR-VP broth, Simmons citrate agar slant (46, 47, 48, 49) Exercise 34

r. Urea hydrolysis—urea broth (50) Exercise 39

Periods 3-7

OBSERVATIONS Select A, B, or C below.

A. Similarity coefficient method

1. Enter all your data on the Data Collection Sheet by circling the number designation for your unknown results. Circle "0" if the test was not done or lost.

   Note: Be careful of using "0". If other results imply a valid score, use it. For example, step No. 7 above indicates only Gram-positives should use manganese agar and do a spore stain. If your organism is Gram-negative, Character 6 would be scored "1" (none) not "0". The fewer "0"'s scored, the better the match will be. Check with your instructor if you have a question.

2. Record the character score in the column immediately to the left of the Character No. column for ease in responding to the computer or key questions.

3. *Now* you are ready to use the computer. Your instructor will provide you with detailed instructions for use of the particular computer. Enter your data as it is requested and wait for the answer.

    a. The computer program has a cut-off of 85%S for identity. If you are lower than this or more than one organism has the same %S, you will need to review, repeat tests, or recode your data. Repeat the computer run again if necessary.

    b. Go to step D below.

B. Dichotomous key—computer version

1. If the dichotomous key is used, it is available in two forms—as a computer program or a printed sheet. In the former, your instructor will provide you with detailed instructions in use of the particular computer. Questions are displayed one at a time. Respond by answering yes or no. The program then takes you to the next question on that branch. Continue responding until your unknown is identified or you are told an error has occurred, in which case you will need to review, repeat tests, or recode your data. Go to step D below.

C. Dichotomous key—printed version

1. If the printed dichotomous key is used, simply follow the questions and branches as indicated until your organism is identified or you come to an error, in which case you will need to review, repeat tests, or recode your data.

D. Take your identified unknown and all the data you have collected and find your unknown in *Bergey's Manual of Systematic Bacteriology.* Compare with your unknown data and decide if this is indeed the correct identification. Write a short report on how the Bergey's data and your data differ or agree and how confident you are in the identification. A very important part of this report is to indicate *what tests could be used to help further clarify the identification.*

THOUGHT QUESTIONS

1. Why is it necessary to have as many characters as possible for a similarity coefficient? What is the practical limit on this?

2. Which would be the better method for use in taxonomy—a simple matching coefficient, a probabilistic coefficient, or a dichotomous key? Give reasons.

3. Would a dichotomous key suffice for all bacteria?

61A. Identification of an Unknown Organism

Data Collection Sheet

Unknown No. _____

Character   **Character Scores:** ND = Not Done, Missing
No.

Cell Morphology and Staining

1. Shape: 0 – ND; 2 – straight rod or coccobacillus; 3 – curved or spiral rod; 5 – spirochete; 6 – coccus; 7 – branched

2. Length of rod or diameter of coccus: 0 – ND; 2 – < 0.5 μm; 3 – 0.5 to 3.0 μm; 4 – > 3.0 μm

3. Width: 0 – ND; 1 – coccus; 2 – < 1 μm; 3 – > 1 μm

4. End of cell: 0 – ND; 1 – coccus; 2 – round end

5. Cell arrangement: 0 – ND; 2 – more than 50% single; 3 – more than 50% pairs; 4 – chains $<$ 5 cells per chain; 5 – chains $>$ 5 cells per chain; 6 – packets (4 or 8) or irregular clusters of cocci; 8 – branching filaments.

6. Endospore: 0 – ND; 1 – none; 2 – cell swollen terminal or subterminal; 3 – swollen central; 4 – cell normal terminal or subterminal; 5 – normal central

7. Air relation: 0 – ND; 2 – aerobic or facultatively anaerobic; 3 – obligate anaerobe; 4 – microaerophilic

8. Gram reaction: 0 – ND; 2 – positive or variable; 3 – negative

9. Motile: 0 – ND; 1 – non-motile; 2 – motile

10. Acid fast: 0 – ND; 1 – no; 2 – yes

Growth Characteristics

11. Colony size (48–72 hours well-isolated): 0 – ND; 2 – < 1 mm; 3 – 1-5 mm; 4 – > 5 mm

12. Colony elevation (48–72 hours well-isolated): 0 – ND; 2 – flat (effuse); 3 – raised; 4 – umbonate; 5 – convex; 6 – pulvinate

13. Colony margin (48–72 hours well-isolated): 0–ND; 1 – entire; 2 – undulate; 3 – lobate; 4 – curled; 5 – erose; 6 – filamentous; 7 – spreading or swarming over whole plate

14. Colony color: 0 – ND; 1 – non-pigmented, off white, white, or gray-white; 2 – blue; 3 – violet or purple; 4 – brown or black; 5 – red or pink; 7 – orange; 8 – green or yellow-green; 9 – yellow

15. Pigment solubility: 0 – ND; 1 – confined to colony (score white, off-white, and non-pigmented here); 3 – diffusible (in agar rather than colony)

16. Pigment fluorescence: 0 – ND; 1 – not fluorescent; 2 – fluorescent (ultraviolet)

17. Colony density (48–72 hours well-isolated): 0 – ND; 2 – transparent (read print through center) or translucent; 4 – opaque

18. Turbidity in broth: 0 – ND; 1 – none; 2 – slight; 3 – moderate to heavy

19. Sediment in broth: 0 – ND; 1 – none; 2 – slight; 3 – moderate to heavy

20. Pellicle on broth: 0 – ND; 1 – none; 2 – ring; 3 – thin barely visible; 4 – moderate to heavy

21. Maximum temperature at which growth is observed to occur: 0 – ND; 2 – 25°C; 3 – 30°C; 4 – 37°C; 5 – 45°C; 6 – 55°C

Physiology and biochemistry (NC = No change or basic; A = acid; AG = acid and gas)

22. Glucose: 0 – ND; 1 – NC; 3 – A; 4 – AG

23. Fructose: 0 – ND; 1 – NC; 3 – A; 4 – AG

24. Galactose: 0 – ND; 1 – NC; 3 – A; 4 – AG

25. Lactose: 0 – ND; 1 – NC; 3 – A; 4 – AG

26. Sucrose: 0 – ND; 1 – NC; 3 – A; 4 – AG

27. Maltose: 0 – ND; 1 – NC; 3 – A; 4 – AG

28. Mannitol: 0 – ND; 1 – NC; 3 – A; 4 – AG

29. Sorbitol: 0 – ND; 1 – NC; 3 – A; 4 – AG

30. Arabinose: 0 – ND; 1 – NC; 3 – A; 4 – AG

31. Xylose: 0 – ND; 1 – NC; 3 – A; 4 – AG

32. Litmus milk: 0 – ND; 1 – not reduced; 2 – reduced

33. Litmus milk: 0 – ND; 1 – no acid curd; 2 – acid curd (coagulated)

34. Litmus milk rennet curd (no acid): 0 – ND; 1 – no rennet (score here if acid formed); 2 – rennet curd formed

35. Blood agar: 0 – ND; 1 – no hemolysis; 2 – beta hemolysis; 3 – alpha hemolysis

36. Starch hydrolysis: 0 – ND; 1 – negative; 2 – positive

37. Gelatin hydrolysis: 0 – ND; 1 – negative; 2 – positive

38. Casein hydrolysis: 0 – ND; 1 – negative; 2 – positive

39. Lipid hydrolysis: 0 – ND; 1 – negative; 2 – positive

40. Nitrite from nitrate: 0 – ND; 1 – negative; 2 – positive

41. Gas from nitrate: 0 – ND; 1 – no gas; 2 – positive (Note: if positive, score No. 40 as 2)

42. Ammonia from peptone: 0 – ND; 1 – negative; 2 – positive

43. Catalase: 0 – ND; 1 – negative; 2 – positive

44. Oxidase: 0 – ND; 1 – negative; 2 – positive

45. H_2S: 0 – ND; 1 – negative; 2 – positive

46. Indole: 0 – ND; 1 – negative; 2 – positive

47. Methyl red: 0 – ND; 1 – negative; 2 – positive

48. Voges-Proskauer: 0 – ND; 1 – negative; 2 – positive

49. Simmons citrate: 0 – ND; 1 – negative; 2 – positive

50. Urease: 0 – ND; 1 – negative; 2 – positive

A. True or False Statements: Circle the correct response.

T   F   1.   All bacterial isolates belonging to a species would be expected to give the same result for a specific biochemical test.

T   F   2.   Plasmids may convert a strain of bacteria either gaining or losing a characteristic depending on whether the plasmid is gained or lost.

T   F   3.   Dichotomous keys do not always work because all strains of a species may not have the same result for a particular test.

T   F   4.   One can successfully use similarity coefficient taxonomic methods with a small number of characteristics, less than 10.

T   F   5.   The ideal for computer Adansonian taxonomy is to do as many tests on an organism or group of organisms as possible, 100 or more.

B. Completion:

6.   The process of arranging organisms into groups based on common characteristics is called

_____.

7.   A group of organisms with common characteristics is referred to as a _____.

8.   Giving a name to an organism is called _____.

9.   When an unknown organism is compared to a group of known organisms, the process is referred to

as _____.

10-11.   A number of methods for identifying organisms exists. The two described in this exercise are

_____ and _____.

12-15.   Ten characteristics are determined for an unknown organism and compared with data from known organisms. The data is given below. Calculate a $\%S_{sm}$ for your unknown organism against *each* of the known organisms below. Using the cut-off from the exercise, determine which, if any, is identical to your unknown. (+ = positive, – = negative, 0 = missing)

	character									
	1	2	3	4	5	6	7	8	9	10
unknown	+	+	–	+	0	–	+	–	–	–
#1	–	+	–	+	–	+	–	–	+	+
#2	+	–	–	+	–	–	+	+	–	–
#3	–	–	+	–	–	–	+	+	+	–

12. $\%S_{sm}$ to #1 _____

13. $\%S_{sm}$ to #2 _____

14. $\%S_{sm}$ to #3 _____

15.   Is your unknown identical to any of these knowns? If so, why?

61B Identification with a Multitest System: API 20E

OBJECTIVES

The student will be able to:

1. identify an unknown member of the *Enterobacteriaceae* using the API 20E system.

2. describe the advantages of the multitest system over the conventional methods.

3. explain the difference between identification and taxonomy as used in this exercise.

A number of commercial kits have been developed involving multiple biochemical tests performed at one time, thus leading to the name **multitest systems.** These include the API, Enterotube, and Micro-ID systems among others. Originally developed for the *Enterobacteriaceae,* kits are now available for other groups as well. Patterns of results are compared to experience with known strains from many laboratories over a long period of time. This bank of data is computerized or supplied as a comprehensive summary of results by the manufacturer of the kit. By this comparison a tentative identification can be made in much less time than the conventional methods. Several precautions must be noted. First, the instructions for the kit must be followed **exactly** and a pure culture is absolutely essential. Second, use of the kit with organisms other than the ones specifically designated must be done with caution. Third, results with the kits often must be correlated with other identifying characteristics such as specimen source and colony morphology on both differential and selective media before an identification can be made. Results must often be confirmed using other techniques such as serology or other biochemical tests. This exercise is intended to introduce the student to the use of a multitest kit for identification of an unknown from the *Enterobacteriaceae.* Once your organism is identified, you must then consult *Bergey's Manual of Systematic Bacteriology* and 2), compare your data, and decide whether the identification is correct or not. The rapid identification form and your analysis are then submitted to the instructor.

MATERIALS (per person or pair)

1. API 20E kit including[a]

    a. API 20E strip
    b. Incubation trays and lids
    c. Report sheet
    d. Differential chart

2. 0.85% saline[a]

3. Sterile capped 13 mm test tubes

4. Sterile mineral oil[a]

5. Sterile applicator sticks

6. Sterile 5 ml Pasteur pipets

7. Test tube racks

8. Marking pen

9. 50 ml plastic squeeze bottle with tap water

10. Zinc dust

11. H_2O_2, 1.5%

12. Kovac's reagent[a]

13. Nitrate A and B reagents[a]

14. Voges-Proskauer reagents[a]

15. Ferric chloride reagent[a]

16. Nutrient agar slant

17. Oxidase reagent

18. An unknown nutrient agar slant culture

[a] Available from API

PROCEDURE (1 day)

Background: The API kit consists of microtubes containing dehydrated substrates. The addition of the bacterial suspension rehydrates these and the bacteria grow. Changes in the substrate can be determined by observation or the addition of reagents after 18-24 hours incubation at 35°-37°C. This kit can be used to determine some Gram-negative non-*Enterobacteriaceae* by modifying the incubation period and the addition of a few tests.

1. Preparation of the bacterial suspension

   a. Add 5 ml of sterile 0.85% saline to a sterile test tube.

   b. With a sterilized loop, transfer a small amount of growth to the saline and emulsify thoroughly. (In clinical practice this would be one well-isolated colony from a selective or differential medium.)

2. Preparation of the strip

   a. Set up an incubation tray and lid and put your name on the flap for identification.

   b. With the squeeze bottle, add 5 ml of tap water to the incubation tray to provide a humid environment during incubation (Figure 61-1).

   c. Remove the API strip from the sealed pouch and place it in the incubation tray (Figure 61-2).

3. Inoculation of the strip

   a. The API 20E strip contains 20 microtubes consisting of a cupule and a tube (inset Figure 61-3).

   b. Using a sterile 5 ml Pasteur pipet, remove some bacterial suspension from the previously prepared tube.

   c. Tilt the incubation tray and fill the tube section of the microtubes by placing the pipet tip against the side of the cupule (Figure 61-3), **except** the *ADH, LDC, ODC, H_2S,* and *URE* microtubes which are best interpreted by being slightly underfilled. Fill both the tube and the cupule section of *CIT, VP,* and *GEL.*

   d. After inoculation fill the cupule section of the *ADH, LDC, ODC, H_2S,* and *URE* tubes with sterile mineral oil (Figure 61-4).

4. With the remaining bacterial suspension, streak a nutrient agar slant. Incubate it with the strip.

5. Place the lid on the tray and incubate the strip for 18-24 hours at 35°-37°C. *Note:* Strips may be removed from the incubator after 18-24 hours on weekends and stored at 2°-8°C until Monday.

OBSERVATIONS (see Table 61-1)

1. After 18 and before 24 hours incubation, record all test reactions not requiring addition of reagents.

2. If the *GLU* tube is negative (blue or green), check with your instructor.

3. If the *GLU* tube is positive (yellow), note if gas bubbles are present and perform the oxidase test.

   a. Add a drop of oxidase reagent to a piece of filter paper.

   b. With a sterile applicator stick (do not use nichrome wire loop as it gives a false positive reaction), transfer some growth from the agar slant to the drop of oxidase reagent on the filter paper. A positive test is a purple color appearing within 30 seconds. If there is no change in color, the test is negative.

4. Add the reagents to the *TDA* and *VP* tubes (Figure 61-5). If positive, the *TDA* reaction will be immediate; whereas, the *VP* test may be delayed up to 10 minutes.

5. Add the Kovac's reagent to the *IND* tube **last.**

6. Perform the nitrate reduction test on all oxidase positive organisms. This must be done last (see Table 61-1).

7. Record all results as positive or negative on the 24 hours line on the form accompanying the kit (or the Results and Observations form). The biochemical tests are grouped in three's and weighted, the numerical weights given as 1, 2, or 4 at the top of the column (see API form). Sum the weighted values (maximum 7) for all positive tests in the group of three and place the sum in the box on the line marked "Profile Number." Repeat until seven profile numbers have been generated. Compare this seven number profile code with the Analytical Profile Index, *Enterobacteriaceae* supplied by API or those provided on the results form and make an identification. Note: If oxidase positive organisms are used, your instructor will supply you with additional media and instructions. Two additional digits can then be added to the Index code.

THOUGHT QUESTIONS

1. How has the data for the strains and the weights given to the tests been collected?

2. If glucose shows no acid in this strip, what tests are then done on the organism?

3. Why does the battery of tests performed here not indicate identity without morphology, growth medium, and source of the organism data?

Table 35-1. Summary of test results, API 20E strip
(from API literature)

Tube	Positive	Negative	Comments
ONPG	yellow (any shade)	colorless	Orthonitrophenylgalactopyranoside
ADH	red or orange	yellow	Arginine dihydrolase
LDC	red or orange	yellow	Lysine decarboxylase
ODC	red or orange	yellow	Ornithine decarboxylase
CIT	turquoise or dark blue	light green or yellow	Citrate, read the cupule area (aerobic)
H2S	black ppt	no black ppt	Hydrogen sulfide, browning is negative
URE	red or orange	yellow	Urea
TDA	brown red	yellow	Tryptophane deaminase. Add 1 drop 10% ferric chloride
IND	red ring	yellow	Indole. Add 1 drop Kovac's reagent.
VP	red	colorless	Voges-Proskauer. Add 1 drop 40% KOH, 1 drop α-naphthol.
GEL	diffusion of pigment	no diffusion of pigment	Gelatin. Any diffusion is positive
GLU MAN INO SOR RHA SAC MEL AMY ARA	yellow or gray yellow	blue or blue green blue or blue green	Fermentation occurs primarily at bottom, oxidation primarily at the top. GLU = glucose, MAN = mannitol, INO = inositol, SOR = sorbitol, RHA = rhamnose, SAC = sucrose, MEL = melibiose, AMY = amygdalin, ARA = arabinose
GLU nitrate reduction Zn	note bubbles, add 2 drops nitrite A, 2 drops nitrite B red yellow	yellow red	Add zinc
MAN INO SOR catalase	bubbles	no bubbles	Add H2O2 and observe for bubbles. Use tube with no gas and, if possible, no acid.

Figure 61-1. API tray

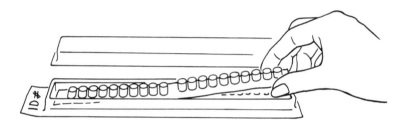

Figure 61-2. Adding API strip

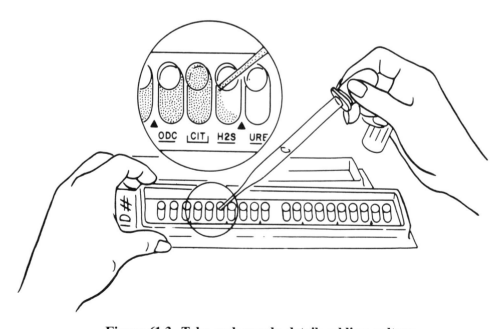

Figure 61-3. Tube and cupule detail; adding culture

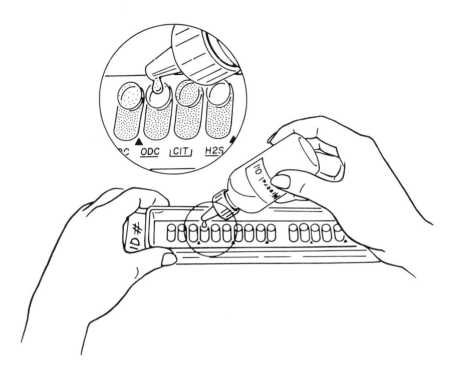

Figure 61-4. Adding mineral oil

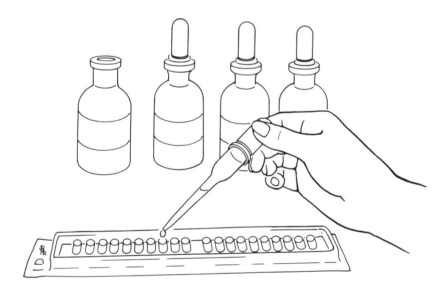

Figure 61-5. Reagent addition

61B. Identification with a Multitest System: API 20E

RESULTS AND OBSERVATIONS

api 2OE® System

Reference Number ——————— Patient ——————————————— Date ———————

Source/Site ——————— Physician ——————————— Dept./Service ———————

	ONPG 1	ADH 2	LDC 4	ODC 1	CIT 2	H₂S 4	URE 1	TDA 2	IND 4	VP 1	GEL 2	GLU 4	MAN 1	INO 2	SOR 4	RHA 1	SAC 2	MEL 4	AMY 1	ARA 2	OXI 4
5 h																					
24 h																					
48 h																					
Profile Number																					

	NO₂ 1	N₂ GAS 2	MOT 4	MAC 1	OF-O 2	OF-F 4
5 h						
24 h						
48 h						
Additional Digits						

Additional Information

Identification

42-012
(11/84)

The codes below will identify six bacterial species provided the results are identical with these strains. If there are differences, the API Index will have to be consulted.

Escherichia coli	5	144	552
Salmonella enteriditis	6	704	552
Klebsiella pneumoniae	5	215	773
Enterobacter aerogenes	5	305	773
Serratia marcescens	5	307	761
Proteus vulgaris	0	476	021

QUESTIONS

A. **True or False Statements:** Circle the correct response.

   T   F   1.   The ONPG test is a test for beta-galactosidase.

   T   F   2.   A positive test for lysine decarboxylase results from the release of a free basic amine.

   T   F   3.   The citrate test is based on the conversion of citrate to lactic acid.

   T   F   4.   The VP test reagents are the same as used for the coliform IMViC test.

   T   F   5.   Acid production at the top of a tube next to the cupule is due to fermentation.

B. **Completion:**

6.   A positive test on one of the carbohydrates depends on the production of _____ .

7.   The addition of mineral oil to certain tubes (e.g., H_2S) is intended to establish _____ _____ .

8-9.   The *Enterobacteriaceae* are generally catalase _____ and oxidase _____ .

10-11.   In this exercise, zinc dust reduces _____ to _____ .

12.   If an organism does *not* reduce nitrate, the addition of zinc dust will produce a _____ test for nitrite.

Soil Microbiology

Microbes in the soil play an important role in the processes of decomposition, mineral cycling, and fertilization. Bacteria and fungi are the chief decomposers, converting plant and animal biomass into humus, carbon dioxide, and other inorganic molecules as well as additional microbial biomass. Plant nutrition and soil animals depend on either the products of these microbes or the microbes themselves. Some very important biogeochemical cycles occur in the soil such as the nitrogen and sulfur cycles studied in this section. The importance of these processes to agriculture and to the biosphere as a whole cannot be overstated because without them life on the earth would be far different or non-existent.

The variety of microbes in the soil is immense with the eubacteria, actinomycetes, and fungi numerically dominant. However, chemoautotrophs and cyanobacteria also occur, the latter being found in the soil crust adding nutrients to the soil through photosynthesis. Only a small sampling of the processes and associated organisms are presented in this section.

Soil and aquatic processes differ very little in nature, especially the aquatic sediments. Sediments serve as a sample source for several of the following exercises. The similarities are so pronounced that many of the exercises in Units XI and XII can be interchanged as examples of either soil or water environments.

62 Microbial Counts of Soil

OBJECTIVES

The student will be able to:

1. prepare a dilution of soil for plating.

2. count a set of soil plates for bacteria, actinomycetes, and fungi.

3. name the media used for soil plate counts.

The variety of microbes in soil is very great and includes many diverse bacteria, actinomycetes, cyanobacteria, fungi, algae, and protozoa as well as multicellular animals. The actual composition and size of the microbial groups varies greatly depending on the **soil type** and the amount and kind of **organic matter** present. Because it is not possible to design a single medium or technique to recover all organisms, standardized media are used for specific groups. In this exercise, a general medium for bacteria, **plate count agar** (PCA), and one for fungi, **rose bengal agar** (RBA), will be used. It is difficult to separate organisms from soil particles and the colonies formed on the plates often do not represent single cells but instead result from several. Thus it is appropriate to call these **colony-forming units** (CFU) rather than numbers of bacteria or fungi. The dilution technique and plate counting procedures introduced in Exercise 23 will be used. The class is divided into pairs, one person doing the bacterial count and one doing the fungal count from a single set of dilution blanks.

MATERIALS (per pair)

1. 3 sterile 99 ml 0.1% peptone water dilution blanks

2. 3 sterile 1 ml pipets and safety bulb

3. 8 Petri plates, sterile

4. 1 flask of plate count agar (PCA), sterile

5. 1 flask of rose bengal agar (RBA), sterile

6. Soil sample

PROCEDURE AND OBSERVATIONS (3-5 days)

Period 1

1. Label the 3 dilution blanks 10^{-2}, 10^{-4}, and 10^{-6}.

2. Label the 8 Petri plates as follows: bacteria 10^{-4}, 10^{-5}, 10^{-6}, 10^{-7}; fungi 10^{-2}, 10^{-3}, 10^{-4}, and 10^{-5}.

3. Weigh out 1 g of soil and add directly to the 10^{-2} dilution blank. Shake well according to the directions in Exercise 23.

4. Make the 10^{-4} dilution by transferring 1 ml from the 10^{-2} blank to the 10^{-4} blank, discard the pipet, and shake. Then transfer 1 ml from the 10^{-4} blank to the 10^{-6} blank, discard the pipet, and shake.

5. With a sterile 1 ml pipet, transfer 0.1 ml of the 10^{-6} blank to the 10^{-7} plate and 1 ml to the 10^{-6} plate.

6. Using the same pipet, place 0.1 ml of the 10^{-4} blank into each of the *two* plates labeled 10^{-5} and 1 ml into each of the *two* plates labeled 10^{-4}.

7. Continue with the same pipet for the 10^{-3} and 10^{-2} plates.

8. Pour PCA into the 4 bacterial plates and RBA into the 4 fungal plates, about 20 ml each, and mix as described in Exercise 23.

9. Incubate the plates at room temperature for 3-5 days.

Period 2

10. Count the plates on the colony counter using the rules found in Exercise 23. Colonies on PCA are mostly bacteria. Actinomycetes surface colonies will appear like a drop of powdered sugar showing a slight indentation of the agar around the colony. Subsurface colonies will be difficult to distinguish from eubacterial colonies. Separate the counts into pigment types as well. On RBA, molds will appear filamentous and yeast colonies creamy and bacteria-like with both types colored red or pink due to the rose bengal. Count both the filamentous and creamy colony types.

11. Gram stain a few representative colonies from each medium noting the Gram reaction and morphology of the cells.

12. Record the results on the results form.

THOUGHT QUESTIONS

1. Bacteria are generally unicellular and fungi filamentous with many reproductive spores. How does this affect the interpretation of the mold counts?

2. Where would you expect to find cyanobacteria in soil?

3. Why was penicillin not used in the fungal medium?

4. How would you determine the presence of protozoa in soils?

5. What is the relationship between bacteria and actinomycetes?

Name _____ Date _____ Grade _____

62. Microbial Counts of Soil

RESULTS AND OBSERVATIONS

Each person should count his/her own plates (bacteria or fungi) and share results by entering the data below.

Organism	Dilution Counted	CFU at that Dilution	CFU/g of Soil
Bacteria			
Actinomycetes			
Pigmented bacteria			
actinomycetes			
Molds			
Yeasts			

Gram reaction and morphology of selected colonies:

Colony Description	Morphology	Gram Reaction
1		
2		
3		
4		
5		
6		

QUESTIONS

True or False Statements: Circle the correct response.

T   F   1.   The medium used here for bacteria is nutrient agar.

T   F   2.   One of the ingredients of the fungal medium inhibiting bacterial growth is chlortetracycline.

T   F   3.   Fungal spores will also be counted on the RBA medium.

T   F   4.   Actinomycetes colonies on PCA appear just like other bacterial colonies.

T   F   5.   Yeast colonies on RBA are filamentous or rhizoid.

T   F   6.   If one makes a series of dilution blanks, using the same pipet to make all the plates is alright if you begin at the lowest dilution.

T   F   7.   1 g of soil added to a 99 ml dilution blank is a 10^{-2} dilution.

T   F   8.   Organic matter in the soil is important in determining what kinds of organisms will be found there.

T   F   9.   Looking at the procedure, you would expect the number of bacteria to be smaller than the number of fungi.

T   F   10.   Mixing the agar and sample from the dilution blank in the plate is not important.

63   Dehydrogenase Activity of Soils

OBJECTIVES

The student will be able to:

1. perform a test for dehydrogenase in a soil sample.

2. use a 2,3,5-triphenyl formazan standard curve.

3. describe the theory of the dehydrogenase test in a general way.

In studies of metabolic activity of soil (or water), some measure of the state of the organisms is necessary to determine whether they are dormant or metabolically active and to what degree. Microbial activity in soils has been measured using assays for a number of enzymes: dehydrogenase, urease, protease, amylase, sulfatase, and phosphatase among others. **Dehydrogenase** is an intracellular enzyme (or enzymes) found in most, if not all, bacteria involved in electron transfer and as such provides a general estimate of the activity of living organisms in soil. 2,3,5-triphenyl tetrazolium chloride (TTC) is a colorless or weakly colored compound which readily accepts two electrons and one proton from dehydrogenase reactions and is reduced to **2,3,5-triphenyl formazan (TPF)** (Figure 63-1), a highly colored compound with an absorption peak at 485 nm in methanol. If organisms are

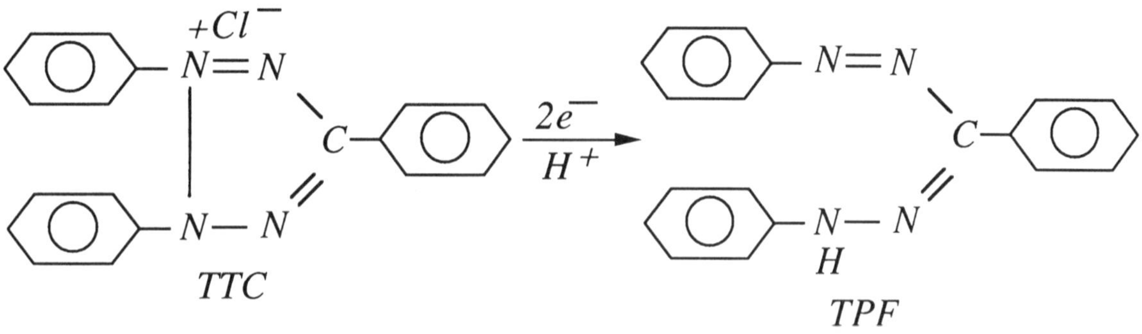

Figure 63-1. TTC Reactions

dormant, few electrons are being transferred and only small amounts of TPF will be formed. If organisms are actively metabolizing, then many electrons will be transferred and considerable TPF will result. By adding a metabolizable substrate, an activity "potential" can be determined. The amount of TPF formed is, therefore, an estimate of the activity of the enzyme in the organisms present.

MATERIALS (per pair)

1. Two soil samples, one of rich garden soil and one of low productivity

2. $CaCO_3$ (lime stone), powdered

3. 2,3,5-triphenyl tetrazolium chloride (TTC), 0.5% aqueous

4. 2,3,5-triphenyl formazan (TPF), 0.5% in methanol (for standard curve)

5. Glucose, 0.5% aqueous

6. 3 large 22 x 150 mm test tubes with rubber stoppers

7. Methanol

8. Water

9. Buchner funnels

10. Whatman No. 5 filter paper to fit the funnels

11. Spectrophotometer and cuvettes

12. 7 sterile 50 ml volumetric flasks

13. 2 sterile 1 ml pipets and safety bulb

14. 2 sterile 10 ml pipets

15. Spatula

PROCEDURE AND OBSERVATIONS (2 days)

I. Preparation

Period 1

1. Weigh out 20 g of the assigned soil and then add 0.2 g of powdered $CaCO_3$. Mix well and place in a large test tube.

2. Repeat step No. 1 twice more adding the mix to separate large test tubes each time.

3. Pipet 3 ml of the 0.5% solution of TTC to the soil in two of the three tubes. Label these 1 and 2. Label the third tube 3.

4. Add water to tubes 2 and 3 until the soil is saturated.

5. Add the 0.5% glucose solution to tube 1 until the soil is saturated.

6. Tamp the soil surface gently to reduce access of air first in tube 3, then tube 2, and finally tube 1. If done in this order, the rod does not need to be rinsed between tubes.

7. Incubate the three tubes at 28°C for 24 hours.

II. Standard TPF Curve (This may be done by the instructor.)

Period 1

8. Dilute the methanol-TPF solution by adding 0.5, 1.0, 3.0, and 6.0 ml to 50 ml volumetric flasks and making up to volume with methanol.

9. Transfer the contents of the flasks one at a time beginning with the lowest concentration to a cuvette and read on the spectrophotometer at 458 nm.

10. Record in the results section the absorbance (OD) for each concentration using methanol as the blank.

11. Using standard graph paper, plot the absorbance (X-axis) vs. the TPF concentration (Y-axis) and connect the points with a straight line. This will serve as a standard curve for determining the TPF concentration formed from the soils.

III. Analysis

Period 2

12. At the end of 24 hours, add 25 ml of methanol to each tube and stir the contents for about 5 minutes.

13. Place a Whatman No. 5 filter paper on a Buchner funnel and pour the slurry from one tube onto the paper. Apply a slight vacuum and draw the methanol through the filter. Before the meniscus of the methanol touches the soil, add an additional 10 ml of methanol. Repeat one more time with 10 ml of methanol. It is important not to let air be drawn through the soil.

14. The combined methanol extracts from a single tube are made to 50 ml in a volumetric flask with methanol. If necessary, the extract may be clarified by centrifugation before being made up to volume.

15. Measure the absorbance at 485 nm using methanol as the blank and record the resulting OD for each tube in the results section.

16. Using the standard TPF curve generated in Part II, convert the absorbance readings into TPF concentrations.

17. Finally, report the results in terms of moles of hydrogen transferred in 20 g of soil per 24 hours during reduction of TTC to TPF. Two electrons and one hydrogen are involved in the formation of one TPF molecule, thus the moles of TPF equals the moles of hydrogen transferred (atomic H).

THOUGHT QUESTIONS

1. What is a dehydrogenase?

2. Did the glucose added to one tube influence the results? Why?

3. Why is air excluded?

ACKNOWLEDGEMENT

We wish to thank Dr. John Skujins, Dept. of Biology, Utah State University for permission to use this exercise.

63. Dehydrogenase Activity of Soils

RESULTS AND OBSERVATIONS

TPF Standard Curve

Conc. TPF mg/l	Absorbance 458 nm
.005	_____
.01	_____
.03	_____
.06	_____

TPF Formation

Tube No.	Absorb.	Conc. mg/l	Moles TPF	Moles H/20 g
1				
2				
3				

QUESTIONS

Completion:

1. The general name of the enzymes demonstrated in this exercise is _____ .

2-3. These enzymes are involved in _____ transfer reactions resulting in a _____ end product.

4-5. The dye being reduced is called _____, while the end product is called _____ .

6-7. Two other enzymes studied in soil are _____ and _____ .

8. The standard curve is necessary in order to determine the _____ of TPF in the soil extract.

9-10. If 3 moles of TTC are reduced to TPF, how many moles of H are involved _____?
Moles of H_2 _____?

64 The Nitrogen Cycle

OBJECTIVES

The student will be able to:

1. outline the nitrogen cycle.

2. name at least one genus of bacteria involved in each step of the nitrogen cycle.

3. write the equations for the various steps of the nitrogen cycle.

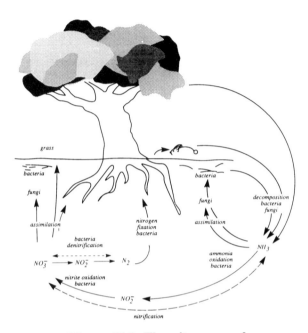

Figure 64-1. The nitrogen cycle

The nitrogen cycle (Figure 64-1) is an example of **biogeochemical cycling** carried out by bacteria. Nitrogen is an essential element in making biological material, chiefly proteins and nucleic acids, and as such requires continual restoration to a useable form. In reduced forms such as ammonia or amines, sufficient energy is available to allow some bacteria to live as **autotrophs** oxidizing the nitrogen of ammonia or nitrite to nitrite or nitrate, respectively. Certain aerobic organisms can utilize the nitrogen in nitrite or nitrate as an electron acceptor thus respiring in the absence of oxygen. The result of this **anaerobic respiration** is the production of nitrogen gas (dinitrogen). Some evolutionists suggest that much of our atmospheric dinitrogen has arisen from bacterial activity. Other prokaryotic organisms have evolved to **fix** dinitrogen from the atmosphere back into an organic form by reducing it to the level of ammonia again. Without this group of microbes, it is conceivable that all nitrogen would eventually become the gaseous form and life as we know it would cease.

There are five distinctive parts to the nitrogen cycle:

1. **Ammonification**—release of ammonia from organic matter;

2. **Nitrification I**—oxidation of ammonia to nitrite;

3. **Nitrification II**—oxidation of nitrite to nitrate;

4. **Denitrification**—reduction of nitrate (or nitrite) to dinitrogen; and,

5. **Dinitrogen fixation**—reduction of dinitrogen to ammonia (or amino acids).

This exercise is divided into 5 parts and the instructor may do any or all as seems appropriate. Work in pairs.

I. Ammonification (2-7 days)

The ability to release ammonia (ammonium ion) from protein is a property of a great many bacteria and fungi. Generally, the nitrogen in protein (or nucleic acids) is used by the growing decomposer organisms as is and is not released as ammonium unless the carbon to nitrogen ratio is heavily in favor of nitrogen (i.e., it is in excess of new cell needs). The strong ammonia odor around cattle feed lots is an example. This property of bacteria was first introduced in Exercise 38 and a specific example presented in Exercise 39. If an experiment is desired, please refer to one of these.

II. Nitrification I. Oxidation of ammonia to nitrite. (10-14 days)

Once released from organic material, ammonia is oxidized to nitrite by several genera of bacteria but chiefly members of the genus *Nitrosomonas*. The reaction is as follows:

$$NH_4^+ + 3/2O_2 \rightarrow NO_2^- + 2H^+ + H_2O \qquad -65.7 \text{ kcal} \qquad\qquad 1$$

The reaction yields very little energy and consequently growth of these organisms is slow with a mean generation time of about 0.32 days at an optimum temperature of 30°-35°C. There is also considerable substrate turnover and very low cell yield, about 1% that of heterotrophs on a suitable substrate. Note that one product is hydrogen ion causing the medium to become more acid.

II. MATERIALS (per pair)

1. 3 tubes of ammonium salts medium, sterile

2. Fertilized soil, preferably one fertilized with an ammonium salt

3. A pure culture of *Nitrosomonas*, if available

4. N, N dimethyl-1-naphthylamine (dimethyl-α-naphthylamine) reagent (NNDNA reagent)

5. Sulfanilic acid reagent

6. Powdered zinc

7. 3 sterile 1 ml pipets and safety bulb

II. PROCEDURE AND OBSERVATIONS (10-14 days)

Period 1

1. Inoculate one tube of ammonium salts broth with a loopful of soil, and a second with the pure culture of *Nitrosomonas*. The third tube serves as an uninoculated control. Label each tube.

2. Incubate all 3 tubes at 30°-35°C for 10-14 days or longer if at room temperature.

Period 2

3. Transfer about half of each broth tube to newly labeled ammonium salts broth tubes with sterile pipets.

4. Add 20 drops of sulfanilic acid reagent to each of these tubes and shake.

5. Add 20 drops of the NNDNA reagent and shake.

6. A deep red or maroon color indicates the presence of nitrite. If there is no red color in the soil tube, however, other organisms may have converted any nitrite formed to nitrate. To test for this, add a small amount of powdered zinc. If the color becomes red or maroon it means that the zinc has reduced nitrate to nitrite. This is interpreted that ammonium *was* oxidized to nitrite and *then* to nitrate showing the presence of *Nitrosomonas*. If no red color appears, there is no nitrate, hence there was no nitrite formed at all. Record results on the observation form.

7. Reincubate the original tubes if required.

III. Nitrification II. Oxidation of nitrite to nitrate (10-14 days)

Most nitrite oxidation is carried out by members of the genus *Nitrobacter*, however, others do occur. As with ammonia oxidation, the oxidation of nitrite to nitrate is a low energy yielding reaction, in fact about 3.5 times less. The reaction sequence is:

$$NO_2^- + \tfrac{1}{2}O_2 \rightarrow NO_3^- \qquad\qquad \text{-18.1 kcal} \qquad\qquad 2$$

The result is low cell yield for a very large substrate turnover. The generation time for *Nitrobacter* is about 1.5 days at an optimum temperature of 34°-35°C.

III. MATERIALS (per pair)

1. 3 tubes of nitrite salts medium

2. Same soil sample as for II above

3. A pure culture of *Nitrobacter*, if available

4. NNDNA reagent as II above

5. Sulfanilic acid reagent as II above

6. Powdered zinc as II above

7. 3 sterile 1 ml pipets and safety bulb

III. PROCEDURE AND OBSERVATIONS (10-14 days)

Period 1

1. Inoculate one tube with a loopful of soil and a second tube with the pure culture of *Nitrobacter*. The third serves as a control. Label all tubes.

2. Incubate all 3 tubes at 35°C for 10-14 days.

Period 2

3. Transfer about half of each tube to newly labeled tubes with sterile pipets.

4. Add 20 drops of sulfanilic acid reagent to each tube and shake.

5. Add 20 drops of NNDNA reagent to each tube and shake.

6. The control tube should show a red or maroon color due to the nitrite. The soil and pure culture tubes may show a weak pink or no color indicating the nitrite has been oxidized to nitrate. To further demonstrate this, add a small amount of powdered zinc to the soil and pure culture tubes. A red or maroon color will appear if nitrate is present, thus confirming the conclusion that the original nitrite in the tube was oxidized to nitrate.

7. Reincubate the original tubes if necessary.

IV. Denitrification. Reduction of nitrate (or nitrite) to dinitrogen (2 days)

The ability to reduce nitrate and nitrite to dinitrogen is found among many obligate aerobes. Generally such reduction does not occur unless the organisms are deprived of oxygen (i.e., anaerobic).

$$2NO_3^- + 12e^- + 12H^+ \rightarrow N_2 + 6H_2O \qquad\qquad 3$$

Organisms such as *Pseudomonas* and *Bacillus* are able to use the nitrogen atom of the molecule as an electron acceptor in the absence of gaseous oxygen. Nitrate is usually reduced first to nitrite, then to nitrous oxide, and lastly to dinitrogen. As demonstrated in Exercise 36, the dinitrogen can be trapped and easily observed. If an experiment is desired please refer to that exercise.

V. Dinitrogen fixation. (3-4 weeks)

Fixation of dinitrogen is brought about by many free-living and symbiotic prokaryotes. The most important ones in nature are the cyanobacteria with heterocysts (see Exercise 4), the genus *Azotobacter,* both free living, and the genus *Rhizobium*, symbiotic dinitrogen fixers associated with leguminous plants. Many other bacteria have been shown to fix dinitrogen under the proper conditions.

$$N_2 + 6e^- + 6H^+ \rightarrow 2NH_3 \qquad\qquad 4$$

Dinitrogen has the structure $N\equiv N$ and the first intermediate is $HN=NH$. A simple assay for the enzyme carrying this reaction out involves the use of acetylene $HC\equiv CH$ as a substrate with the production of ethylene $H_2C=CH_2$ which can be detected by gas chromatography. Apparently the enzyme for this step is not very specific. Two groups of dinitrogen fixers are presented here. Either or both may be studied.

V. MATERIALS (per pair)

1. 3 flasks of mannitol salts, nitrogen-free broth, sterile
2. 3 prepoured Petri plates of mannitol salts agar, sterile
3. Pure culture of *Azotobacter chroococcum*
4. Clover, alfalfa, lupine, or other legumes with nodules
5. Methylene blue stain
6. Soil sample, preferably one not recently fertilized. A corn field after harvest would be good.
7. Nessler's reagent for ammonium
8. Sulfanilic acid reagent
9. Powdered zinc
10. NNDNA reagant

V. PROCEDURE AND OBSERVATIONS (3–4 weeks)

Azotobacter

Period 1

1. Inoculate one flask with several loopfuls of soil, a second with the pure culture of *Azotobacter,* and the third as an uninoculated control.
2. Incubate the flasks at 30°C until growth appears on the surface.

Periods 2–10

3. Streak a mannitol salt agar plate from each flask showing growth and incubate these until colonies appear in approximately 1–2 weeks.
4. Place 3 or 4 ml of one flask into 3 test tubes. Test for ammonium, nitrite, and nitrate (Zn powder), respectively. Repeat for the other flasks. Record results in the observation form.

Periods 14–28

5. Make Gram stains of organisms from representative colonies.

   Note: From the soil plate, colonies may appear which are not *Azotobacter.* This is due to the fact that soil contains enough nutrient to allow some non-dinitrogen fixers to grow and produce enough nutrient to carry over onto the agar plates. Care should be taken in interpretation of these plates.

Rhizobium

Period 1

1. Examine the roots of the legumes provided for the presence of small nodules which contain the *Rhizobium* cells. Make a drawing of the root-nodule parts on the observation sheet.
2. Carefully clean any adhering soil off and cut out one nodule.

3. Place it in drop of water on a slide and slice it into very small pieces with a razor blade or scalpel.

4. Add a drop of methylene blue and put a coverslip over the preparation. Then place a double layer of paper towel, bibulous paper, or other tissue over the coverslip and press down with the thumb using uniform pressure to avoid breaking the coverslip. Squash the nodule slices as much as possible.

5. Observe under the high power objective of the microscope. Look for swollen, club-shaped, irregular bacteroids inside or between the root cells. Make drawings on the observation sheet.

THOUGHT QUESTIONS

1. What are the conditions necessary for the functioning of the nitrogenase enzyme?

2. The rhizosphere of certain plants contains dinitrogen fixers. What are some of these organisms? and plants?

3. Describe the *Azolla* symbiosis. What are the organisms involved? To what practical use is it put?

4. Write a brief scenario depicting

   a. the consequence of the disappearance from the earth of all nitrogen fixing prokaryotes;

   b. the death of all the nitrifying bacteria;

   c. if no ammonifying bacteria existed on earth.

Name _____ Date _____ Grade _____

64. The Nitrogen Cycle

RESULTS AND OBSERVATIONS

I. **Ammonification.** If Exercise 38 is done, complete this table, otherwise omit this part. Record as + or negative for ammonia.

Organism	Ammonia Production		
	2d	4d	7d
Control			
Pseudomonas aeruginosa			
Bacillus subtilis			
Soil sample			

II. **Nitrification I.** Ammonia broth. Record nitrite as + or −.

Organism	Nitrite Production	
	10d	__d
Control		
Soil sample		
Nitrobacter		

III. **Nitrification II.** Nitrite broth. Record as nitrite or nitrate + or −.

Organism	Nitrite		Nitrate	
	10d	__d	10d	__d
Control				
Soil sample				
Nitrobacter				

IV. Denitrification. If Exercise 37 is done as part of this exercise, use this form; otherwise omit.

Organism	Nitrite 2 d	Zinc Test	Conclusions
Control			
Soil sample			
Pseudomonas aeruginosa			
Bacillus subtilis			
Staphylococcus aureus			

V. Dinitrogen fixation. Record as + or – for each test.

Organism	Growth	Ammonium	Nitrite	Nitrate
Control				
Soil sample				
Azotobacter				

Colony morphology   Cell morphology and Gram stain

Sketch of plant roots with nodules

Sketch of bacteroids in nodules as observed under high power.

QUESTIONS

Completion:

1.   The nitrogen cycle is a specific example of _____ cycling.

2-6.   Name the organism carrying out each of the following and indicate whether it is an oxidation, a reduction or no change.

   2.   amino acid-NH_2 → ammonium   _____

   3.   ammonium → nitrite   _____

   4.   nitrite → nitrate   _____

   5.   nitrate → dinitrogen   _____

   6.   dinitrogen → ammonium   _____

7.   The ability of an aerobic organism to use inorganic compounds other than oxygen as an electron

   acceptor is called _____ .

8-9.   The conversion of ammonium to nitrate is called _____ ,

   while the conversion of nitrate to dinitrogen is called _____ .

10.   The incorporation of dinitrogen into amino acids is called _____ .

11-15.   Write the equations for each of the 5 steps of the nitrogen cycle.

16.   On the back of this page, diagram the nitrogen cycle.

65 Sulfur Oxidizers

OBJECTIVES

The student will be able to:

1. grow and isolate a culture of thiobacilli from soil.

2. recognize the colony morphology of thiobacilli on a selective medium.

3. write the equations for sulfur oxidation by thiobacilli.

Sulfur oxidizers are bacteria requiring sulfur in a reduced form as a source of energy (i.e., **sulfur autotrophs**). These bacteria are Gram-negative, obligate aerobes which oxidize H_2S, thiosulfate, sulfur, or other intermediate states of sulfur oxidation to sulfur or sulfate while fixing carbon dioxide.

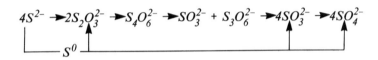

Figure 65-1. Sulfur oxidation

Morphologically they range from gliding filaments such as *Beggiatoa* to the rod shaped **thiobacilli**. These bacteria are of considerable interest for a number of reasons. The filaments often form slimy masses in waters with considerable H_2S at the anaerobic interface. Some of the thiobacilli convert H_2S to H_2SO_4 reducing the pH to as low as 0.1. These organisms grow at the expense of the sulfur in **iron pyrites** causing the environment to become very acid. Pyrites commonly occur in coal deposits and waters from coal mines are often sufficiently acid to kill fish and other forms of life in the receiving streams. The ability of these organisms to use the sulfur in various metallic sulfides is used industrially to release copper from CuS by a recycling process.

Two procedures are presented here—enrichment of thiobacilli from natural soils or water and a pure culture study. Either or both may be used.

MATERIALS (per pair)

I. Enrichment

1. Sample of soil, preferably one previously fertilized with sulfur

2. 2 flasks of thioparus broth, sterile

3. Shaker for the flasks

4. pH meter

5. 50 ml beakers for pH

6. 1 sterile 1 ml pipet and safety bulb

II. Isolation and/or pure culture study

1. Thioparus agar plates, sterile

2. Pure culture of *Thiobacillus thiooxidans*

3. Bromcresol purple indicator in dropper bottle

PROCEDURE AND OBSERVATIONS (5-15 days)

I. Enrichment

Period 1

1. Determine the pH of the broth using a small amount from an uninoculated flask. Discard this after determining the pH.

2. Inoculate one or more flasks of thioparus broth with 1 g each of soil (or sulfur waters).

3. Place the flasks on a shaker and incubate at 30°C in the dark for 4-5 days. Darkness prevents the growth of the photosynthetic sulfur oxidizers.

Period 2 (may be omitted)

4. Subculture 1 ml from each flask to a new flask and incubate for an additional 4-5 days.

II. Isolation or pure culture

Period 3

5. After 5 days incubation or when growth in thioparus broth is apparent, streak a loopful of broth for isolation on one or more thioparus agar plates. A pure culture of *T. thiooxidans* may be used instead and part I omitted altogether.

6. After subculturing, determine the pH of the broth culture.

7. Incubate the plates at 30°C until growth occurs (5-10 days). Plates may be placed in plastic baggies to prevent dehydration.

8. Colonies will be small, whitish and appearing granular.

Period 4

9. Make a wet mount for motility determination from one or two of the agar plate colonies.

10. Gram stain cells from the same colonies.

11. Finally, flood the plate with bromcresol purple indicator and observe for acid (yellow) halos around the colonies. The amount of acid formed may be very small and be barely noticeable.

THOUGHT QUESTIONS

1. Describe the industrial method used to extract copper from sulfide ores.

2. How do the anaerobic sulfur oxidizers grow?

65. Sulfur Oxidizers

RESULTS AND OBSERVATIONS

I. Broth, initial pH _____ final pH _____

Describe the appearance of the broth:

II. Colony description

Motility

Gram reaction

Morphology

Acid production

QUESTIONS

Completion:

1-2.   The genus of bacteria studied in this exercise is _____

which is Gram-_____.

3.   Acid mine waters result from the oxidation of the sulfur in _____.

4.   Thioparus broth uses _____ as the source of sulfur.

5.   Write the equation for H_2S oxidation to sulfate.

66   Hydrogen Sulfide Producers

OBJECTIVES

The student will be able to:

1. grow sulfate reducers in a selective medium.

2. recognize colonies of sulfate reducers on a selective medium.

3. write the equation for sulfate reduction.

4. name one genus of sulfate reducers.

Hydrogen sulfide can be produced from organic matter as was demonstrated in Exercise 33. Hydrogen sulfide can also be produced by a group of bacteria using **sulfate** as an **electron acceptor** in the absence of oxygen. The electron source is either organic matter or hydrogen depending on the organism involved. This use is not assimilation but is a means of disposing of metabolically generated electrons where the sulfate serves the same function as oxygen and is sometimes referred to as **sulfate respiration**.

$$4H_2 + SO_4^{2-} + 2H^+ \rightleftharpoons H_2S + 4H_2O \qquad\qquad 1$$

$$2CH_3CHOHCOOH + SO_4^{2-} + H_2 \rightleftharpoons 2CH_3COOH + 2CO_2 + 2H_2O + H_2S \qquad\qquad 2$$

$$CH_3COOH + SO_4^{2-} + 2H^+ \rightleftharpoons 2CO_2 + 2H_2O + H_2S \qquad\qquad 3$$

These organisms cannot respire using oxygen, however. If H_2S is produced in excess of precipitation reactions (notably with iron as black FeS) and solubility, then the gas escapes to the atmosphere giving the strong "rotten egg" odor associated with waterlogged soils, swamps, estuaries, or other areas of anaerobic activity. High sulfate and high organic matter predisposes to bacterial H_2S production. *Desulfovibrio* is a representative genus of this group.

MATERIALS (per pair)

1. 1 sterile 300 ml BOD bottle (insert string between stopper and neck to prevent breakage when autoclaving)

2. Black mud from stream, lake, estuary or other source

3. 1 flask of Starkey modified broth medium, sterile

4. 5 tubes Starkey modified agar medium, sterile

5. Vaspar sufficient for about 1 cm deep on each tube, about 25-30 ml

6. 5 sterile Pasteur pipets and bulb

7. 5 Petri plates, sterile

8. 5 sterile 1 ml pipets and safety bulb

PROCEDURE AND OBSERVATIONS (1-2 weeks)

Period 1

1. Add about one gram of black anaerobic lake, stream, or swamp mud to a sterile BOD bottle. Discard cap string.

2. Promptly fill with freshly prepared Starkey modified broth.

3. Place the cap in the bottle so that no air is entrapped. Then fill the rim with broth. Check the bottles daily and replace evaporated liquid from the rim with distilled water.

Fill bottle   *Place cap*   *Fill rim*

4. Incubate the bottles in the dark at 30°C until the contents turn black. This may take 1–2 weeks.

Period 2

5. When growth is plentiful as indicated by an intense black color, subculture 1 ml to a tube of melted, tempered Starkey modified agar and mix well by rolling rapidly between the hands (or use a vortex mixer).

6. With a new sterile pipet, subculture 1 ml of that tube to another tube, discard the pipet and mix well as before.

7. Repeat step No. 6 three more times for a total of 5 tubes.

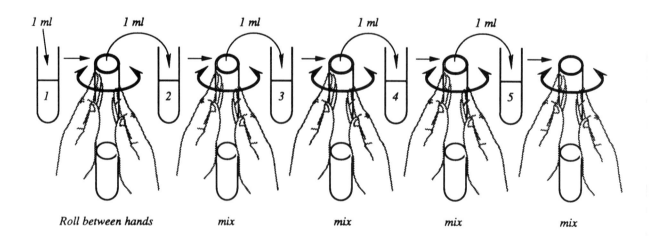

Roll between hands   *mix*   *mix*   *mix*   *mix*

8. Let the tubes solidify and overlay each with vaspar to about 1 cm depth.

9. Incubate at 30°C in the dark until black colonies appear. Continue incubation for a few days after the lower dilutions turn black.

10. Using the tube at the highest dilution showing black colonies, insert a Pasteur pipette along the glass wall to the bottom of the tube and apply air pressure. Blow the agar into a Petri plate.

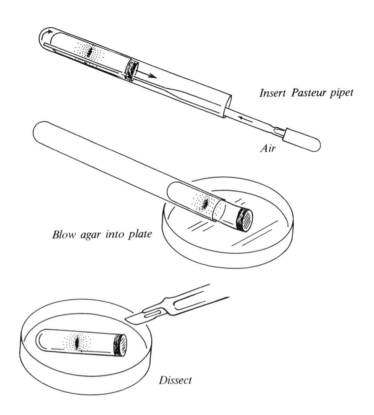

Insert Pasteur pipet

Air

Blow agar into plate

Dissect

11. Dissect the agar in such a way as to find the colony (or colonies) producing the blackening. Smear a colony on a glass slide and Gram stain the cells.

THOUGHT QUESTIONS

1. Could you design a quantitative method for counting the numbers of these organisms in soil?

2. What are the conditions necessary for the growth of these organisms?

3. Describe a habitat involving these organisms *and* the sulfur oxidizers.

Name _____ Date _____ Grade _____

66. Hydrogen Sulfide Producers

RESULTS AND OBSERVATIONS

Draw the appearance of the bottle.

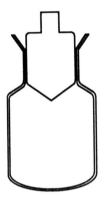

Describe the appearance of the bottle in words. Include a comment on its odor (do not open until ready to subculture). Give an explanation for the odor, or lack of it.

Make drawings of the tubes after blackening appears.

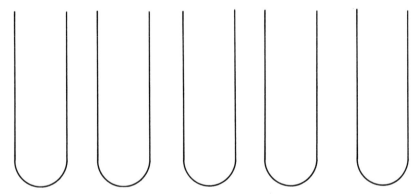

Write a description of the tubes' appearance.

Describe the morphology and Gram reaction of the organisms.

QUESTIONS

Completion:

1. _____ is one of the genera in this group.

2-3.   The electron acceptor for these organisms is _____

and the resulting product is _____ .

4.   The black material you observe in the bottle and the tubes is _____ .

5-6.   Name two environmental requirements for an abundance of the these organisms to occur.

5. _____

6. _____

7.   Write an equation for the conversion of sulfate to sulfide.

Aquatic Microbiology

Water covers 70% of the earth's surface and most of that is sea water with a salinity of about 35 g 0/00 chiefly NaCl. Although fresh water is a relatively small part of the total water volume, it is important to humans out of proportion to its size because of its use for drinking water, and for agricultural and industrial uses. All of the processes carried out by soil microbes as discussed in Unit XI, are also found in the aquatic environment whether fresh or marine, including all of the biogeochemical cycles. The exercises presented in Unit XII are intended to show some of the additional aspects of these processes as well as the very important bacterial tests for the health quality of drinking water.

Water as a habitat for microbes varies directly with the amount of organic matter. Under eutrophic (high organic matter) conditions, there are large numbers of bacteria; while under oligotrophic (low organic matter) conditions there are few bacteria. Within the water, whether it be a lake, stream, or the ocean, most microbes are attached to surfaces such as rocks, the bottom etc., or within the sediments. Bacteria in the water column are usually few in number in oligotrophic conditions but much higher in eutrophic conditions.

67 Microbial Counts of Water

OBJECTIVES

The student will be able to:

1. prepare a dilution of water for plating.

2. explain the reason for the "standard plate count."

3. explain why surface plating should result in more bacterial colonies than the standard plate count.

4. count the plates prepared in the two methods and explain the differences.

A wide variety of bacteria are found in water as in soil. The **sediment** organisms are very "soil-like" being mostly **Gram-positive** and **non-pigmented**. Bacteria in the **water column** and on **surfaces**, however, are primarily **Gram-negative** and usually **chromogenic** (pigmented). Many of the bacteria in water, especially in oligotrophic conditions, are **psychrophiles** or **psychrotrophs** which do not grow at temperatures above 20°–25°C and are actively killed by exposure to the temperature of tempered agar media. These bacteria are best counted by using a **surface plating technique** with incubation at 20°C. Public health researchers have recognized that organisms in water able to grow at 35°C (usually non-pigmented) suggest pollution of the water by animal feces, especially if in high numbers. A technique for measuring this group of organisms is presented here as well as the surface plating technique. The plate count at 35°C, otherwise known as the **"Standard Plate Count Technique,"** is not unequivocal since some of these organisms occur naturally in water and sediments, although usually in low numbers. Fungi also occur in water, especially in shallow water sediments. Many (e.g., *Saprolegnia*) are specialized for this habitat. Exercise 7 presents some techniques used in isolating these aquatic fungi. Of course algae, protozoa, and higher animals also occur in water.

This exercise is designed to be performed in pairs, one person doing the surface plate technique and the other the standard plate count technique.

MATERIALS (per pair)

A. Surface Plate Technique

   1. 5 prepoured Petri plates of plate count agar (PCA), sterile

   2. 1 sterile 99 ml dilution blank, 0.1% peptone water

   3. 3 sterile 9 ml dilution blanks, 0.1% peptone water in screw capped tubes

   4. 1 sterile 10 ml pipet and safety bulb

   5. 4 sterile 1 ml pipets

   6. 1 bent glass spreading rod (glass rod bent to hockey stick shape)

   7. Water sample

B. Standard Plate Count

   1. 5 Petri plates, sterile

   2. 1 flask of plate count agar, sterile

   3. 1 sterile 1 ml pipet and safety bulb

PROCEDURE AND OBSERVATIONS (7 days)

A. Surface Plate Technique

   Period 1

   1. Label the 5 prepoured PCA plates 10^{-1} to 10^{-5}.

   2. Pipet 11 ml of water sample into the 99 ml dilution blank. Label it 10^{-1}.

   3. Using a new sterile pipet each time, transfer 1 ml from the 99 ml blank to one 9 ml blank (10^{-2}), then 1 ml of that to another 9 ml blank (10^{-3}), and again 1 ml of that to a 9 ml blank (10^{-4}). Discard each pipet as used. This dilution series will be used for Part B as well.

4. Beginning with the highest dilution, pipet 0.1 ml from the 10^{-4} blank on to the surface of the 10^{-5} plate. The partner should dip the glass spreading rod in alcohol and flame. Spread the drop on the plate by rotating the plate under the stick or the stick around on the plate until the drop is evenly distributed. Then pipet 0.1 ml of the 10^{-3} blank onto the surface of the 10^{-4} plate and spread immediately. The glass spreading rod does not need to be sterilized between plates if done in this manner. Continue on to the lowest dilution with the same pipet and hockey stick.

5. Before inverting the plates, set them aside for about 1/2 hour so the spread drops can be absorbed.

6. Incubate the plates at 20°C for 5 days to 1 week.

Periods 2-3

7. Count all colonies according to the rules in Exercise 23 and enter the total in the table on the results form.

8. Count chromogenic (pigmented) colonies — yellow, red, green, blue and whether the pigment is diffusible or restricted to the colony. *Note:* Bright green colonies are often eukaryotic algae.

9. Place the plate, cover off, under a long-wave ultraviolet lamp (Mineral Lamp) and count all colonies which fluoresce, if any. Record this result in the observation table.

B. Standard Pour Plate

Period 1

1. Label 5 Petri plates 10^0 to 10^{-4}.

2. Using the same dilution blanks prepared for Part A, pipet 1 ml of the highest dilution into the 10^{-4} plate, and with the same pipet, 1 ml of the 10^{-3} dilution into the 10^{-3} plate. Continue in like manner through the dilutions. Finally pipet 1 ml of the original water sample into the 10^0 plate and discard the pipet.

3. Pour about 20 ml of PCA into each plate and mix as instructed in Exercise 23.

4. Incubate these plates at 35°C for 48 hours.

Period 2

5. Count the plates according to the rules for plate counting found in Exercise 23. Don't forget to include the lens shaped subsurface colonies.

6. Record the total counts in the observation table.

7. Count chromogens — yellow, red, colorless colonies, etc. and record these in the table.

THOUGHT QUESTIONS

1. What function do the pigments of aquatic bacteria serve?

2. How would you grow cyanobacteria from a water sample?

3. How does eutrophication of a water system relate to Exercise 70?

67. Microbial Counts of Water

RESULTS AND OBSERVATIONS

Bacterial Group	Dilution Counted	Total Bacteria per ml	
		20°C	35°C
Total			
Chromogens fluorescent			
yellow			
red			
other			
Comments			

Comment on the differences between the 20°C and 35°C plates.

Considering the Public Health Standard Plate Count limit of <500 per ml for drinking water and swimming pool water (remember, these are chlorinated) what does your result suggest?

QUESTIONS

Completion:

1. A colony of bacteria which is pigmented (e.g., sky blue) is said to be _____ .

2-3. Bacteria from the plankton (water column) are usually Gram-_____ and _____ ; whereas, those in the sediments are more often Gram-_____ and _____ .

4-5. Many bacteria in fresh water and perhaps most in sea water grow at temperatures below 20°C and would be called _____ or _____ .

6. Most bacteria in water are found on _____ .

68
Water Quality Analysis: MPN Technique

OBJECTIVES

The student will be able to:

1. perform the MPN coliform test.

2. name the three steps in the MPN coliform test.

3. describe the media used in each step of the test.

4. describe a positive test for each step of the test.

5. define the term *fecal coliforms*.

6. calculate an MPN from a seven tube, three dilution table.

7. recognize coliform growth and characteristic colonies.

Water can be analyzed for disease potential by performing the **MPN** (most probable number) test or the membrane filter test. These are quantitative bacteriological tests for a group of bacteria called **coliforms** which occur in large numbers in the intestinal tract of man and animals. While not normally pathogens themselves, they do indicate the presence of sewage and thereby pathogens, because they come from the same site in the body. Almost any human and many animal intestinal pathogens, bacteria, viruses, and parasites, can be transmitted through water, often leading to large epidemics. The coliform group includes *Escherichia coli, Enterobacter aerogenes*, and a number of closely related species, all having the ability to ferment lactose with gas production.

The MPN test for coliforms consists of three steps: a presumptive test, a confirmed test and a completed test (Figure 68-1). It attempts to determine the numbers of organisms in the water which are Gram-negative and ferment the carbohydrate lactose with the production of gas at 35°C. They must be facultative anaerobes and nonsporeformers.

The first step is the **presumptive** test. A set of tubes of lauryl sulfate tryptose lactose (LST) broth is inoculated with samples of water and incubated. Lauryl sulfate is a surface active detergent which inhibits the growth of Gram-positive organisms while encouraging the growth of coliforms. Coliforms use up any oxygen present in the broth and then ferment the lactose producing acid and gas under anaerobic conditions. Gas formation in 24 or 48 hours is a positive test.

Positive tubes from the presumptive test are subcultured into brilliant green lactose bile (BGLB) broth to provide the **confirmed** test. BGLB broth, in addition to containing lactose, also contains two components inhibitory to Gram-positive bacteria. Brilliant green is a dye related to crystal violet and belongs to the triphenylmethane dye series. Ox bile is a surface active agent which also inhibits the growth of Gram-positive bacteria. Gas formation in 24 or 48 hours "confirms" the results of the presumptive step. The number of coliforms per 100 ml of water is then calculated from the distribution of positive and negative tubes in the test by referring to an appropriate table (Table 68-1). Results are reported as coliform MPN per 100 ml of water.

In some cases the organisms must be isolated and stained to provide the **completed** test. Positive BGLB tubes are streaked on eosin-methylene blue (EMB) agar. The two dyes, eosin and methylene blue, also inhibit the growth of Gram-positive organisms. Typical colonies (Table 68-2) are isolated on nutrient agar slants and inoculated into LST broth. If gas is now formed in 24 or 48 hours, a Gram stain is made from the growth on the slant. If the cells are Gram-negative and there is no indication of spores, the completed test is considered to be positive. Further biochemical studies (IMViC) may be performed on isolated cultures.

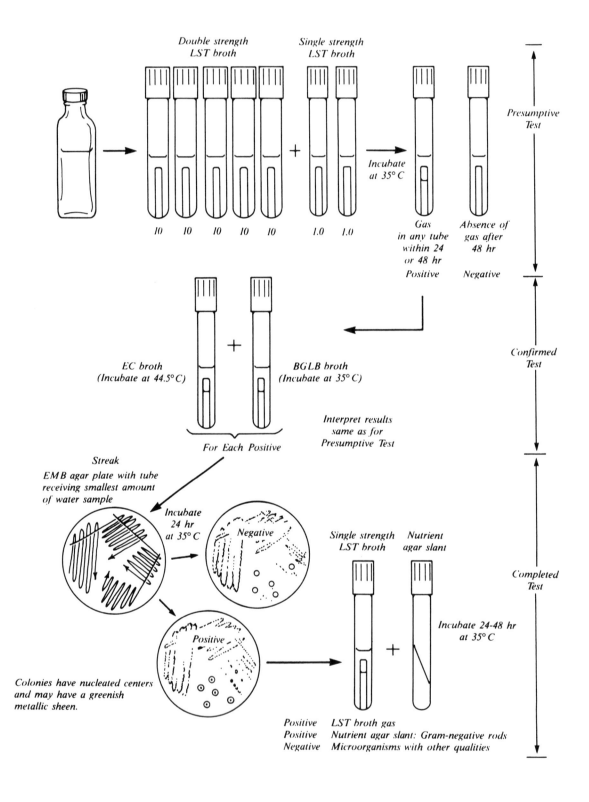

Double strength
LST broth

Single strength
LST broth

10   10   10   10   10   1.0   1.0

Incubate
at 35° C

Gas
in any tube
within 24
or 48 hr

Positive

Absence of
gas after
48 hr

Negative

*Presumptive
Test*

EC broth
(Incubate at 44.5° C)

BGLB broth
(Incubate at 35° C)

For Each Positive

Interpret results
same as for
Presumptive Test

*Confirmed
Test*

Streak

EMB agar plate with tube
receiving smallest amount
of water sample

Incubate
24 hr
at 35° C

Negative

Positive

Colonies have nucleated centers
and may have a greenish
metallic sheen.

Single strength
LST broth

Nutrient
agar slant

Incubate 24-48 hr
at 35° C

Positive   LST broth gas
Positive   Nutrient agar slant: Gram-negative rods
Negative   Microorganisms with other qualities

*Completed
Test*

Figure 68-1. Outline of steps in the MPN coliform test

All three tests are necessary to prove that an organism in a water sample is in truth a coliform. In actual practice, when it has been shown that the presumptive and confirmed tests give essentially the same results, then the completed step is generally not done because of the time it takes.

A modification of the confirmed test allows enumeration of fecal coliforms (*Escherichia coli* Type I). These particular strains are closely associated with the human intestinal tract. Positive presumptive tubes are subcultured into EC broth in addition to the BGLB broth and incubated in a 44.5°C water bath. EC medium contains bile and lactose. The bile inhibits Gram-positive bacteria while the high temperature selects only those organisms able to grow at this temperature. Gas in 24 hours is a positive test for fecal coliforms.

The official MPN method calls for 5 tubes at each of three dilutions for greater accuracy. However, in this exercise five tubes at the lowest dilution (largest sample volume) plus one tube at two others is used to conserve equipment.

Coliform organisms in **treated** water, and many others also, are generally determined now by the membrane filter method which is quicker and employs a much larger volume of water. The MPN method still is the method of choice when water is turbid or contains many bacteria or algae and is used also with foods.

This exercise will introduce the student to one of the most widely used methods of coliform determination in natural waters. The purpose of the membrane filter method is the same although the technique differs.

MATERIALS (per pair)

1. 1 empty sterile dilution blank. Collect 100 ml of a water sample from any stream, lake, pool, gutter, or other source. Samples should be collected on the day of the lab, or, if it is necessary, on the day before and refrigerated until used. Do not use drinking water.

2. 5 tubes double strength LST broth, sterile

3. 3 tubes single strength LST broth, sterile

4. 7 tubes BGLB broth, sterile

5. 7 tubes EC broth, sterile

6. 1 EMB agar plate, sterile

7. 1 nutrient agar slant, sterile

8. 1 sterile 10 ml pipet and safety bulb

9. 1 sterile 1 ml pipet

PROCEDURE AND OBSERVATIONS (6 days) See Figure 68-2 for daily schedule.

A. Presumptive Test

Period 1

1. Shake the water sample 25 times in a one foot arc in 7 seconds.

2. Pipet 10 ml into each of the 5 double strength LST broth tubes.

3. Pipet 1 ml into one of the single strength LST broth tubes and 0.1 ml into the second single strength LST broth tube.

4. Incubate the tubes at 35°C.

Period 2

5. At the end of 24 hours, agitate each tube vigorously to release any gas dissolved in the medium. The presence of any gas is a positive presumptive test. Record your results in the table provided. Negative tubes must be reincubated for an additional 24 hours.

B. Confirmed Test and Fecal Coliforms

Periods 2–3

1. For each LST broth tube that shows gas at 24 or 48 hours, transfer one loopful of growth to BGLB broth and a second loopful to EC broth.

2. Incubate the BGLB broth tubes at 35°C and the EC broth tubes in a thermostatically controlled water bath at 44.5°C.

3. The EC broth tubes are read at 24 hours. Gas is a positive test. Record your results in the table provided.

Periods 4–5

4. Read the BGLB broth tubes at 24 and 48 hours. Gas is a positive test. Record your results in the table provided. Save one or more positive tubes for Part C.

5. Determine the MPN for total coliforms using the distribution of positive and negative tubes in the confirmed test and the MPN table (Table 68-1) provided.

6. Determine the MPN for fecal coliforms using the distribution of positive and negative tubes in the fecal coliforms test and the MPN table (Table 68-1) provided.

C. Completed Test

Period 5

1. In practice, this step would be done for *each* positive BGLB tube. Only one tube will be used here.

2. Streak one positive (gas) BGLB tube (or EC tube) for isolation on an EMB agar plate. Incubate at 35°C for 24 hours.

3. A typical isolated colony (see Table 68-2 for description) is selected and inoculated into one tube of single strength LST broth and streaked on one nutrient agar slant. These are incubated at 35°C and observed at 24 and 48 hours.

Periods 6–7

4. If no gas appears in 48 hours, the test is negative.

If gas appears in the LST both tube insert, a Gram stain is made of the nutrient agar slant culture. If cells are Gram-negative and no spores are present, the completed test is positive for that tube.

If spores are present, the culture must be re-isolated on EMB and proceed again as in step No. 3.

5. Record your results in the table provided.

D. IMViC Reactions (Optional)

1. If desired, some idea of the species of coliforms may be gained by applying the IMViC tests to the nutrient agar slant culture.

2. At least two more re-isolations on EMB should be done to insure purity before proceeding.

3. Refer to Exercise 23 for procedures of these tests.

THOUGHT QUESTIONS

1. Does the presence of coliforms in water always mean a health hazard? Distinguish between raw water and treated water.

2. Can there be health hazard from water if coliforms are absent? Why?

3. Discuss the difference between fecal coliforms and total coliforms. Where does each group originate?

Table 68-1. MPN Index and 95 percent confidence limits

NUMBER OF TUBES SHOWING A POSITIVE REACTION OUT OF				95 PERCENT CONFIDENCE LIMITS	
5 of 10 ml each	1 of 1 ml each	1 of 0.1 ml each	MPN INDEX per 100 ml	Lower	Upper
0	0	0	<2	0	5.9
*0	0	1	2		
0	1	0	2	.05	13
*0	1	1	4		
1	0	0	2.2	.05	13
*1	0	1	4.4		
1	1	0	4.4	.52	14
*1	1	1	6.7		
2	0	0	5	.54	19
*2	0	1	7.5		
2	1	0	7.6	1.5	19
*2	1	1	10		
3	0	0	8.8	1.6	29
*3	0	1	12		
3	1	0	12	3.1	30
*3	1	1	12		
4	0	0	15	3.3	46
4	0	1	20	5.9	48
4	1	0	21	6.0	53
*4	1	1	27		
5	0	0	38	6.4	330
5	0	1	96	12	370
5	1	0	240	12	370
5	1	0	240	12	3700
5	1	1	>240		

* These tube combinations are unlikely. If they occur in more than 1% of the tests, it indicates faulty technique or other problem.

Source: *Standard Methods for the Examination of Water and Wastewater*, 13th ed., New York: The American Public Health Association, 1971.

Table 68-2. Differentiation of coliforms on EMB agar

	Escherichia coli	*Enterobacter aerogenes*
SIZE	Well-isolated colonies are 2-3 mm in diameter.	Well-isolated colonies are larger than *Escherichia coli*; usually 4-6 mm in diameter or more.
CONFLUENCE	Neighboring colonies show little tendency to run together.	Neighboring colonies run together quickly.
ELEVATION	Colonies slightly raised; surface flat or slightly concave, rarely convex.	Colonies considerably raised and markedly convex; occasionally the center drops precipitately.
APPEARANCE BY TRANSMITTED LIGHT	Dark, almost black centers which extend more than 3/4 across the diameter of the colony; internal structure of central dark portion difficult to discern.	Centers deep brown; not as dark as *Escherichia coli* and smaller in proportion to the rest of the colony. Striated internal structure often observed in young colonies.
APPEARANCE BY REFLECTED LIGHT	Colonies dark, button-like, often concentrically ringed with a greenish metallic sheen.	Much lighter than *Escherichia coli*, metallic sheen not observed except occasionally in depressed center when such is present.

Source: Reprinted with permission from Bacteria Fermenting Lactose and Their Significance in Water Analysis by Max Levine. *Iowa State College of Agriculture and Mechanic Arts Official Publication. Vol. 20, No. 31, Bulletin 62, 1921.*

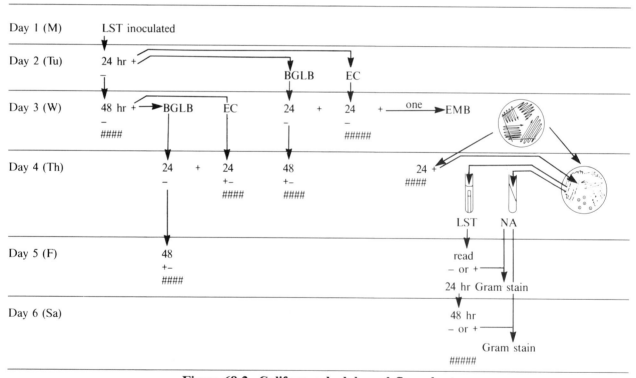

Figure 68-2. Coliform schedule and flow chart

Name _____ Date _____ Grade _____

68. Water Quality Analysis: MPN Technique

RESULTS AND OBSERVATIONS

Water Sample _____

Test	Sample Volume (ml)							MPN
	10	10	10	10	10	1.0	0.1	
Presumptive LST broth	/	/	/	/	/	/	/	XXX
Confirmed BGLB broth	/	/	/	/	/	/	/	
Fecal Coliforms EC broth								
Completed LST broth								
Gram stain								

+ = Gas
− = No Gas
/ = 24 and 48 hr observations

QUESTIONS

A. **True or False Statements:** Circle the correct response.

    T   F   1.   MPN means most probable numbers of bacteria per milliliter.

    T   F   2.   A positive presumptive test consists of acid production only.

    T   F   3.   EC broth is used to detect fecal coliforms.

    T   F   4.   Coliforms are normally considered to be pathogens.

    T   F   5.   Drinking water is examined for the presence of coliform organisms mainly because they are normal intestinal inhabitants.

T F 6. The completed step of the MPN test is always performed to determine the bacteriological content of drinking water.

T F 7. BGLB broth is used in the coliform presumptive test.

T F 8. The membrane filter method can be used to analyze drinking water.

T F 9. Incubation temperature is not critical in performing the MPN or membrane filter tests.

T F 10. The Gram stain is a necessary part of the completed test.

B. Completion:

11–14. List 4 diseases which are water-borne.

11. _____   13. _____

12. _____   14. _____

15. Why use coliforms instead of directly isolating pathogens from water?

_____

16. The water analysis test is designed to detect the presence of _____ .

17–21. What is the definition of a coliform? _____

_____

22–24. List the 3 steps, in order, of the MPN test.

22. _____

23. _____

24. _____

25. _____ agar is used to isolate typical coliforms for further study.

26–30. List 5 chemical agents used in the MPN test that inhibit the growth of Gram-positive organisms while encouraging the growth of coliforms.

26. _____   29. _____

27. _____   30. _____

28. _____

31–32. Name the two most prominent species of coliforms

_____

_____

33. To what bacterial family do the coliforms belong? _____

69 Water Quality Analysis: Membrane Filter Technique

OBJECTIVES

The student will be able to:

1. perform the membrane filter technique for coliforms and fecal coliforms.

2. name the selective media used for these two groups of coliforms.

3. recognize the appearance of coliform colonies on the two media.

4. name two species of the coliform group.

The **membrane filter** technique for coliforms (see Exercise 68 for further discussion of coliforms) is widely used in public health analysis of water quality because of the ease of performance and the speed of obtaining results. A water sample is drawn through a membrane filter with pores of $0.45\,\mu$m diameter. The filter is then transferred to the surface of an agar medium or a blotter pad soaked with a liquid medium and incubated at 35°C for total coliforms or 44.5°C for fecal coliforms. Typical colonies are then counted at 24 hours, a marked saving in time over the MPN method. Unfortunately, in contrast to the MPN method, the membrane filter method cannot be used on all types of water samples. Water high in turbidity, silt or even bacteria often clog the filter as do heavy blooms of algae. A heavy coat of algae or bacteria on the filter surface can suppress coliform growth or alter the typical coliform colony morphology. Stressed coliforms (e.g., in chlorinated sewage effluent) do not grow well on many of these media and the MPN method is usually required on these waters.

MATERIALS (per pair)

1. 6 sterile 50 × 12 mm Petri plates with tight cover

2. 6 sterile 47 mm diameter membrane filters with pads

3. 1 nonsterile 1-liter filter flask

4. 1 filter unit, graduated, with top, sterile

5. 6 ml mEndo broth-MF, sterile

6. 6 ml lactose agar, sterile

7. 15 ml mFC agar, sterile

8. 1 sterile 10 ml pipet and safety bulb

9. 1 flask with 200 ml distilled water, sterile

10. 250 ml water sample supplied by instructor or collected by student in a sterile empty Mason jar from almost any source except tap water

PROCEDURE (2 days)

Period 1

1. Flame a pair of forceps and place a sterile blotter pad from the sterile filter-pack in the bottoms of 3 of the special Petri plates (Figure 69-1).

2. Pipet 2 ml of mEndo broth-MF onto each pad and replace covers (Figure 69-2).

3. Pipet 5 ml of melted mFC agar into the bottoms of each of 3 of the Petri plates and let solidify.

4. Then pipet 2 ml of melted lactose agar onto the surface of the mFC agar and let solidify. Once the lactose agar is added, the plates should be used within 1 hour.

5. Assemble the filter funnel on the flask as illustrated in Figure 69-3.

6. Unscrew the funnel top and with an alcohol-flamed forceps, place a sterile membrane filter in place with the grid side up and center it (Figure 69-3). *Note:* The forceps *must be cool* before attempting to pick up a filter. Screw on the funnel top being careful not to screw it down too tightly since this will tear the filter.

7. Carefully pour about 50 ml of sterile distilled water on top of the filter (Figure 69-4). Then pipet 1 ml of the water sample into the funnel. Return the pipet to the water sample and let it stand there.

8. Apply the vacuum gently. Just as the liquid level approaches the filter, rinse the sides with a small amount of the sterile distilled water, and let the vacuum draw all of the water through the filter.

9. Unscrew the funnel top with the vacuum still applied. With a sterile forceps, remove the filter (Figure 69-5) and carefully "roll" onto the pad of mEndo broth-MF (Figure 69-6). Avoid trapping bubbles of air. Label the plate 1 ml.

10. Repeat steps No. 7, 8, and 9 finally transferring the filter to one of the mFC plates labeled 1 ml.

11. Repeat steps No. 7, 8, and 9, this time using 10 ml of water sample instead of 1 ml. Label this plate 10 ml.

12. Repeat steps No. 7, 8, and 9 one more time for the mFC plate. Label this 10 ml.

13. Now place a filter on the funnel block and screw the funnel down gently. Pour the water sample into the funnel (no vacuum) until the meniscus is at the 50 ml mark.

14. Apply the vacuum and rinse the sides with sterile distilled water until the water is drawn through.

15. Remove the funnel and transfer the filter to the last mEndo broth-MF plate. Label it 50 ml.

16. Repeat steps No. 13, 14, and 15, transferring the filter to the last mFC plate labeled 50 ml.

17. Incubate the mEndo broth-MF plates at 35°C with the *cover up* for 24 hours.

18. Incubate mFC plates at 35°C for *2 hours, cover down.* Then transfer the plates to 44.5°C for 22 hour. The plates can be inverted (bottom up) and immersed in a thermostatically controlled water bath.

Figure 69-1

Figure 69-2

Figure 69-3

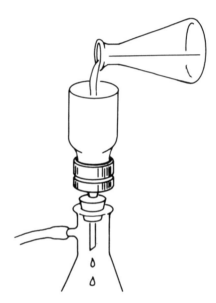

Figure 69-4

Figure 69-5

Figure 69-6

OBSERVATIONS

Period 2

19. Examine the mEndo broth-MF plates using a low power (10–15X magnification) dissection microscope. Coliform colonies are red or pink showing a bright golden-red metallic sheen. Colonies without the golden sheen are non-coliforms. Count the coliform colonies and record the results in the form provided.

20. Examine the mFC plates in the same fashion. Fecal coliform colonies are blue regardless of shade. All others are not coliforms. Count and record in the results form.

21. Note that coliform results are usually reported per 100 ml rather than per ml.

THOUGHT QUESTIONS

1. What other microbial measures of water polution can be used?

2. How is drinking water processed for safety?

3. Do coliforms, even fecal coliforms, always mean fecal pollution? Why?

4. What are some of the limitations of the membrane filter method?

Name _____ Date _____ Grade _____

69. Water Quality Analysis: Membrane Filter Technique

RESULTS AND OBSERVATIONS

Class data will be collated on the chalkboard in a table similar to that below. Put your data on the first line of the table below and then on the chalkboard. When all the data is collated, then complete the table below. Record colonies counted in the appropriate column. If < 20 or > 200, cross it out and do not use the count on that plate. The count per 100 ml is calculated as follows:

$$\text{count}/100 \text{ ml} = \frac{\text{count on the filter}}{\text{ml filtered}} \times 100$$

If more than one plate has between 20 and 200, calculate the count per 100 ml for each and average. If no plates are in the range 20–200, use the one nearest to it.

Coliform Counts

Sample Source	TC Count ml			Total Coliform Count per 100 ml	FC Count ml			Fecal Coliform Count per 100 ml
	1	10	50		1	10	50	
1								
2								
3								
4								
5								
6								
7								
8								
9								
10								

TC = Total Coliform
FC = Fecal Coliform

QUESTIONS

A. **True or False Statements:** Circle the correct response.

    T   F   1.   Colonies of fecal coliforms on mFC medium are red.

    T   F   2.   A golden sheen is characteristic of coliforms on mEndo broth-MF medium.

    T   F   3.   The membrane filter used for the coliform test has a pore size of 0.45 μm diameter.

    T   F   4.   Coliforms surviving chlorination are best detected by the membrane filter technique.

    T   F   5.   mFC medium contains ox-bile.

B. **Completion:**

6-7.   The name of the medium used for the total coliform membrane filter count is

        _____ and that for the fecal coliform count is _____.

8-9.   Name two prominent genus-species of the coliforms (do *not* abbreviate).

    8. _____

    9. _____

10-11.   The membrane filter technique gives a result in _____ hours while the MPN method

    takes a minimum (through the confirmed test) of _____ hours.

12.   _____ may interfere with this technique by clogging the filter.

13-14.   The incubation temperature for fecal coliforms is _____$°$C and for total coliforms

    is _____$°$C.

70 Methane (Biogas) Production

OBJECTIVES

The student will be able to:

1. establish a small methane generator.

2. determine the relative amount of methane in the gas phase above the generator.

3. write the formula for the origin of methane.

4. name the group of bacteria to which the methanogens belong.

5. name one genus and species of the methanogens.

The **archaebacteria** are an ancient line of prokaryotes whose modern representatives inhabit extreme environments — high temperature, saturated salt (see Exercise 44), acid, or highly anaerobic conditions. The archaebacteria differ from the eubacteria in a number of features, one of the most prominent being the lack of peptidoglycan (murein) in the cell wall. The wall of these organisms contains either pseudomurein or protein alone. One specialized group of these bacteria produces **methane** gas under extremely anaerobic conditions from CO_2 and H_2. Most species use formate and a few can also use methanol, methylamines, and acetate either to form methane or as a source of carbon. An example is *Methanosarcina formicum*, forming methane according to the following equations:

$$4H_2 + H^+ + HCO_3^- \rightarrow CH_4 + 3H_2O \qquad\qquad 1$$
$$H_2O + H^+ + 4HCOO^- \rightarrow CH_4 + 3HCO_3^- \qquad\qquad 2$$

Methanogens are found wherever there is a high organic matter load and conditions are anaerobic. The best known habitats are the rumen (and the intestinal tract of warm-blooded animals including man), sediments of lakes and marine environments, and anaerobic digestors in sewage treatment. As a group, they are being investigated commercially for the production of methane from waste organic matter (biogas) and for use on farms to supply part of the farm fuel requirements. A farmer with 100 dairy cattle can produce 39,600 m^3 (1.4 x 10^6 ft^3) of methane annually which is equal to 20,300 liters (5,365 gal) of fuel oil. It can thus be a significant source of energy. Research is also being done on biogas from municipal garbage, sewage sludge, and farm crops.

Methane formation from biomass proceeds first with the hydrolysis of polymers to monomers by a mixed group of bacteria. Then, via fermentative pathways of a variety of bacteria, the monomers are converted to acids, alcohols, CO_2, and H_2 with the acidity of the biomass slurry increasing, and the loss of any oxygen present. The methane bacteria begin growing only when the oxygen is gone and sufficient CO_2 (and other single carbon compounds depending on the species) and H_2 are present. Removal of the hydrogen even allows some thermodynamically unfavorable reactions to take place. For example:

$$CH_3\text{–}CH_2OH + H_2O \rightleftharpoons CH_3 - COOH + 2H_2 \qquad\qquad 3$$

This reaction is normally to the left unless the hydrogen is removed and the methanogens do just that. One species of methanogens uses acetate:

$$CH_3 - COO^- + H_2O \rightarrow CH_4 + HCO_3^- \qquad\qquad 4$$

Since these bacteria are very difficult to grow and oxygen is toxic to them, this experiment is designed to illustrate the production of methane under very simple conditions. The experiment is based in part on one published by Lennox et al. *Amer. Biol. Teacher* 45:128-138, 1983.

MATERIALS (per group — see diagram)

1. 1 1 liter flask

2. 1 2-hole rubber stopper with glass tubes inserted through the holes

3. 2 soft rubber or plastic hose pieces — one 10-15 cm long, one 3 cm long

4. 2 clamps for the hoses

5. 1 syringe needle bent in a U-shape and fitted to the 10-15 cm hose piece as illustrated in Figure 70-1

6. 1 deep beaker and tape for attaching it to the flask neck

7. 1 small test tube 13 × 100 mm

8. 1 methylene blue anaerobic indicator attached to a thread

9. A quantity of fresh cow manure or sewage sludge. If these are not available, human feces or any rich organic material supplemented with formate and bicarbonate and made into thick slurry would do.

10. Beaker with 12% NaOH

11. 1 or 2 wooden applicator sticks

12. A millimeter rule

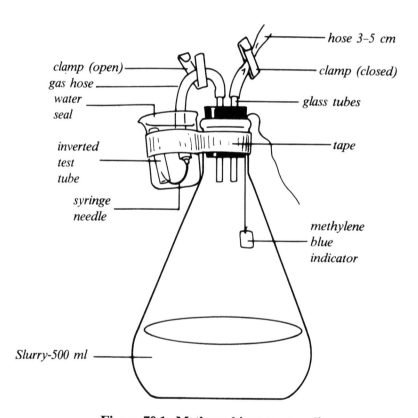

Figure 70-1. Methane biogenerator diagram

PROCEDURE AND OBSERVATIONS (1–3 weeks)

Period 1

1. Prepare a flask and rubber stopper as illustrated in the figure above. Tape the beaker to the neck of the flask and fill with water.

2. Prepare 500 ml of a slurry of fresh manure of 1:5 in water. Pour the 500 ml into the flask. Other students may prepare and use 500 ml slurries of 1:7 and 1:11 instead. Sewage sludge can be used without dilution although bicarbonate may be added.

3. Suspend the methylene blue indicator by the thread well above the slurry and put the rubber stopper in place. Clamp the short rubber hose tightly. This port may be used for sampling the gas in the head space or adding materials to the slurry, if desired, using a syringe with a long needle or other sampling device.

4. Fill the short test tube with water and invert it in the beaker in a manner to prevent air entering. Place the syringe needle into the test tube opening. The clamp on the gas hose is available for transferring tubes but must be open at all other times to prevent build-up of pressure and possible explosion.

Periods 2-10

5. Incubate the entire unit at 37°C for a period of up to 30 days. Check on the water level in the beaker periodically and add more as needed. Also observe color changes of the anaerobic indicator and note the day it becomes colorless.

6. When gas appears, insert a millimeter rule into the beaker along side of the test tube and measure the length of the gas column inside the gas tube. Record the result in the table provided. Repeat at least twice a week.

7. After half or more of the test tube has been filled with gas, the methane may be measured by carefully placing a thumb over the opening of the tube and then removing it from the water.

8. Measure the total length of gas in the tube with the rule and record the value.

9. Carefully place the base of the tube in a container of 12% NaOH. Rinse your fingers promptly.

10. As the CO_2 is removed by the hydroxide, liquid will be drawn up into the tube. It is important to keep the liquid levels inside and outside the tube at the same level by adjusting the position of the tube up and down as needed. When no further change occurs, measure the height of the remaining gas in the tube and record the value. The remaining gas is methane.

11. While only approximate, the percent methane should be within a few percent of the actual value, between 50-65%.

Final Period

12. After the experiment is complete, remove the tube from the hydroxide slowly, draining the liquid out. Turn the tube upright and place it behind a safety glass in a chemical hood. Insert a flaming applicator stick into the tube. If the room and hood are darkened, the methane will be seen to flame blue.

THOUGHT QUESTIONS

1. What is the biochemical pathway of methane synthesis?

2. What other organisms compete with the methanogens for hydrogen gas in these reactions?

3. What is the relationship between the archaebacteria and the eubacteria?

Name _____ Date _____ Grade _____

70. Methane (Biogas) Production

RESULTS AND OBSERVATIONS

Starting date _____

Days to 1st
methylene blue change _____   **mm of gas production**

Days to 1st gas _____   _____

Days to 2nd obs _____   _____

Days to 3rd obs _____   _____

Days to 4th obs _____   _____

Days to 5th obs _____   _____

Days to 6th obs _____   _____

Days to 7th obs _____   _____

Days to 8th obs _____   _____

Days to 9th obs _____   _____

Days to 10th obs _____   _____

Final gas volume _____

Volume after NaOH _____

% methane _____

Results of flame test:

QUESTIONS

Completion:

1. The name of the group to which the methanogens belong is the _____ .

2. A methanogen genus and species name is _____ .

3-4. Write the reaction for methane formation from

    3. CO_2 and H_2

    4. acetate

5-9. Methane-producing bacteria will not grow in the presence of _____
or without the inorganic molecules _____ and _____
or the organic compound _____ .
Some will grow on _____ , however.

10. Name one distinguishing feature of the methanogens which sets them aside from the true bacteria.

11. In the bioreactor used in this experiment, what is the purpose of the methylene blue indicator tab?

12. What could be added to the bioreactor slurry to make additional methane?

71 Winogradsky Column and Immersed Slide

OBJECTIVES

The student will be able to:

1. explain what a Winogradsky column is.

2. describe microbial succession in a Winogradsky column.

3. describe the microbial composition of the layers of a standard Winogradsky column.

4. prepare and use an immersed slide.

The Winogradsky column provides a method for showing microorganismal **succession** and **enrichment** of specialized groups of bacteria. A natural sample of sediment from a lake or a stream (or a soil sample) is enriched with a nutrient substrate depending on the purpose of the column. The substrate may be almost anything with calcium sulfate, calcium carbonate, and shredded paper commonly used for simple succession. A well developed column might look like Figure 71-1. Although only one column type is suggested here, other column types can be made by changing the nutrients added, the lighting conditions, or temperature of incubation. One or two columns can usually serve the entire class.

The **immersed slide** is simply a slide placed in the water which then serves as an **interface** for the attachment of bacteria and other organisms. The bacteria generally are attracted to these surfaces where organic matter tends to accumulate. In moving water organisms attached to surfaces are exposed to more nutrient as the water flows past the surface than a suspended cell. This is a special advantage in streams or the ocean where currents play a big role in the movement of water. Not all organisms attach to surfaces, however. Generally, bacteria attach first and begin to grow forming microcolonies. These are followed some time later by algae and then protozoa. The kinds are dependent on the water, the kinds of organisms present, the time of year, and the nutrient state of the water.

MATERIALS (per group or class)

1. Mud and water sufficient for the columns from a local stream or lake, perhaps more than one source

2. 1 or more graduated cylinders, 500 ml or 1 liter size

3. Incandescent lights, 60 watts, one or more

4. Plastic sandwich bag, one per column

5. $CaCO_3$ (limestone) powdered, 3-5 g per column

6. $CaSO_4$ (plaster of Paris), 3-5 g per column

7. Finely shredded paper, Whatman No. 1, 1-2 g per column

8. Na_2S, 1 g per column

9. Spatula

10. Balance

11. Glass slides

12. Plastic, water proof tape, 1.75 cm wide

13. Plastic monofilament fish line

14. Phenol erythrosin stain

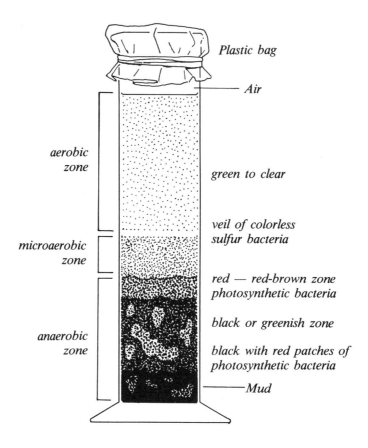

Figure 71-1. Location of the zones is highly variable in a Winogradsky column

PROCEDURE (up to 3 months or more)

Period 1

1. In a suitable container, collect enough mud for 5–10 cm depth of mud in the column and sufficient water to fill the column. Eliminate rocks, twigs, and other large debris.

2. Take the amount of mud to be used in the column and mix 3-5 g of $CaSO_4$, 3-5 g of $CaCO_3$, 1 g of Na_2S, and 1-2 g of shredded paper with it.

3. Place the mud in the cylinder and add water (from the sample site) to within 5–10 cm of the rim. Stir the mud to release trapped air. Mark the water level. Place a plastic bag over the top to retard evaporation.

4. Incubate at room temperature near an incandecent lamp (60 watt) but far enough away to avoid heating. Daylight may be used but do not expose the column to direct sunlight as overheating results. Fluorescent lamps (about 20 watts) can be used but the photosynthetic bacteria may grow poorly or not at all due to the lack of infrared radiation.

5. Prepare a glass slide by taping a plastic monofilament line to the top of the slide (A) with a small piece of plastic tape.

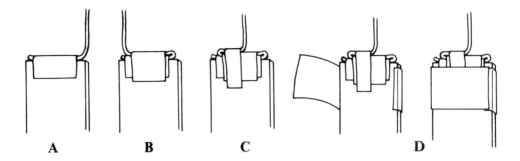

Figure 71-2. Preparation of suspended slide

Stretch the tape as tightly as possible. Fold the monofilament line back across the slide end and place one more piece of tape on the end (B). Return the monofilament to the center of the slide end and seal it down with 1/2 a piece of tape (C) so that the slide hangs vertically. Then stretch a piece of tape around the end at a right angle to the monofilament line (D) at least once, stretching it tightly while doing so.

OBSERVATIONS

Week 1 et seq.

1. Make general observations on the appearance of the column at weekly intervals noting any changes in color, growth, etc.

2. After 4 weeks or so, suspend one prepared glass slide for each student in the column. Several suspended in the more interesting areas of the column should be used. (This and step no. 3 may be omitted).

3. After the slides have been in the column for 48-72 hours, remove and treat each one as follows:

    a. Carefully remove the plastic tape and line and place the slide on a paper towel. Polish the adhering material off the down side by rubbing back and forth on the towel.

    b. Stain the slide with phenol erythrosin or methylene blue 3-5 minutes. Rinse quickly and let air dry. Do not blot.

    c. Observe under oil immersion and make drawings on the forms provided.

Final Period

4. After completing 6-8 weeks incubation, use a long glass tube (2-3 mm inner diameter) as a pipet and remove a sample from an interesting looking area and make a wet mount as described in Exercise 7. Rinse the glass tube with tap water between samples at different levels.

5. Using the low power objective, observe and make drawings of the different types of organisms observed. Repeat using high dry and oil immersion. The wet mount observations are best done on a phase contrast microscope if available.

THOUGHT QUESTIONS

1. How would you make one of these columns if you wanted methane bacteria? nitrifying bacteria? sulfur oxidizers? sulfate reducers?

2. Why do the bacterial photosynthesizers require incandescent light?

3. Explain why two columns made from the same mud and water sample result in different patterns of community structure after 6-8 weeks.

71. Winogradsky Column and Immersed Slide

RESULTS AND OBSERVATIONS

1. Draw the appearance of the columns and any changes occurring over the incubation period.

2. Make drawings of the stained suspended slides.

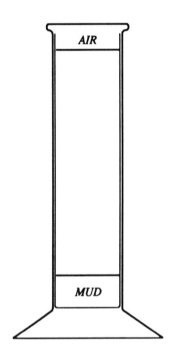

3. Make drawings of the wet mounts from the different layers.

QUESTIONS (you may need to refer to Parts I and XII)

Completion:

1. The column used in this exercise is named after a famous Russian microbiologist Serge _____ .

2. The process of encouraging the growth of a special group of bacteria (e.g., nitrifiers) is called _____ .

3. A source of carbon for autotrophs is added to the columns in the form of _____ .

4. _____ is a genus of obligate anaerobic organisms converting sulfate to H_2S .

5. _____ is a genus of obligately aerobic bacteria oxidizing H_2S to S or sulfate.

6. _____ is a genus of obligately anaerobic bacteria converting H_2S to S or sulfate.

7. _____ is a genus of cyanobacteria fixing nitrogen in these columns.

8–9. The name of the slide put in the water is the _____ .

It is an example of an _____ between the water on the one hand and the glass on the other.

72 Bioluminescent Bacteria

OBJECTIVES

The student will be able to:

1. describe the appearance of bacterial luminescence.
2. outline the biochemistry of the light producing reaction.
3. describe the organism and the group producing light.

One of the more interesting phenomena in microbiology is the production of light by organisms. **Light** is emitted by many microbes and higher animals; in at least some of the latter, light is the result of bacterial **symbionts** residing in tissues or special organs. Among the prokaryotes, light production is found in certain species of *Vibrio* and *Photobacterium*. These bacteria are often placed with the family *Enterobacteriaceae* as Gram-negative facultative anaerobes. However, they differ considerably from that family in a number of characteristics (e.g., they are oxidase positive and are polarly flagellated when motile). The bioluminescent bacteria are exclusively marine in origin and often observed on the skin of spoiling fish as well as in light emitting organs.

The **bioluminescent** bacteria emit a blue-green light with a maximum near 490 nm. Light is emitted continuously as long as **oxygen** is plentiful. As oxygen is depleted light emission ceases. The emission of light by these organisms is one of the most sensitive tests for the detection of oxygen. The pathway of emission is a side reaction of the electron-cytochrome-oxygen transport chain as follows:

$$e^- \rightarrow NADH_2 \rightarrow flavins \rightarrow cytochromes \rightarrow O_2$$

$$FMNH_2 + O_2 + R\text{-}CHO \xrightarrow{\quad luciferase \quad} FMN + H_2O + R\text{-}COOH + hv$$

The enzyme luciferase reacts with the flavin mononucleotide forming a complex which is then oxidized by oxygen creating an excited intermediate. When this intermediate returns to the ground state in the presence of an aldehyde (dodecanal), a photon of light is emitted and the aldehyde oxidized to an acid.

In this exercise you will demonstrate light emission and examine the characteristics of a pure culture.

MATERIALS (per pair)

1. 1 flask of a light emitting luminous broth culture of *Photobacterium phosphoreum*
2. 1 flask of luminous agar, sterile
3. 4 Petri plates, sterile
4. Filter paper and oxidase reagent (Kovac's)

PROCEDURE (2-3 days)

Period 1

1. Take the flasks into a completely dark room or use the laboratory if it can be completely darkened. Allow your eyes to adjust to the darkness for about five minutes. Observe the aerating cultures. Be prepared to describe the appearance on your report form when you return to light conditions.

2. Remove one of the aerating flasks from the stirrer or turn off the air. Let the flask sit quietly for a period of time. Note the gradual disappearance of the light until only the top layer is glowing. What does this appearance suggest?

3. Return the now darkened flask to the stirrer or restore the air. Note what happens.

4. Record your observations on your report form.

5. Return to the laboratory and pour 4 luminous agar plates. Allow them to solidify.

6. With a sterilized loop, each person streaks the organism from the flask onto two plates. Streak in the form of a message or words such as your name or anything that suits you.

7. Incubate the plates inverted at 15°-18°C.

OBSERVATIONS

Periods 2-3

8. Because the growth rate of these organisms is variable, you will have to look at your plates at 12, 18, 24, and 30 hours until growth is visible. Take plates with growth into a darkened room and observe as in step No. 1 above.

9. Draw your message on the report form in the space provided.

10. Each person makes a Gram stain of the growth from one of the plates and performs an oxidase test (Exercise 35).

THOUGHT QUESTIONS

1. Why have animals sought symbiotic associations with these bacteria?

2. Design a test for oxygen using these bacteria.

3. How does the biochemistry of the bacterial reaction differ from that of the firefly luminescence?

72. Bioluminescent Bacteria

RESULTS AND OBSERVATIONS

1. Draw the flask as it is aerated and not aerated. Describe the appearance in words beside the drawing.

    Aerated   Unaerated

2. Draw one of your plates with the message on it.

3. Draw the morphology and indicate the Gram reaction below.

QUESTIONS

Completion:

1.   _____ is the enzyme involved in the light reaction.

2.   The electrons involved in these reactions originate from the _____ chain or pathway.

3-4.   The aldehyde involved is _____ and the product of its oxidation is an _____ (chemical type).

5.   An essential chemical in this reaction is _____ .

6-9.   These bacteria are oxidase _____ and are _____ flagellated, while the *Enterobacteriaceae* are oxidase _____ and _____ flagellated.

10.   To isolate luminescent bacteria you would have to go to the _____ .

UNIT *XIII*

Food Microbiology

It has often been said, "we are what we eat." In addition to converting the nutrients of foods to our own use, there are other important aspects of foods. These include spoilage, food-borne illness organisms, the number of organisms as a quality control item, and the conversion of one food to another by encouraging the growth of certain microbes. This last category includes food fermentations such as cheese, pickles, beer, wine, soy sauce, and salami. Almost all foods contain living microbes, with the exception of canned foods and a few others. It is necessary that microbes be limited in number (except for fermented foods) lest the food be spoiled and that pathogens be excluded. Most people are suprised to learn that so many microbes are found in the food they eat. Thus it is extremely important to handle foods so that the microbes do not grow, thereby limiting the potential for food-borne illness as well as spoilage. Unit XIII illustrates the microbial quality of several food types, some health aspects of foods, and the production of one fermented food type.

73 Standard Plate Count of Food

OBJECTIVES

The student will be able to:

1. prepare, dilute, and plate a food sample.

2. count colonies according to the rules for counting plates.

3. explain the results to a friend.

4. discuss in a general way the reasons for concern with bacteria in food.

Bacteria and fungi occur in most foods in varying quantities. Generally, numbers are fairly **low**, less than 100,000 per g or ml depending on the food, unless growth has occurred. Spoiling food may contain 10^7 or more per g or ml. The number of bacteria (or **colony forming units-CFU**) is determined by homogenizing a food sample in a diluent, making a dilution series (Exercise 14) and plating the dilutions with **standard plate count agar (PCA)**. The plates are then incubated and the number of bacteria (or CFU) are determined per g or ml. An evaluation can then be made of the **quality** of the food based on the normal condition of that food. **Large** numbers (10^5–10^7) can generally be interpreted to mean the food has been held under conditions **permitting growth** of bacteria. In many foods, especially previously cooked foods, this suggests that food-borne illness organisms may also have grown. However, a food may be **dangerous** to health with very little growth and the standard plate count may not be very useful in these cases. In many situations, selective media for particular pathogens can be used instead. Standards for some foods have been established using the plate count (e.g., milk). The standard plate count is not useful with all foods, such as fermented foods (cheese, pickles, etc.), in which organisms are encouraged to grow. Again special media for specific groups can be used in these cases.

Two food types will be studied in this exercise — hamburger and two spices, black pepper and chili powder. The results will provide the student with some information on the bacteria in commonly used food items. Exercise 76 deals with another aspect of black pepper and you may want to coordinate the two exercises.

MATERIALS (groups of 3 pairs)

1. A sample of fresh hamburger from a local market and cans of black pepper and chili powder
2. 1 sterile Waring blender jar with aluminum foil cover (for hamburger)
3. 7 sterile 99 ml dilution blanks (hamburger 3, pepper 2, chili 2)
4. 9 Petri plates, sterile
5. 7 sterile 1 ml pipets and safety bulb
6. 1 flask plate count agar (PCA) for 9 plates, sterile
7. Spatulas

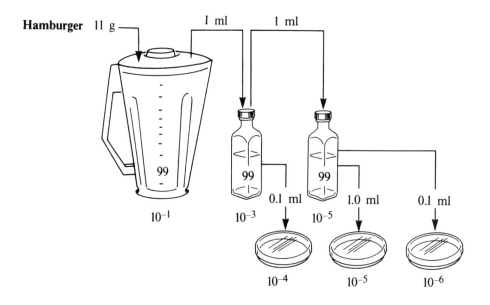

Figure 73-1. Hamburger dilution scheme

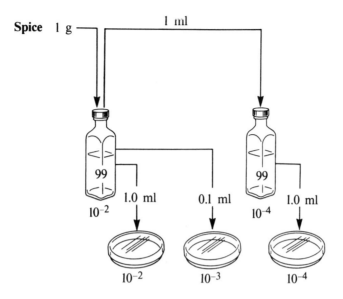

Figure 73-2. Spice dilution scheme

PROCEDURE (2–5 days)

Hamburger (See Figure 73-1)

Period 1

1. Weigh 11 g of hamburger aseptically into a sterile blender jar with a flamed and cooled spatula.

2. Add one 99 ml dilution blank to the jar and blend 1-2 minutes at low speed and 1 minute at high speed. This is the 10^{-1} dilution.

3. Pipet 1 ml of the 10^{-1} dilution to a second 99 ml dilution blank labeled 10^{-3}. Discard the pipet and shake the blank 25 times in a one foot arc in 7 seconds.

4. Pipet 1 ml of the 10^{-3} dilution to a third blank making the 10^{-5} dilution. Discard the pipet and shake the blank well.

5. With a new pipet, transfer 0.1 ml of the 10^{-5} dilution to a plate labeled 10^{-6}. Then with the same pipet transfer 1 ml of the 10^{-5} dilution to a plate labeled 10^{-5}, blowing out the last drop. With the same pipet transfer 0.1 ml of the 10^{-3} dilution to a plate labeled 10^{-4}. Discard the pipet.

6. Pour enough tempered (45°-50°C) PCA into each plate to just cover the bottom (about 20 ml). Mix carefully as instructed in Exercise 23 and let solidify.

7. Incubate the plates at 32°C for 48 hours (or 5 days at room temperature).

Black Pepper and Chili (See Figure 73-2)

Period 1

1. Weigh 1 g of spice directly into a 99 ml dilution blank with a flamed and cooled spatula. Shake vigorously as previously instructed. This is the 10^{-2} dilution.

2. Pipet 1 ml of the 10^{-2} dilution into a second 99 ml dilution blank labeled 10^{-4}. Discard the pipet and shake the blank 25 times in a one foot arc in 7 seconds.

3. Pipet 1 ml of the 10^{-4} dilution into a plate labeled 10^{-4}.

4. With the same pipet, transfer 0.1 ml of the 10^{-2} blank to a plate labeled 10^{-3}.

5. With the same pipet, transfer 1 ml from the 10^{-2} blank to a plate labeled 10^{-2}.

6. Pour enough tempered (45°-50°C) PCA into each plate to just cover the bottom (about 20 ml). Mix carefully as instructed in Exercise 23 and let solidify.

7. Incubate the plates at 32°C for 48 hours (or 5 days at room temperature).

OBSERVATIONS

Period 2

1. Using the rules for counting plates in Exercise 23, count all the colonies on qualified plates for each food using a colony counter and record the results on the record form.

2. Note any differences between colony morphology on the plates for the three foods.

3. Make a Gram stain of cells from a few surface colonies from each food and record the Gram reaction and morphology of each.

THOUGHT QUESTIONS

1. How can the total count be related to the health hazard of a food?

2. How would a total count of 10^7 CFU/g in hamburger be compared to a total count of 10^7 CFU/g of cooked turkey stuffing?

3. If you had 10^7 CFU/g of hamburger and the meat is then cooked, what would you now expect the count to be? Would it be safe to eat?

73. Standard Plate Count of Food

RESULTS AND OBSERVATIONS

1. Record the number of bacteria observed in the table below.

Food	Dilution Counted	No. of Colonies on Plate	Total CFU/g
Hamburger			
Black pepper			
Chili powder			

2. Comment on colony morphology between foods.

3. Gram reaction and morphology of organisms from the three foods.

QUESTIONS

True or False Statements: Circle the correct response.

T	F	1.	The term "colony forming unit" means the same as "bacterial count".
T	F	2.	Fresh foods rarely have microbes on them.
T	F	3.	A spoiled food will often have $<10^7$ bacteria/g.
T	F	4.	The total plate count is directly related to health hazard.
T	F	5.	Bacterial counts in spices are low; therefore, spice used in food presents no problem.
T	F	6.	A most important interpretation of large numbers of bacteria in food is that the food has been held under conditions permitting growth.
T	F	7.	The medium used here is plate count agar.
T	F	8.	Some foods have microbial standards for quality and health.
T	F	9.	The standard plate count is commonly used on fermented foods.
T	F	10.	11 g of hamburger ground in 99 ml of dilution water is a 10^{-2} dilution.
T	F	11.	Spices, such as chili powder and curry, when used in foods prevent food poisoning.

74 Standard Plate Count of Milk

OBJECTIVES

The student will be able to:

1. identify five general sources of milk contamination.

2. name five bacterial diseases transmitted to humans through milk.

3. discuss the methods of milk pasteurization.

4. perform a standard plate count of milk.

5. calculate the plate count per ml of milk.

Since milk contains a variety of nutrients and has a pH of 6.8, it a good medium for the growth of many different bacteria. Milk has an initial microbial flora at the time it is drawn from the cow. However, unless good sanitation practices are followed, milk may be contaminated by many more microorganisms and especially those which cause disease. Such sources of contamination include the cow, the milking area, milking equipment, personnel, and processing.

In order to make milk safe for human consumption, pasteurization is applied to most commercially processed milk. The holding or vat method of pasteurization consists of raising the temperature of milk to 63°C and holding it for 30 minutes. An alternative method known as flash pasteurization is available and is more frequently used. This procedure involves the heating of milk to 72°C and holding it for 15 seconds. A recently developed ultra high temperature pasteurization using temperatures above 121°C for 1–2 seconds is also available. Regardless of the method employed, the pasteurization procedure is designed to kill pathogenic microorganisms found in milk, particularly *Coxiella burnetti* the causative agent of Q-fever, the most heat resistant of these milk-borne pathogens. Many diseases are potentially transmitted to humans in milk (e.g., from the cow — tuberculosis (bovine), brucellosis, *Streptococcus*, *Salmonella*; from human milk handlers — typhoid fever, scarlet fever, diphtheria, tuberculosis (human), hepatitis; from soil and dirty equipment — listeriosis, *Salmonella*).

The quality and safety of milk is monitored by state and local health departments using standards set forth by the U.S. Food and Drug Administration, the American Public Health Association, and the Dairy Industry. One of the most widely used tests is to determine the total number of bacteria in a milliliter of raw or pasteurized milk as an indication of how the milk was handled at the farm, during shipment, and after pasteurization. This test is known as the standard plate count and uses plate count agar tested under specific conditions and approved for this use. According to accepted standards, raw milk (from individual supplies) may not have more than 75,000 bacteria per ml before pasteurization and must have less than 15,000 per ml after pasteurization. Note that a well run milk farm will produce raw milk with a total count of less than 10,000. Just because a raw milk has a low bacterial count does not mean it is safe. Public health records show that pathogens may be present even if the count is 1–2,000 per ml.

The purpose of this exercise is to introduce the student to a widely used method for monitoring the quality of milk. A procedure for both pasteurized and raw milk is included. In most cases raw milk will not be available in the local market area due to health restrictions on its sale so pasteurized milk is the sample of choice. Select a market milk as fresh as possible since the total number of bacteria rises with time while refrigerated.

MATERIALS (per pair)

A. Pasteurized Milk

1. Carton of pasteurized milk

2. 1 sterile 99 ml dilution blank

3. 8 Petri plates, sterile

4. Flask of plate count agar, sterile

5. 2 sterile 1 ml pipets and safety bulb

B. Raw Milk

1. Carton of raw milk

2. 2 sterile 99 ml dilution blanks

3. 6 Petri plates, sterile

4. Flask of plate count agar, sterile

5. 3 sterile 1 ml pipets and safety bulb

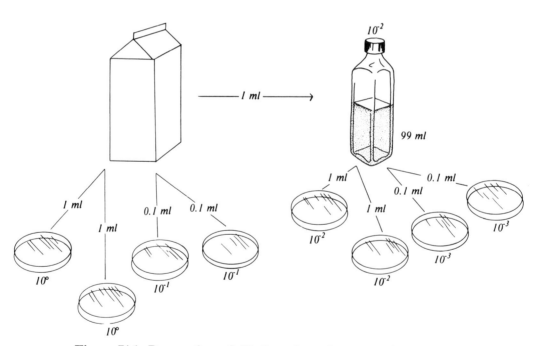

Figure 74-1. Preparation of dilution plates for pasteurized milk

PROCEDURE (2 days)

A. Pasteurized Milk

Period 1

1. Label eight Petri plates in pairs, 10^{-0}, 10^{-1}, 10^{-2} and 10^{-3}. Include your name, date, etc. as well (Figure 74-1).

2. Before opening, shake the carton of milk 25 times in a one foot arc in 7 seconds.

3. Aseptically transfer 1 ml from the carton of milk into a 99 ml dilution blank and then discard the pipet. This transfer results in a 10^{-2} dilution. Shake the blank as before.

4. Pipet 1 ml from the carton of milk into each of the 2 plates labeled 10^0. Do not discard the pipet.

5. Using the same pipet from step no. 4, transfer 0.1 ml from the carton of milk into each of the 2 plates labeled 10^{-1}. Discard the pipet.

6. Select another pipet and transfer 1 ml from the 99 ml dilution blank into each of the 2 plates labeled 10^{-2}. Do not discard the pipet.

7. Using the same pipet from step no. 6, transfer 0.1 ml into each of 2 plates labeled 10^{-3}. Discard the pipet.

8. Introduce 15-20 ml of cooled plate count agar into each plate. As each plate is poured, thoroughly mix the medium with the aliquot of milk sample by rotating the plates *gently* in a figure-8.

9. After solidification, invert the plates, and incubate at 32°C for 48 ± 3 hours.

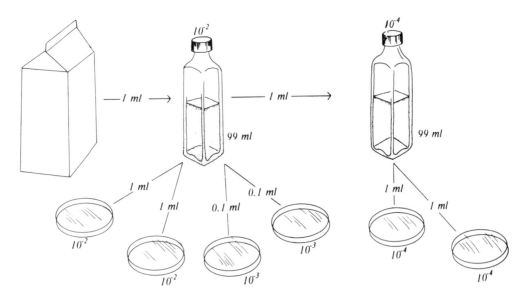

Figure 74-2. Preparation of dilution plates for raw (unpasteurized) milk

B. Raw Milk

Period 1

1. Label eight Petri plates in pairs, 10^{-1}, 10^{-2}, 10^{-3}, and 10^{-4}. Include your name, date, etc. (Figure 74-2).

2. Before opening, shake the carton of milk 25 times in a one foot arc in 7 seconds.

3. Aseptically pipet 1 ml from the carton of milk into the first 99 ml dilution blank and then discard the pipet. This transfer results in a 10^{-2} dilution. Shake the blank as before.

4. Pipet 1 ml from the 10^{-2} dilution blank in a second 99 ml dilution blank and then discard the pipet. This transfer results in a total dilution of 10^{-4} in the second blank. Shake the blank as before.

5. Pipet 1 ml from the 10^{-2} dilution blank into each of the 2 plates labeled 10^{-2}. Do not discard the pipet.

6. Using the same pipet from step No. 5, transfer 0.1 ml from the 10^{-2} dilution blank into each of the 2 plates labeled 10^{-3}. Discard the pipet.

7. Select another pipet and transfer 1 ml from the 10^{-4} dilution blank into each of the 2 plates labeled 10^{-4}. Discard the pipet.

8. Introduce 15-20 ml of cooled plate count agar into each plate. As each plate is poured, thoroughly mix the medium with the aliquot of milk sample by rotating the plate gently in a figure-8.

9. After solidification, invert the plates and incubate at 32°C for 48 ± 3 hours.

OBSERVATIONS

Period 2

1. Regardless of the sample, count plates with colony numbers between 30-300 using the procedure and rules of Exercise 23.

2. Enter the counts on the report form and calculate the standard plate count (SPC) per ml of milk.

THOUGHT QUESTIONS

1. Name a few other foods which are pasteurized together with times and temperatures.

2. What is a reasonable definition of pasteurization?

3. What do coliforms mean in raw milk? Pasteurized milk? What are the milk standards for this group?

74. Standard Plate Count of Milk

RESULTS AND OBSERVATIONS

A. **Pasteurized Milk**

Dilution	Reciprocal of Dilution	Colonies/plate	Average Colonies/plate	SPC/ml
10^0				
10^{-1}				
10^{-2}				
10^{-3}				

B. **Raw Milk**

Dilution	Reciprocal of Dilution	Colonies/plate	Average Colonies/plate	SPC/ml
10^{-2}				
10^{-3}				
10^{-4}				

QUESTIONS

A. True or False Statements: Circle the correct response.

T   F   1.   A colony count determines the numbers of both living and dead bacteria introduced into a pour plate.

T   F   2.   A countable plate must have 10 to 300 colonies.

T   F   3.   Raw milk often has no more bacteria than pasteurized milk.

T   F   4.   Nutrient agar can be used instead of plate count agar.

T   F   5.   A darkfield Quebec colony counter and a mechanical hand tally counter should be used to count colonies.

T   F   6.   A pour plate in which the colonies are well distributed makes the final colony count more accurate.

B. Completion:

7–11.   List 5 sources of contamination of milk.

7. _____

8. _____

9. _____

10. _____

11. _____

12.   The _____ method is used by the American Public Health Association to determine viable bacterial populations in milk.

13–14.   Milk dilution plates are incubated at _____ °C for _____ hours.

15.   Pasteurization methods are designed to kill _____ .

16–17.   According to public health law acceptable milk for market must have less than _____ bacteria/ml in pasteurized milk and less than _____ bacteria/ml in raw milk.

18–19.   List 2 methods of pasteurization.

18. _____

19. _____

20–22.   List 3 diseases of man introduced into milk by uncleanliness of the animals, equipment, etc.

20. _____

21. _____

22. _____

23–25.   List 3 diseases transmitted to man by drinking milk from infected cows.

23. _____

24. _____

25. _____

75 Preparation and Analysis of Yogurt

OBJECTIVES

The student will be able to:

1. make yogurt.

2. make a quantitative viable plate count of the number of organisms present in the product.

3. make a quantitative direct microscopic count of the organisms present in the product.

4. identify by name and describe the morphological appearance of cells and colonies of the two bacteria involved.

Yogurt and acidophilus fermented milk products have been used for centuries by peoples of the Near East. Very likely it was originally a means of preserving milk which, incidentally (and unknown to the users, of course), killed disease organisms as a result of the lactic acid produced.

Yogurt fermentation is brought about by inoculation of boiled milk with two lactic acid bacteria, *Streptococcus thermophilus* and *Lactobacillus bulgaricus*. The final product is quite acidic with a white appearance and a custard-like texture due to coagulation of milk protein by lactic acid. Fruit or flavors mask the acidity and improve acceptability.

Acidophilus fermentation is brought about by inoculation of boiled milk with *Lactobacillus acidophilus*. The final product is white, extremely acid (much more than yogurt), and somewhat granular or lumpy. Fruit or flavors materially improve acceptability.

Foods and many other substances are often examined directly for the presence of bacteria. It is useful to see and count organisms which may be dead and not able to grow (e.g., a heated food involved in a food-borne illness outbreak). The direct microscopic examination is a technique that allows one to stain and count organisms present in the sample. A major limitation of this technique is the need for at least 500,000 per gram of food in order to see enough cells under the microscope to make a reliable count. This limits its use to foods in which bacteria have grown to sizeable numbers.

This exercise is intended to introduce the student to the making of yogurt and analysis of the product for bacterial content using the standard plate count and direct microscopic count methods.

MATERIALS (per person)

A. Preparation of Yogurt

1. Powdered skim milk and tablespoon

2. 1 liter beaker or flask

3. Milk supplied by student (500 ml or 1 pint)

4. Long-handled teaspoon or dowel for stirring

5. 2 plastic hot cups or glass jars with covers (200 ml or 6-8 oz.)

6. Plain yogurt inoculum

7. Thermometer (non-mercury)

B. Analysis of Yogurt

1. 1 sterile 0.1 ml pipet and safety bulb

2. 4 sterile 1 ml pipets

3. 5 sterile 99 ml dilution blanks

4. Spatula

5. 3 Petri plates, sterile

6. LAB agar flask, sterile

7. Bent glass rod

8. Candle jar

9. 3% H_2O_2

PROCEDURE (3-5 days)

I. Yogurt Preparation

Period 1

1. Obtain 500 ml (one pint) of fresh, pasteurized milk (whole or skim) (see Note 1).

2. Add at least 2 level tablespoons of powdered skim milk. More can be added if a firmer product is desired.

3. Bring the mixture to a boil over medium heat for 30 seconds, stirring constantly. Add a non-mercury thermometer and cool to 45°–46°C (112°–115°F).

4. The inoculum used in class is a carton of grocery store plain yogurt without added flavor. Use about 1-2 teaspoonfuls of the store product per 500 ml of milk. Use a spoon boiled in the original milk or separately. Dried prepared culture may be obtained from Hansen's Laboratory, Inc., 9015 W. Maple St., Milwaukee, Wisconsin 53214. Local health food stores sometimes carry dried or live preparations.

5. Mix well with the boiled spoon.

6. Pour the mixture into pre-boiled warm cups or dishes and cover with aluminum foil or other closure. Plastic hot cups can be used directly. Fill to within several millimeters of the rim. Incubate (see step 6a below) at 42°C (109°F) for 9-15 hours or until desired firmness is obtained.

   a. Incubation: If a 42°C incubator is unavailable in the lab, use the 37°C incubator and incubate for 18 hours. At home, use an oven at 42°C with a pilot light or an electric bulb, or an electric oven with bulb. Change the light bulb wattage until the desired temperature is obtained. Use a thermometer to check the temperature in any case.

Period 2

7. Place cups in a refrigerator until cool and serve. Sugar, flavors, jam, or preserves may be added, if desired. One cup should be saved without flavor for part II below.

8. Samples of the above batch (without added flavors) may serve as an inoculum for the next batch and be stored in the refrigerator up to 10 days. Use 1-3 teaspoonfuls (boiled spoon) of this per liter (quart) of newly boiled milk for continued culturing (see Note 2).

II. Analysis of Yogurt

Period 2

A. Viable Count

1. After refrigeration for 1-2 days, prepare a 10^{-1} dilution. Weigh the yogurt container and remove 11 g with a flamed, cooled spatula adding it aseptically to a 99 ml dilution blank. Shake well (see Exercise 14). Save this and subsequent dilution blanks for the direct microscopic count below.

2. Make the 10^{-3} through 10^{-6} dilutions in steps of 10^{-1}.

3. Pour three plates of LAB agar and let solidify.

4. Pipet 0.1 ml from each of the 10^{-6}, 10^{-5}, and 10^{-4} dilutions onto the surface of appropriately labeled plates and spread with a sterile bent glass rod.

5. Incubate the plates at 37°-42°C for 2-4 days in candle jars (Figure 75-1) or, if available, a CO_2 incubator.

B. Direct Microscopic Count

1. With a wax pencil and a template, outline a one centimeter square area on the underside of a clean glass slide.

2. Pipet 0.01 ml of the 10^{-1} dilution onto the top of the slide over the square cm area. With a bent inoculating needle (NOT loop) spread the drop evenly over the area. Dry the film in a warm place.

3. Fix and Gram stain the dried smear and examine the slides under oil immersion.

OBSERVATIONS

Period 2

1. For the direct microscopic count, make the following observations on 10-20 fields. (If there are too many bacteria to count, prepare another slide from the next higher dilution.):

    a. Count the total number of bacteria or clumps of bacteria in each field and determine an average per field.

    b. Describe the various morphological types of bacteria in each field, count them and average.

    c. The average count per field can be converted to count per g of original sample using the direct microscopic formula:

    (Average count/field) × (dilution factor) × (microscope factor) = count/g

    To determine microscope factor use a micrometer disk and measure the diameter (d) of the microscope field in millimeters (mm). Calculate the area: $mm^2 = \pi(d/2)^2$. Then calculate the microscope factor (MF) using the following formula:

$$\frac{100 \times 100}{mm^2 \ field \ area} = MF$$

where: 100 = No. of 0.01 ml volumes/1 ml; and 100 = No. of $mm^2/1 \ cm^2$.

Period 3

2. After incubation of the plates in the candle jars, make the following observations:

    a. Count colonies on the plates and describe the dominant types. Large, opaque white colonies are *Streptococcus thermophilus* and small, translucent colonies are *Lactobacillus bulgaricus*.

    b. Examine representative colonies by making Gram stains. Describe the morphology of organisms found.

    c. After completing the above, flood the plate with 3% H_2O_2 and count colonies as catalase positive (showing gas formation) and negative (no gas formation).

3. Enter data from the microscopic examination and the plate counts in the tables provided.

Note[1]: Larger volumes may be made by increasing the proportion of each item correspondingly.

Note[2]: An inoculum carried this way gradually deteriorates, producing a less desirable product. Replenish the inoculum periodically from a new commercial source.

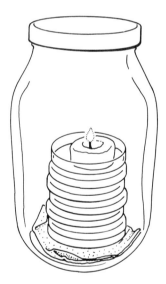

Figure 75-1. A candle jar

THOUGHT QUESTIONS

1. How would the making of yogurt reduce the incidence of disease associated with milk?

2. What is acidophilus milk? What is the name of the organism used to make this product? Is it made in a manner similar to yogurt?

Name _____ Date _____ Grade _____

75. Preparation and Analysis of Yogurt

RESULTS AND OBSERVATIONS

A. Description of Yogurt

Odor _____

Texture _____

Taste _____

B. Microscopic Count

Cell Type	Average No./Field	Dilution Factor	Microscope Factor	Count/gram
cocci				
rods				
Total				

C. Description of the morphological forms of bacteria observed:

D. Plate Count

Colony Type	Average No. of Colonies	Dilution Factor	Count/gram	Gram Reaction	Catalase Reaction
Total					

E. Colony Descriptions:

QUESTIONS

A. **True or False Statements:** Circle the correct response.

    T   F   1.   Production of lactic acid is a prime characteristic of yogurt.

    T   F   2.   Yogurt can be made from whole milk.

    T   F   3.   The optimum yogurt incubation temperature is 25°C (room temperature).

    T   F   4.   Once made, a yogurt inoculum is good for 20 years.

    T   F   5.   Adjusting the wattage of light bulbs permits the use of an insulated picnic hamper as an incubator.

    T   F   6.   A candle jar is higher in oxygen than normal air.

    T   F   7.   *Streptococcus thermophilus* colonies are large, translucent and white.

B. **Completion:**

8–9.   The coccus member of the yogurt making pair is named _____

    _____ and the rod-shaped member is _____

    _____ .

10–11.   Both bacteria involved in yogurt making are Gram- _____

    and catalase _____ .

12.   The catalase test is performed using _____ as an enzyme substrate.

13-14.   The coccus member of the yogurt pair is a _____ lactic

    fermenter and the rod is a _____ lactic fermenter.

15.   The medium used to grow the yogurt bacteria is specially formulated for that purpose and is called

    _____ agar.

16.   Colonies of the rod-shaped bacteria are _____ (morphology).

17.   The desired incubation temperature for yogurt making is _____ °C.

18.   The purpose of the candle jar is to:

19.   What kind of spoilage of yogurt is most likely?

76 Bacterial Spores in Foods

OBJECTIVES

The student will be able to:

1. explain why bacterial spores are important in foods.

2. perform a test for mesophilic bacterial spores.

3. explain the use of heat in this analysis.

Sporeforming bacteria of the genera *Bacillus* and *Clostridium* are important spoilage agents in certain foods, primarily canned foods, because of the extremely high **heat resistance** of the spores (see Exercise 43). The introduction of spores into canned food products must be kept at a minimum in order to reduce survival and subsequent spoilage. The major **sources** of spores are **flour**, **spices**, and **sugar**. Canners often have standards for these ingredients specifying a maximum acceptable number. This exercise illustrates a simple procedure for demonstrating the presence of mesophilic spores in black pepper, although other spices or flour could be used.

MATERIALS (per pair)

1. Black pepper, ground, any brand

2. Waring blender jar, sterile

3. 3 sterile 99 ml distilled water dilution blanks

4. 1 sterile 10 ml pipet and safety bulb

5. 3 sterile 1 ml pipets

6. 2 sterile 22 mm diameter tubes, capped

7. Thermometer

8. 5 Petri plates, sterile

9. 1 flask PCA (Plate Count Agar), sterile

PROCEDURE (2-3 days)

Period 1

1. Heat a water bath to 82°-83°C and maintain it there.

2. Weigh 11 g of black pepper into a sterile blender jar and blend with a 99 ml dilution blank.

3. Pipet 10 ml to each of two large 22 mm diameter tubes making sure sediment is transferred also.

4. Place the thermometer in one of the tubes and cap the other loosely.

5. Heat the tubes in the 82°-83°C water bath with agitation.

6. When the tube with the thermometer reaches 80°C, hold both tubes for 10 minutes at that temperature.

7. Remove the capped tube and cool quickly in ice or by holding the bottom of the tube in a stream of cold tap water.

8. Shake the cooled tube and pipet 1 ml to another dilution blank (10^{-3}). Discard the pipet. Shake that blank well and pipet 1 ml to another blank (10^{-5}). Discard the pipet.

9. Label 5 Petri plates 10^{-1} to 10^{-5}.

10. Beginning with the 10^{-5} blank, pipet 1 ml to the 10^{-5} plate. Then pipet 0.1 ml of the 10^{-3} blank to the 10^{-4} plate. Continue until 1 ml of the 10^{-1} blank (the heated tube) is added to the 10^{-1} plate.

11. Pour 20 ml of PCA into each plate, mix in a figure-8 motion, and allow to solidify.

12. Incubate, cover down, at 32°C for 48-72 hours.

OBSERVATIONS

Period 2

13. Count colonies on the plates using the rules of Exercise 23. Record the results in the observations table. Don't forget to count the subsurface colonies.

THOUGHT QUESTIONS

1. How do spores affect the canning process?

2. What sporeforming organisms cause food-borne illness?

3. How would you alter the procedure of this exercise to measure thermophilic sporeformers? Anaerobic mesophilic sporeformers?

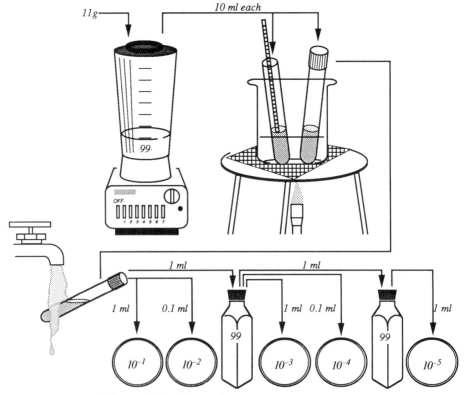

Figure 76-1. Flow diagram for spores in foods

76. Bacterial Spores in Foods

RESULTS AND OBSERVATIONS

1. Mesophilic sporeformers at 32°C

Food	Dilution	CFU on plate	CFU per g
Pepper			

2. Make a statement about the meaning of your result.

3. If the pepper was used in Exercise 73, explain the differences between the two results.

QUESTIONS

Completion:

1-2.   The two prominent sporeforming genera are ———————————————— and

———————————————— .

3-4.   In addition to pepper and other spices, two other sources of spores in foods are

———————————————— and ———————————————— .

5-6.   The temperature and time used to destroy vegetative cells are ——— °C and ——— minutes.

7.   ———————————————— is a genus-species of the sporeformers which causes food-borne illness.

8.   If you incubated the plates at 55°C instead of 32°C, these organisms would be called

———————————————— sporeformers.

77   Histamine Production in Foods

OBJECTIVES

The student will be able to:

1. explain the nature of scombroid or histamine poisoning.

2. indicate the origin of the histamine.

3. name a bacterial genus producing histamine.

Scombroid poisoning is a type of food poisoning associated with members of the marine fish suborder Scombroidae (tuna, mackerel, bonita, kingfish, swordfish) as well as a few others such as mahi-mahi. The poisoning results from the growth of certain bacteria, particularly members of the family *Enterobacteriaceae* (*Morganella, Klebsiella, Enterobacter, Escherichia,* and others) on the flesh of the fish when held under conditions allowing growth. These fish have a particularly high level of the amino acid **histidine** in the flesh which spoilage bacteria decarboxylate to form the **vasoactive** basic amine **histamine**. When such fish is ingested during a meal, humans react by exhibiting symptoms of histamine poisoning — decreased blood pressure, flushed face, prostration, headache. The fish have usually been held unrefrigerated for some time. If sufficient time elapses, considerable histamine is produced, on the order of 2000 mg per meal, and there may be no organoleptic changes. Because histamine is stable to ordinary cooking and canning procedures, heating a food prior to eating does not prevent the illness. The bacteria are introduced during handling after harvesting. Chicken skins are also high in histidine and chicken has been reported as a cause of histamine poisoning. Many other foods, particularly fermented foods, such as cheese, beer, etc., contain smaller amounts of histamine as the end product of fermentation but symptoms usually appear only in very sensitive individuals and are usually mild.

Histamine is not the only vasoactive amine. Others include **tyramine** from tyrosine, **tryptamine** from tryptophan, and **glutamine** from glutamic acid. All are found in foods, especially fermented ones and all are vasoactive to some degree, the last named being a pressor amine causing elevated blood pressure and prostration associated with a food-borne illness involving Won-Ton soup, the so-called Chinese restaurant syndrome.

This exercise demonstrates the ability of *Morganella* (*Proteus*) *morganii* and organisms from fish to produce histamine from histidine.

MATERIALS (per pair)

1. Sample of fish (tuna, mackerel, mahi-mahi)

2. Blender jar, sterile

3. 3 sterile 1 ml pipets and safety bulb

4. 3 sterile 99 ml dilution blanks

5. Histidine agar (must not be overheated), sterile

6. 5 Petri plates, sterile

7. 18-24 hour nutrient broth culture of *Morganella morganii*

PROCEDURE (3 days)

Period 1

1. Weigh 11 g of fish, primarily the skin or surface, into the blender jar. Pour in a 99 ml dilution blank and homogenize 2 minutes at low speed and 1 minute at high speed.

2. Label 4 Petri plates 10^{-2} to 10^{-5} (Figure 77-1) and the 5th plate "*Morganella*".

3. Prepare the 10^{-3} and the 10^{-5} dilutions.

4. Pipet the appropriate volume of the dilutions into the labeled plates excepting the one labeled *Morganella*.

5. Pour about 20 ml of histidine agar into each plate including the *Morganella* plate and mix well.

6. Streak the *Morganella* plate for isolation with the pure culture of *Morganella morganii*

7. After solidification, overlay each plate with tempered histidine agar and allow that to solidify. This supresses colony spreading on the surface.

8. Incubate the plates at 35°C for 48–72 hours.

OBSERVATIONS

Periods 2-3

9. Examine the plates at 48 and 72 hours looking for purple colonies with a purple halo against the yellow background of the medium. The purple color results from histamine production. Organisms unable to produce histamine either do not grow or appear yellowish.

10. On the dilution plates, count these and record the number on the Results and Observations form.

11. Gram stain cells from a few colonies and record the results on the form.

12. Make a drawing of the *Morganella* plate showing a colony and the purple zone around it.

THOUGHT QUESTIONS

1. Another exercise in this manual dealt with amines in another context. What was it?

2. What kinds of foods are amines most likely to be found in? Why?

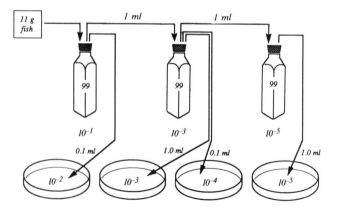

Figure 77-1. Dilution series

77. Histamine Production in Foods

RESULTS AND OBSERVATIONS

1. Count of histamine producers from fish

Dilution counted	Count	CFU/g

2. Cell observations

Colony No.	Gram Reaction	Morphology
1.		
2.		
3.		
4.		
5.		

3. Drawing of the *Morganella* plate

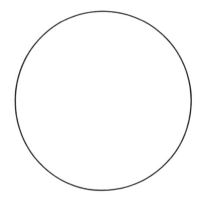

QUESTIONS

A. **True or False Statements:** Circle the correct response.

T   F   1.   Tuna and trout have been associated with scombroid poisoning.

T   F   2.   Histamine is the chemical which causes the symptoms associated with scombroid poisoning.

T   F   3.   Tyramine is a vasoactive amine produced from the decarboxylation of tryptophan.

T   F   4.   The Chinese restaurant syndrome is a food-borne illness caused by histamine.

B. **Completion:**

5.   _____ is the fish family most frequently associated with scombroid.

6.   Name a genus of bacteria producing scombroid poisoning: _____

7.   How would you prevent scombroid poisoning?

8.   Are there other amines derived from amino acids which cause illness in man? What are they?

UNIT *XIV*

Medical Microbiology

One of the great successes of microbiology has been in the understanding and conquest of infectious disease. Although there are still many unknowns, infectious disease is no longer the threat to life that it once was. This has resulted from success in identifying a particular organism with a specific disease, understanding how the organism is transmitted, and the discovery of antibiotics in treatment of disease, and of chemicals to kill or inhibit microbes.

As in all parts of the natural environment, the human body is a habitat for numerous microbes, some just waiting for an opportunity to cause trouble. The teeth, throat, and hands are prime sources of problems intimately involving microbes. The use of antibiotics, antiseptics, and germicides to control bacteria on or in the body and elsewhere requires knowledge of their effectiveness. The emergence of new disease agents and the development of resistance to chemical agents requires continual effort to stay ahead of the problem.

Unit XIV provides some experience in analyzing the microbial flora of parts of the body and tests for effectiveness of chemicals on microbes.

78   Normal Flora of the Human Throat

OBJECTIVES

The student will be able to:

1. properly perform the methods of obtaining a throat culture specimen and subsequent isolation of microorganisms from a throat swab.

2. list four significant cultural characteristics that can serve as an aid in the identification of the isolates.

3. list at least four organisms that are part of the normal flora of the human throat.

4. name the differential medium used in the cultivation of a throat specimen.

Under normal conditions the mouth and throat contain **considerable numbers** of microorganisms. Most of these are harmless but some are potential pathogens. Sometimes virulent organisms may be present but not producing disease, although the same species may be the cause of disease in other individuals.

Organisms commonly isolated from healthy individuals include *Staphylococcus* spp., *Streptococcus* spp., *Proteus* spp., diphtheroid bacilli, *Branhamella catarrhalis, Klebsiella pneumoniae,* other Gram-negative bacilli, lactobacilli, and *Haemophilus influenzae.*

Because most of these organisms have fastidious growth requirements, a **differential** medium (e.g., blood agar) is used for their cultivation. The reaction given by a bacterial species growing on a blood agar plate can be used as a valuable aid in the identification of certain pathogens.

MATERIALS (per person)

1. 5% sheep blood agar plate, sterile

2. 1 cotton swab, sterile

3. 1 tongue depressor

4. Clean microscope slides

5. Gram stain reagents

PROCEDURE (2 days)

Period 1

1. Divide the blood agar plate into 2 segments as in Figure 78-1.

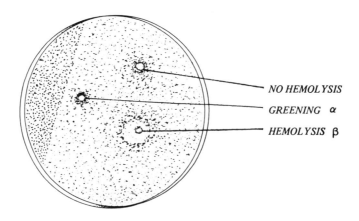

Figure 78-1. Types of hemolysis

2. Have your partner swab your throat with a sterile cotton swab. Use a tongue depressor to hold the tongue down and to assure easy access to the throat. Insert the swab through the mouth to the tonsillar area without touching the tongue or any other oral surface. You should constantly rotate the swab as you obtain the specimen (Figure 78-2).

3. Take the swab with your throat specimen, streak and rotate over the smaller sector (original inoculum sector) of the blood agar plate. Discard the swab.

4. Using a sterile inoculating loop, streak the original inoculum sector over the remaining sector so as to obtain well-isolated colonies.

5. Incubate the plate at 37°C for 24 hours.

OBSERVATIONS

Period 2

6. After incubation, examine the plate for both alpha- and beta-hemolytic colonies (Figure 78-1). Make smears and Gram stain any hemolytic colonies of either type. Examine the stained slides carefully and note Gram reaction, cell shape, and cell arrangement. Observe for significant cultural characteristics that might serve as an aid in identification.

7. Record your results in the table provided.

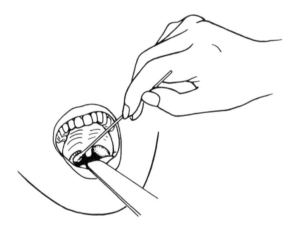

Figure 78-2. Proper method for taking a throat culture

THOUGHT QUESTIONS

1. How does the natural throat flora prevent more serious organisms from establishing themselves?

2. How can a pathogenic organism be present in the throat and not cause disease?

3. How does the particle size of droplets or droplet nuclei determine where in the upper respiratory tract they impinge?

78. Normal Flora of the Human Throat

RESULTS AND OBSERVATIONS

Colony	Size (mm)	Chromogenesis	Type of Hemolysis	Gram Reaction	Morphology (shape/arrangement)

QUESTIONS

A. True or False Statements: Circle the correct response.

T   F   1.   The presence of *Streptococcus pyogenes* in a throat culture always indicates "strep throat."

T   F   2.   The viridans group streptococci are the most prominent organisms of normal throat flora throughout life.

T   F   3.   If a throat swab cannot be cultured immediately, it should be placed in a tube of transport medium to prevent drying.

T   F   4.   A predominance of a specific organism in a throat culture usually indicates that it is responsible for a pathogenic condition in the throat.

T   F   5.   Colony size, color, hemolysis type, and Gram reaction are useful indicators of the means necessary for the final identification of an organism from a throat culture.

T   F   6.   The throat swab is used to streak the entire surface of your original isolation plate.

T   F   7.   Hemolysis is produced in erythrocytes.

T   F   8.   Pathogenic streptococci are generally beta-hemolytic.

B. Completion:

9–12.   List four organisms or genera that are part of the normal flora of the human throat.

9. _____ 11. _____

10. _____ 12. _____

13–15.   _____ is the differential medium used to culture the throat specimen, with incubation at _____ °C for _____ hours.

79 Dental Caries Susceptibility

OBJECTIVES

The student will be able to:

1. relate the acid production of certain mouth bacteria to dental caries susceptibility.

2. name the primary microorganisms linked to dental caries.

3. list the significant ingredients of Snyder test agar.

Dental caries result when certain bacteria ferment carbohydrates on the tooth surface. The fermentation process produces lactic acid or other organic acids which decalcify the tooth enamel causing decay to begin.

Streptococcus mutans has been considered to be the predominant organism responsible for dental caries. However, other organisms found as part of the normal mouth flora also produce acids and can contribute to the carious process.

The **Snyder test** is a simple method of determining caries susceptibility by measuring the rate of acid production from the metabolism of glucose by mouth microorganisms. As the microbes utilize the glucose present in the medium, the acids produced lower the pH below the uninoculated medium pH of 4.8. When the pH becomes 4.4 or lower, the pH indicator bromcresol green turns yellow. The susceptibility of an individual to caries is determined by the time it takes for the medium to turn yellow.

MATERIALS (per person)

1. 1 Snyder test agar deep, sterile

2. Paraffin cube (size $\sim$ 3 cm^3)

3. 1 Petri plate, sterile

4. 1 sterile 1 ml pipet and safety bulb

PROCEDURE (3 days)

Period 1

1. Melt a Snyder test agar deep and cool to 45°C.

2. While the deep cools, allow a paraffin cube to soften under your tongue and then chew it for 3 minutes. Do not swallow your saliva. Collect all of the saliva in a sterile empty Petri plate over the 3 minute period. Discard the paraffin.

3. Vigorously stir the saliva sample with the tip of a sterile 1 ml pipet for 30 seconds to more evenly distribute the organisms.

4. Aseptically pipet 0.2 ml of saliva into the cooled Snyder test agar.

5. Roll the tube between the palms of your hands until the saliva is evenly mixed with the medium (Figure 79-1). Allow it to solidify in an upright position.

6. Incubate the tube at 37°C.

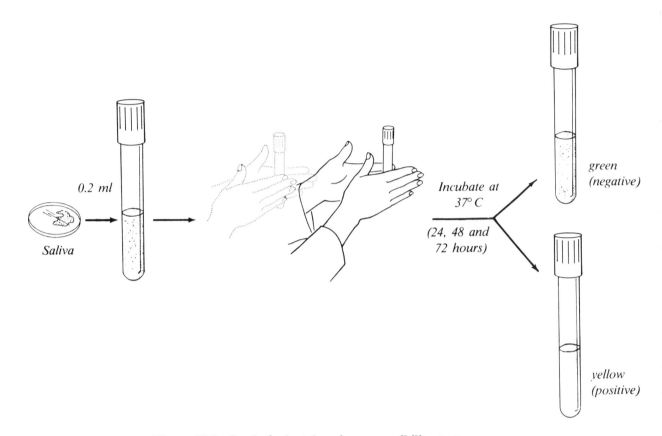

Figure 79-1. Snyder's dental caries susceptibility test

OBSERVATIONS

Periods 2-4

7. Examine after 24, 48, and 72 hours to see if the pH indicator has turned yellow. Study the following table to determine the degree of your dental caries susceptibility. Record your results in the table provided.

Table 79-1. Caries susceptibility scale

Caries Susceptibility	Medium turns yellow in		
	24 hrs	48 hrs	72 hrs
Marked	+		
Moderate	−	+	
Slight	−	−	+
None	−	−	−

THOUGHT QUESTIONS

1. What is plaque and what role does it play in periodontal disease?

2. *Streptococcus mutans* is only one of the organisms thought to be involved in caries formation. What is another?

3. What organisms cause the disease known as trench mouth or Vincent's disease?

79. Dental Caries Susceptibility

RESULTS AND OBSERVATIONS

Sample	Incubation Interval			Degree of Caries Susceptibility
	24 hrs	48 hrs	72 hrs	
Control				
Saliva				

+ = positive
– = negative

QUESTIONS

A. **True or False Statements:** Circle the correct response.

T   F   1.   Bromcresol purple is the pH indicator in Snyder test agar.

T   F   2.   When the pH indicator in Snyder test agar turns yellow, the test is positive.

T   F   3.   Interpretation of the Snyder test results depends only on the amount of acid produced.

T   F   4.   Tooth decay generally begins at pH 4.4.

T   F   5.   Carbohydrates are fermented to organic acids to produce tooth decay.

T   F   6.   Lactic acid is an organic acid.

B. **Completion:**

7–9.   _____ is the primary organism involved in dental caries.

It is a Gram-_____ nonsporeforming _____ (morphology).

10–11.   List the 2 main ingredients in Snyder test agar.

10. _____

11. _____

12–15. List 4 measures to prevent dental caries.

12. _____

13. _____

14. _____

15. _____

16–17. Do the results of this exercise agree with your case history of caries? Explain. _____

_____

_____

80 Handwashing and Skin Bacteria

OBJECTIVES

The student will be able to:

1. define the terms "transient" and "resident" microbes relative to the skin and hands.

2. explain the importance of handwashing or scrubbing to medicine, food preparation, and general health.

3. describe the general characteristics of the transient and resident bacteria.

The skin of humans and other animals serves as a habitat for many microbes living in secretions and on skin tissue. Most of these **resident** microbes are Gram-positive bacteria and yeasts harmless under normal conditions which even offer some protection from possibly pathogenic organisms. Protection is afforded in a number of ways, such as direct competition, and production of acids and other inhibitory metabolites. The skin, especially the hands, acquire a large number of organisms through contact with many environmental sources of microbes. These microbes are not normal to the skin and usually don't grow but are not destroyed by the resident bacteria, at least immediately. These microbes are termed **transient** microbes and are very easily removed from the skin in contrast to the resident forms which are very difficult to remove and cannot be removed completely. The nature of these organisms is highly varied, including Gram-positive and Gram-negative bacteria, yeasts, molds, viruses, and parasites depending on the source.

The transient bacteria are most important on the hands, since hands are so intimately involved in many of the portals of entry and exit of pathogens. These bacteria are easily transferred to food, cuts, surgical openings, and directly to the mouth or other body opening. The Austrian physician Ignatz Semmelweis observed in 1846-47 that puerperal fever in women just after giving birth was related to medical students not washing their hands before examining the women. Nurses usually washed and during a period when the students were absent and only the nurses present, Semmelweis noted that the puerperal fever rate declined. He established a policy requiring the medical students to scrub their hands before examining the patients and as a result the puerperal fever rate dropped from 12% to slightly more than 1% in one year. This and later observations led to the surgical scrub used today in medical practice.

The hands are important in other ways as well. Examples include the transfer of food-borne illness organisms from feces after a bowel movement, from the nose and mouth, and from food-to-food (e.g., *Salmonella* organisms). Hands can also transfer organisms directly to the mouth and may play a very important role in the transmission of certain respiratory and intestinal diseases.

This exercise is intended to introduce the student to transient organisms and the importance of handwashing as a method of hygiene.

MATERIALS (per group of four)

1. 2 washbasins with 1000 ml of sterile tap water
2. 2 sterile surgical scrub brushes
3. 2 sterile 1 ml pipets and safety bulb
4. 1 flask plate count agar (PCA), sterile
5. 1 flask violet red bile agar (VRB), sterile
6. 1 flask mannitol salt agar (MSA), sterile
7. 18 Petri plates, sterile
8. Hand lotion
9. 70% alcohol
10. L-shaped glass rod
11. Liquid soap (e.g., Ivory)

PROCEDURE (2 days)

Period 1

A. Scrubbing

1. The group is divided into the washer, helper, and the plate makers.

2. The person assigned to wash, removes a sterile scrub brush from its wrapping while the helper removes the protective lid from the first bowl. The scrubber then wets both hands and the brush in the bowl.

3. The scrubber scrubs first one hand then the other for 30 seconds each. Scrubbing includes the palms and the backs of the hands down as far as the wrist bone, the fingers and under the nails. The helper reads instructions and times and directs the scrubber as needed.

4. At the end of the scrub, the pair assigned to plate now removes the bowl and makes the first set of plates (see part B below).

5. The scrubber now moves to a running water tap and, with the aid of the helper lathers both hands with soap, scrubbing them with the same brush as used in step No. 3 for one minute each. The hands are scrubbed in the same manner as previously described. Finally, the hands are thoroughly rinsed.

6. The helper now takes the used scrub brush, hands a sterile one to the scrubber and then uncovers the second bowl.

7. The scrubber wets both hands in the bowl and repeats the scrubbing of step No. 3 except that each hand is scrubbed 1 minute. At the end of scrubbing, the bowl is removed by the plating team for the second set of plates. The helper provides the scrubber with some hand lotion.

B. Plating

1. For bowl No. 1, lay out 12 plates according to Figure 80-1. Label 3 plates VRB and 1 ml, 0.5 ml, and 0.1 ml, respectively. Label 3 plates MSA and the same volumes. Label 6 plates PCA, 2 with 1 ml, 1 with 0.5 ml, and 2 with 0.1 ml.

2. Take the L-shaped glass rod, rinse it with 70% alcohol and flame it. When cool, hold the long part of the rod between the palms of your hands. Lower the shorter end into bowl No. 1. Roll the rod rapidly between the palms so that the lower part revolves back and forth mixing the water of the bowl. If available, a magnetic stir bar can be sterilized in the bowl and the water mixed by the magnetic stir unit.

3. Pipet the appropriate volume from bowl No. 1 into each labeled plate. Pour melted cooled agar into the proper Petri plates, mix, and allow them to solidify.

4. For bowl No. 2 only 6 PCA plates are prepared. Mix, pipet, and pour plates as described above and illustrated in Figure 80-1.

5. Incubate all plates inverted at 37°C for 24 hours.

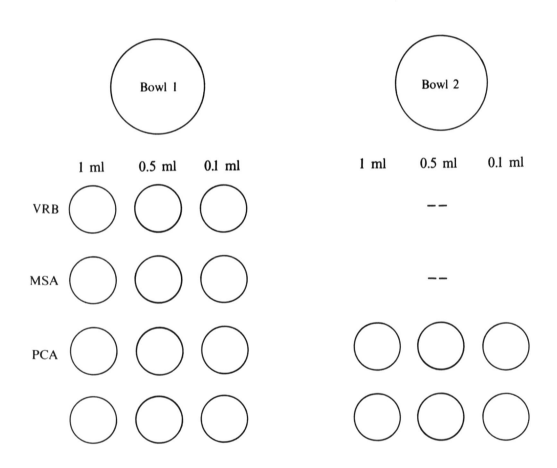

Figure 80-1

OBSERVATIONS

Period 2

1. Count colonies on all plates using the following criteria:

   a. VRB. Count all deep purple colonies (usually with a purple zone of precipitated bile around them) and ignore others. These are coliforms, bacteria usually associated with the intestinal tract. Most people have a few on their hands even when washed. These are usually considered transient bacteria.

   b. MSA. Mannitol salt agar is very selective for staphylococci which are usually resident bacteria. *Staphylococcus aureus*, however, can be either resident or transient. Count all colonies growing on this medium.

   c. PCA. This is a general purpose medium which will grow most skin organisms whether resident or transient. Count all colonies on this medium.

2. Record counts in the table on the report form. Convert the count per ml of basin water to count per hand as follows:

$$\frac{\text{count/ml} \times 1000}{2} = \text{count per hand}$$

3. Select 2 or 3 representative colonies on each plate and make Gram stains. Report the morphology and Gram reaction in the space provided on the report form.

INTERPRETATION

Most people will have a few coliforms on the hands and quite a few others. These will be removed fairly easily. The PCA count should be significantly lower in the second bowl. A third scrub would reduce the PCA count further but not as much as the first scrub.

THOUGHT QUESTIONS

1. Medical implants such as steel joints, contact lenses, and plastics are often colonized by a resident bacterium *Staphylococcus epidermidis*. What factors aid this and other organisms in colonizing such implants?

2. Can transient bacteria ever become resident bacteria?

80. Handwashing and Skin Bacteria

RESULTS AND OBSERVATIONS

		Count/Volume			Count/ml in Bowl	Count/Hand
		1 ml	0.5 ml	0.1 ml		
Bowl No. 1	PCA					
	MSA					
	VRB					
Bowl No. 2	PCA					

Morphology and Gram stain

1.

2.

3.

4.

5.

6.

7.

8.

9.

10.

What was the percent reduction in total count between the two washings?

$$\frac{(\text{PCA count/ml in bowl 1}) - (\text{PCA count/ml in bowl 2})}{(\text{PCA count/ml in bowl 1})} \times 100 = \%$$

Was there a change in morphological types and/or Gram reaction between the bowls? If so, what was the change?

_____

_____

QUESTIONS

A.   True or False Statements: Circle the correct response.

T   F   1.   Bacteria are the only microbes found in the resident microbe group.

T   F   2.   The transient microbes may include mold spores.

T   F   3.   Typhoid fever may be spread by hands in contact with food.

T   F   4.   Viral diseases would not be expected to be transmitted by hands.

T   F   5.   The resident bacteria are usually harmless.

T   F   6.   The Gram-positive bacteria are usually more common among the transient bacteria than the resident group.

B.   Completion:

7.   Bacteria which are easily removed from the skin are called the _____ bacteria.

8.   Bacteria normally living in or on the skin are called _____ bacteria.

9.   Handling a chicken with salmonellae on the skin would contribute to the _____ bacteria on your hands.

10–11.   The man who first observed the relationship between handwashing and disease was

_____. The disease he helped reduce by requiring medical students

to wash their hands was _____.

12.   This disease was caused by _____ (organism).

13.   It is/is not (cross out one) common to find coliforms on the hands.

14.   Most resident bacteria are Gram-_____ .

81 Antimicrobial Susceptibility Testing

OBJECTIVES

The student will be able to:

1. perform an antimicrobial susceptibility disk test.

2. measure a zone of inhibition.

3. distinguish between an antibiotic and a disinfectant.

2. describe the Kirby-Bauer test.

2. discuss the variation encountered in such tests as this.

Antibiotics by definition are chemical agents which are produced by living organisms either killing or inhibiting the growth of other organisms. Antibiotics belong to a larger group of antimicrobial agents affecting growth and used in medicine called chemotherapeutic agents. Other chemotherapeutic agents, such as the sulfa drugs, are made chemically. Because many of the antibiotics now can be made chemically or modified chemically, the distinction is blurred a bit. In this exercise, the term antibiotic will be used for all of these chemical agents. Antibiotics are generally distinguished from antiseptics and disinfectants (see Exercise 82) on a number of points. Antibiotics are generally effective in very small quantities and are usually very specific for one group of organisms. Among the antibiotics directed against prokaryotes, most are produced as secondary metabolites by three genera of microbes, *Bacillus* and *Streptomyces* from the bacteria, and *Penicillium* from the fungi.

In clinical or hospital practice, the attending physician not only may wish to know the identity of an infecting organism but may want to know the kind of chemotherapeutic agent to use in controlling the infection. The most effective agent, or better, the antibiotics which would be *ineffective*, can be determined by a simple laboratory test — the Kirby-Bauer test.

The **Kirby-Bauer method** of antibiotic sensitivity testing has evolved over a number of years to solve the problem of the many variations that are observed in such testing. The test is basically a diffusion test using a standard medium under standard conditions with a particular test organism. A paper disk is saturated with a known antibiotic concentration and placed in the center of a Petri plate previously heavily inoculated with a test organism. After incubation, any zone of inhibition (area of no growth) around the disk is measured and related to a standard for that compound and concentration. From this, the test organism can be said to be resistant, sensitive, or intermediate. No two tests are exactly alike so standard concentrations are used. Variation occurs with such things as the volume of medium in the dish, the medium composition, the amount of inoculum, the solubility of the test agent, and many other factors. All of these factors must be controlled as much as possible. The standard medium for this method is Mueller-Hinton agar. These variations make comparison between different antibiotics difficult, but it is useful for comparing different concentrations of the same antibiotic and differences between organisms. Standard strains of *Staphylococcus aureus* and *Escherichia coli* are used as controls for inhibitory zone diameter. Although the strains used in this exercise are not the standard strains, they may be used in that manner.

This exercise is intended to introduce the student to a standard clinical laboratory procedure for determining antibiotic sensitivity.

MATERIALS (per group of 4 students)

1. 18-24 hour old broth cultures of *Staphylococcus aureus, Escherichia coli, Pseudomonas aeruginosa,* and *Saccharomyces cerevisiae*

2. 100 ml Mueller-Hinton agar, sterile

3. 4 Petri plates, sterile

4. 4 cotton swabs, sterile

5. Commercial antibiotic dispenser or individual disks

6. Forceps (if needed)

7. 70% alcohol (if forceps are needed)

8. Calipers or plastic millimeter rule

PROCEDURE (4 days)

Period 1

1. One student in the group of four pours four Petri plates of Mueller-Hinton agar. The agar should be the same depth in all the plates. Allow them to solidify.

2. Label each plate with the name of one of the four organisms assigned.

3. Each student then swabs one plate with the assigned organism. Aseptically remove a swab from its container and wet it in the broth culture. Remove excess fluid by rolling the swab against the inside of the tube. Streak the swab uniformly across the entire surface of the plate, then rotate the plate 90° and repeat. Repeat the swabbing once more at a third angle. Discard the swab in an autoclave bag or the disinfectant solution provided. At the end of this step, each person in the group will have one plate inoculated with a different organism.

4. With a commercial multiple disk dispenser, remove the Petri plate top, place the dispenser over the agar surface and press firmly on the plunger. This results in depositing several disks onto the agar surface. Some devices press the disk down to ensure contact. If your device does not automatically tamp the disks, use flame-sterilized forceps to gently press each disk onto the agar surface. (Often these devices will not work if one dispenser is empty; check for empty holders before hand.)

5. With individual dispensers, release a disk one at a time around the margin of the Petri plate, about 1.5 cm inside the rim and about 2 cm apart.

6. If no dispenser is available, transfer disks one at a time using sterilized forceps as described in step No. 5.

7. Incubate the *S. cerevisiae* plate at 25°-30°C for 48 hours, and all others at 35°-37°C for 24 hours. Invert the plates.

OBSERVATIONS

Periods 2 and 3

8. After incubation, observe each plate for zones of inhibition around the disks (i.e., a zone of no growth or clearing). Note whether partial growth inhibition occurs in the zone instead. Plates should be examined against a dark background as illustrated in Figure 81-1.

9. Measure the diameter of the zone with the calipers or with a millimeter rule to the nearest millimeter. Be sure the edge of the rule bisects the center of the disk and the disk is included in the measurement. Record the name of the antibiotic and the measurement in the table provided. From Table 81-1, determine if your organism is resistant, intermediate, or sensitive to the antibiotic and enter an R, I, or S to the right of the measurement.

10. Record any unusual appearance: resistant colonies, concentric rings or bands of heavier growth, heavy growth ring at zone margin, precipitates in the zone or along its margin, etc.

THOUGHT QUESTIONS

1. What is the mode of action on the organism of each of these antibiotics?

2. If colonies grow in the clear zone after a period of incubation, what are they? How could you tell?

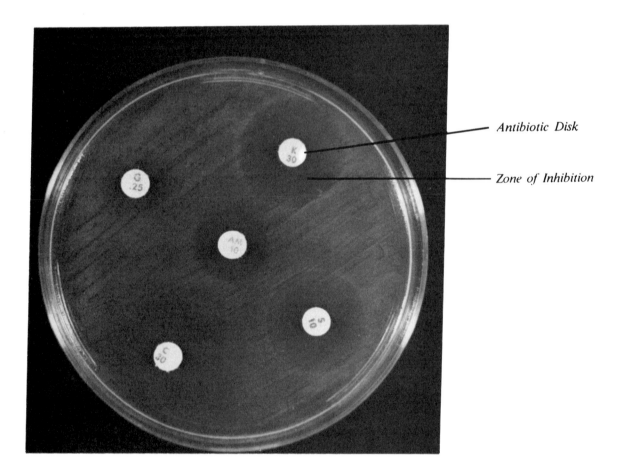

Antibiotic Disk

Zone of Inhibition

Figure 81-1. Example of antibiotic disks and zones of inhibition

Table 81-1. Antibiotic zone size interpretive chart (BBL Sensidisc data)

Antibiotic	Code	Conc.	Zone dia., mm Resistant	Zone dia., mm Intermediate	Zone dia., mm Sensitive
			<		>
Ampicillin, Gram neg & enterococ.	AM10	10 mcg	11	12–13	14
Ampicillin, staph & highly sensitive	AM10	10 mcg	20	21–28	29
Bacitracin	B10	10 U	8	9–12	13
Carbenicillin, *Pseudomonas* spp.	CB50	50 mcg	12	13–14	15
Cephaloglycin	CG30	30 mcg	16	17–26	27
Cephaloridine	CD30	30 mcg	11	12–15	16
Cephalothin	CF30	30 mcg	14	15–17	18
Chloramphenicol	C30	30 mcg	12	13–17	18
Clindamycin	CC2	2 mcg	11	12–15	16
Erythromycin	E15	15 mcg	13	14–17	18
Gentamicin	GM10	10 mcg	12		13
Kanamycin	K30	30 mcg	13	14–17	18
Lincomycin	L2	2 mcg	9	10–14	15
Methicillin	DP5	5 mcg	9	10–13	14
Nafcillin, Oxacillin	NF1, Ox1	1 mcg	10	11–12	13
Nalidixic acid	NA30	30 mcg	13	14–18	19
Neomycin	N30	30 mcg	12	13–16	17
Nitrofurantoin	F/M300	300 mcg	14	15–16	17
Novobiocin	NB30	30 mcg	17	18–21	22
Oleandomycin	OL15	15 mcg	11	12–16	17
Penicillin G, staphylococci	P10	10 U	20	21–28	29
Penicillin G, other organisms	P10	10 U	11	12–21	22
Polymyxin B	PB300	300 U	8	9–11	12
Rifampin	RA5	5 mcg	24		
Streptomycin	S10	10 mcg	11	12–14	15
Triple sulfa	SSS.25	250 mcg	12	13–16	17
Tetracycline	Te30	30 mcg	14	15–18	19
Vancomycin	Va30	30 mcg	9	10–11	12

81. Antimicrobial Susceptibility Testing

RESULTS AND OBSERVATIONS

Antibiotic	Disk Conc'n	Inhibition Zone Diameter (mm)			
		S. aureus	E. coli	P. aeruginosa	S. cerevisiae

Other observations (note the antibiotic and organism):

QUESTIONS

A. True or False Statements: Circle the correct response.

T F 1. The best antibiotic is one toxic to both prokaryotes and eukaryotes.

T F 2. An antibiotic is usually effective in small doses.

T F 3. Standard strains of bacteria are used as controls in the Kirby-Bauer method.

T F 4. A variation in zone size with the standard strain often means the test was performed differently than it should have been.

T F 5. Antiseptics and antibiotics are essentially the same.

B. Completion:

6. The _____ method is a standardized disk diffusion test for determining antibiotic sensitivity.

7–10. Name four factors which may affect the diameter of the inhibitory zone in any particular test.

7. _____

8. _____

9. _____

10. _____

11. _____ agar is the medium used to perform this test.

12–14. Name the three microbial genera responsible for the most antibiotics.

12. _____

13. _____

14. _____

15. In the space below explain why *Saccharomyces cerevisiae* was not affected by these antibiotics.

82

Action of Disinfectants and Antiseptics

OBJECTIVES

The student will be able to:

1. perform a disk plate inhibition assay for a disinfectant.

2. accurately measure a zone of inhibition.

3. distinguish between antiseptics, disinfectants, and sanitizers.

4. explain some of the reasons for variation in zone size between chemicals.

Antiseptics, disinfectants, and sanitizers are chemical agents used to kill microbes under different conditions. Antiseptics originally were agents that either killed pathogens or inhibited their growth allowing the body defenses to finish the job. These agents were used on skin or animate objects. **Disinfectants** had much the same connotation, except they were used only on inanimate objects. Today, disinfectants must kill vegetative cells but not endospores of bacteria. Since some viruses escape inactivation by disinfectants, the current definition of disinfectant is under review. **Antiseptics** are defined essentially the same except for the inhibitory or bacteriostatic property. Antiseptics are commonly used on animate surfaces today. **Sanitizers** are chemical agents widely used in the food and restaurant industries. They are intended to kill a predetermined number of vegetative cells (not endospores) on an **already well cleaned** surface. Public health standards dictate 1 cell out of more than 1,000,000 can survive (i.e., a 99.9999+% reduction).

A number of tests are approved by the U.S. Food and Drug Administration, including the **Phenol Coefficient Test** (the effect of the agent on several pathogenic bacteria compared to phenol as a standard) and the **Use Dilution Test** (the effectiveness of the agent under actually used conditions). These are generally very demanding tests and require special equipment. In this exercise a method is used which allows the student to see the inhibitory effects of the chemical. It is not a quantitative test, however, since each chemical agent behaves differently (see below). A standard base medium is poured into a Petri plate and the surface swabbed heavily with a test culture. A filter paper disk is saturated with the test chemical, drained, and placed on the agar surface in the center of the dish. After a period of incubation, any zone of inhibition is measured and recorded. A number of interesting additional observations can be made. Sometimes a ring of increased growth is seen at the rim of the inhibitory zone — a number of explanations have been proposed for this. Some agents cause mutations and occasionally resistant colonies arise in the inhibitory zone with prolonged incubation.

This method, as with antibiotics, should not be used to directly compare these chemical agents. Each chemical is different in structure, solubility and thus diffusion, adherence to the filter paper disk, interaction with medium constituents, and the effect on the bacteria themselves. Similar kinds of chemicals behave in a similar manner and dilutions of the same chemical are comparable.

MATERIALS (groups of four)

1. 18-24 hour old cultures of *Staphylococcus aureus, Escherichia coli, Bacillus subtilis,* and *Saccharomyces cerevisiae*

2. 20 sterile Petri plates (5 each)

3. 1 flask of nutrient agar, sterile

4. 1 glass Petri plate with 25 paper disks, sterile

5. 4 loosely wrapped cotton swabs, sterile

6. 70% alcohol

7. 5 chemical disinfectants, antiseptics, or sanitizers. Each student is encouraged to bring at least one.

8. 5 forceps (1 per chemical)

9. Calipers or plastic millimeter rule

PROCEDURE (2–3 days)

Period 1

1. Each student is assigned to a group of four, one person to each available organism.

2. Each student pours 5 Petri plates from the flask provided and allows them to solidify. Label the cover with the name of the organism provided.

3. After the plates have solidified, aseptically remove a cotton swab from its container, and wet it in the broth culture assigned. Remove excess fluid by rolling the swab against the inside of the tube. Streak the swab uniformly across the entire surface of the plate, then rotate the plate 90° and repeat. Repeat the swabbing once more at a third angle. Return the swab to the culture tube and repeat this procedure for **each** plate. Discard the swab in an autoclave bag or the disinfectant solution provided. At the end of this step, each student in the group will have five plates inoculated with one organism; four different organisms in the group.

4. Dip a forceps in alcohol and flame in the Bunsen burner. Allow the forceps to cool and pick up a paper disk. Dip the disk into the chemical to saturate it. Remove the disk from the chemical and touch it gently to the side of the container to draw off excess. Then place the disk in the center of one of your Petri plates. Label the Petri dish cover with the **name** of the chemical and its **concentration**.

5. Repeat the previous step with each of your plates, each time using a **different** chemical. At the end of this procedure, each student will have one organism and 5 different chemicals.

6. Incubate the *S. cerevisiae* plates at 30°C for 24-48 hours. Incubate the remaining plates at 35°-37°C for 24 hours.

OBSERVATIONS

Period 2

7. After incubation, observe each plate for a zone of inhibition (i.e., a zone of no growth or clearing). Note if only partial growth inhibition occurs or if well separated colonies occur in the zone of inhibition. Plates should be examined against a dark background as in Exercise 81 (Figure 81-1).

   Measure the diameter of the zone with the calipers or with a millimeter rule to the nearest millimeter. Be sure the edge of the rule bisects the center of the disk and the disk is included in the measurement. Record the measurement in the table provided. Record any unusual appearance: resistant colonies, concentric rings or bands of heavier growth, heavy growth ring at zone margin, precipitates in the zone or along its margin, etc.

THOUGHT QUESTIONS

1. What agency approves the disinfectants for use?

2. What is the practical meaning of a 99.9999+% kill on a utensil?

3. If known, what is the mode of action on the cells of these chemicals?

Name _____ Date _____ Grade _____

82. Action of Disinfectants and Antiseptics

RESULTS AND OBSERVATIONS

Disinfectant/ Antiseptic	Conc'n	Inhibition Zone Diameter (mm)			
		S. aureus	*E. coli*	*B. subtilis*	*S. cerevisiae*

Other observations (note the chemical and organism):

QUESTIONS

A. **True or False Statements:** Circle the correct response.

    T   F   1.   Sanitizers are used on unwashed utensils.

    T   F   2.   Zones of inhibition are measured and recorded in inches.

    T   F   3.   All disinfectants are equally effective against a given organism.

    T   F   4.   The term antiseptic is a synonym of the term disinfectant.

    T   F   5.   An agent used as a gargle would commonly be called a disinfectant.

    T   F   6.   The "zone of inhibition" refers to the clear area around a chemical agent in which no bacteria are growing.

B. **Completion:**

7.   The _____ is a regulatory test to measure the effect of a disinfectant on pathogens.

8.   _____ are agents used to kill bacteria on well cleaned food handling equipment.

9.   The suffix _____ means "to kill."

10.   The suffix _____ means "to arrest," "to stop," or "to inhibit."

11.   Agents used to kill or inhibit growth of vegetative cells are generally called

_____ .

12–13. List two major differences between an antibiotic and a disinfectant.

    12. _____

    13. _____

83 Use-Dilution Testing of Disinfectants

OBJECTIVES

The student will be able to:

1. perform a Use-Dilution test.

2. describe the practical meaning of such a test.

3. determine the Use-Dilution of a disinfectant under clean conditions and when organic matter (dirt) is present.

4. define the phenol coefficient.

Disinfectants and sanitizing agents are widely used in hospitals, restaurants, laboratories, and the food processing industry to reduce in number or prevent the growth of microorganisms causing disease or spoilage. Chemical agents used for this purpose are many and, unless properly applied, may not achieve the desired control. If too much is used, it is wasteful and expensive and can lead to taste and odor problems as well as irritating the skin or the nasal passage.

In order to be properly used, some comparison between the chemicals is needed as well as a measure of effectiveness in actual use. Exercise 82 on disinfectants and antiseptics does not demonstrate the effectiveness of such agents when in actual use. A widely used standard of comparison for these chemicals is the **Phenol Coefficient Test** as prescribed by the Association of Official Analytical Chemists (AOAC) in their "Official Methods of Analysis," 15th ed., 1990 (AOAC, 1111 N. 19th St., Suite 210, Arlington, VA 22209). This test uses phenol as the standard against a typical Gram-negative pathogen, *Salmonella typhimurium*, and a pyogenic organism, *Staphylococcus aureus*. The phenol coefficient is defined as the dilution of disinfectant killing the organism in ten minutes, but not in five minutes, divided by the dilution of phenol with the same result. Many chemical agents do not act biologically in the same manner as phenol, and the phenol coefficient is merely a useful comparative standard.

Under actual conditions of use, disinfectants are not always as effective as the phenol coefficient would predict. Thus an alternate test for determining the most effective dilution of the disinfectant for actual use has been developed called the **Use-Dilution Test**. Two versions of this test are used officially. In the United States the **AOAC method** is widely used, and in England the **Kelsey-Sykes Test** (*Pharmaceutical Journal* 213:528-530, 1974) is used. The Kelsey-Sykes test also includes the effect of "dirt" on the disinfectant, an important consideration since many agents are reduced in effectiveness and some completely inactivated by organic matter.

The following experiment is a simplified version of the AOAC method with a "dirt" effect. Students should beware of comparing results of this exercise with bottle labels or published data since the official method is different.

MATERIALS (per group of 6 students)

1. 1 glass Petri plate with 61 steel brads, sterile

2. 48-54 hour nutrient broth culture of *Staphylococcus aureus*

3. 60 sterile test tubes

4. 6 nutrient broth tubes, sterile

5. 6 containers (1 per person) with sufficient diluted disinfectant for the test

6. 4 glass Petri plates with circular filter papers inside, sterile

7. 6 inoculating needles bent at the tip into a hook to pick up the nails (prepare using non-sterile nails) as follows:

8. 3 flasks of distilled water, sterile

9. 3 flasks with yeast cake suspension, autoclaved

10. 2 sterile 10 ml pipets

11. 2 sterile 1 ml pipets

12. Safety bulb

13. 6 sterile 250 ml beakers or flasks

14. 2 forceps

PROCEDURE (2 days) See flow diagram in Figure 83-1.

Period 1

1. Six students should work together on one disinfectant, three using "clean" conditions and three using "dirty" conditions in accordance with Table 83-1.

Table 83-1. Phenol example

Clean			Dirty		
Student No.	Dilution Letter	Phenol Conc. % (w/v)	Student No.	Dilution Letter	Phenol Conc. % (w/v)
1	A	5.0	4	D	5.0
2	B	2.0	5	E	2.0
3	C	1.0	6	F	1.0

Table 83-2 shows some phenol coefficients, use-dilutions, and recommended starting concentrations for dilutions A & D. Calculate the remaining dilutions per Table 83-2 footnote c. Each student will be responsible for one dilution under either clean or dirty conditions.

Table 83-2. Disinfectant concentrations

Disinfectant	Approx. Phenol Coef.	Use-dilution Conc.[a, b]	Test Conc. A & D[c] (%)
Phenol	1.0	5.0% (1–20)	5
Lysol	5.0	1.0% (1–100)	1
Mercurochrome	1.7	2.5% (1–40)	2.5
Merthiolate	50	0.1% (1–100)	0.1
Tincture of Iodine with 3% Alcohol	6.3	0.8% (1–125)	0.8[e]
Lugol's Iodine	5.0	1.0% (1–100)	1.0[e]
Formaldehyde	0.7	7.0% (1–14)	7.0
Ethyl Alcohol	0.04	70%	70
Isopropyl Alcohol	0.06	70%	70
Hydrogen Peroxide	—	as is	as is
Sodium Hypochlorite (laundry bleach)	—	0.02% (1–5000)	0.02[e]
Steritex (Quat)	25	0.2% (1–500)	0.2
Roccal (Quat)	25	0.2% (1–500)	0.2
Pine Oil[d]	4	0.3% (1–300)	0.3[d]

[a] This is the concentration recommended for practical use.

[b] General method for calculation of the use-dilution concentration is the phenol coefficient x20 = parts of water to mix with 1 part of disinfectant. The reciprocal of this number is the % concentration.

[c] Concentrations for tubes B & E and C & F can be approximated as 40% and 20%, respectively, of the recommended A & D concentration (Table 83-1). If this does not prove satisfactory, repeat using other concentrations.

[d] Many household disinfectants contain 10–30% pine oil plus some alcohol. Use label information to obtain dilutions A & D (Table 83-1).

[e] Halogens and some others may require that concentrations for D, E, and F be increased by 10 times in the presence of organic matter (Table 83-1).

2. Pour one tube (12–15 ml) of a 48–54 hour nutrient broth culture of *S. aureus* over the 61 sterile nails in the glass Petri dish and let stand for at least 15 minutes.

3. Remove the nails with the sterile (flamed) special inoculating needle hook to a sterile Petri plate with an absorbent filter in the bottom, 31 brads to one dish and 30 to the second.

4. After excess liquid has been absorbed, dump the brads onto the filter paper in another sterile dish and allow them to dry thoroughly in a 37°C incubator.

5. If not already prepared, each student prepares 120 ml of the assigned disinfectant dilution as follows (phenol example): Place a 250 ml sterile flask or beaker on a balance and aseptically add 6 g (or ml) of phenol. Then add 120 g of sterile distilled water for a 5% (w/v) solution. Reasonable accuracy is required. For 2%, add 2.4 g (or ml) and 120 g of water. For 1%, add 1.2 g (or ml) and 120 g water. Students preparing the "dirty" solution proceed in the same manner *except* the autoclaved yeast suspension is used instead of the distilled water.

6. Using a sterile 10 ml pipet, each student then aseptically adds 10 ml of the disinfectant dilution to each of 10 sterile tubes properly labeled with the dilution and numbered 1 to 10 and the letter of the dilution being used.

7. To begin the experiment, pick up one brad from the dish with 31, using sterilized (and cool) forceps and drop the nail into a nutrient broth tube. Label "control." This is the growth control.

8. Each student then labels 10 nutrient broth tubes with the dilution letter and the tube number (1 to 10), corresponding exactly to the ten disinfectant tubes.

9. Then each student, using sterile forceps, drops one brad (with the head *up*) into each of the ten disinfectant tubes, one at a time at intervals of one minute.
   Note: Brads must be removed later at one minute intervals.

10. When the last brad has been placed in its tube, sterilize the specially formed inoculating needle and at exactly 10 minutes from placing the first brad in the first tube, remove it, allow it to drain by touching it to the glass on the inside of the disinfectant tube at an angle, then drop it into the correspondingly labeled nutrient broth tube. Proceed in a like manner at one minute intervals with the other tubes. The one minute interval allows sufficient time to retrieve the brad, transfer it, and *sterilize* the needle before going to the next tube.

11. All 61 tubes are then incubated for 48 hours at 37°C. (*Note:* Tubes may incubated longer than 48 hours if necessary.)

OBSERVATIONS

Period 2

12. Record tubes as + if growth occurs and – if there is no growth. Enter your data in the table provided in the results section. Obtain the remaining data from the other five members of your group.

13. Results showing growth from any of the ten tubes indicates that dilution to be unsafe for use.

14. In some cases neutralizers are used in the broth medium (Table 83-3) or the brad may be subcultured to a second set of broth tubes if the agent has inhibitory effects after transfer (i.e., it is rinsed in the first tube and deposited in the second).

THOUGHT QUESTIONS

1. Why does "dirt" or organic matter have an effect on disinfectants?

2. Describe the differences between the AOAC and Kelsey-Sykes use-dilution tests.

3. Which of the following would you expect to be *most* affected by the presence of organic matter—phenol or chlorine? Explain why.

Table 83-3. Disinfectant neutralizers[a]

Disinfectant	Neutralizer
Halogens[b]	Sodium thiosulfate
Quats[b]	Lecithin, stearate, Lubrol W
Phenolics	Tween 80, charcoal, ferric chloride
Hexachlorophene	Tween 80
Formalin	Ammonium
Hydrogen peroxide	Catalase
Mercurials	Sodium thioglycollate
Mercuric chloride	Sodium sulfide

[a] References:
Conference on environmental aspects of institutional infections.
U.S. Public Health Service, CDC, Altanta GA, pp. 20–21. November 1960.
J. Applied Bacteriol. 23:318–344. 1960.

[b] The most commonly used disinfectants.

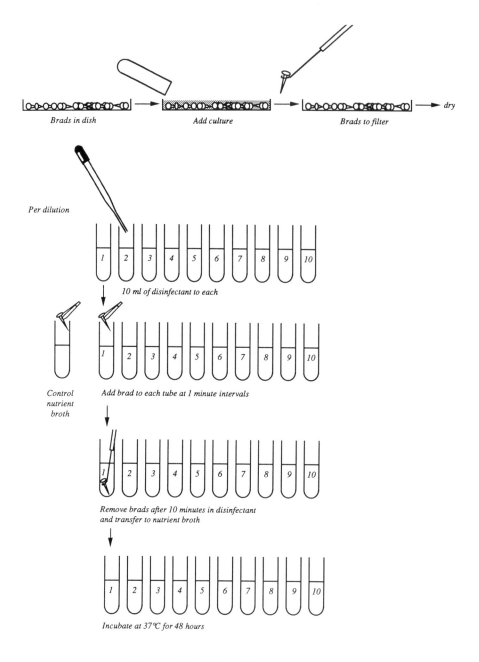

Brads in dish → *Add culture* → *Brads to filter* → dry

Per dilution

| 1 | 2 | 3 | 4 | 5 | 6 | 7 | 8 | 9 | 10 |

10 ml of disinfectant to each

Control nutrient broth

| 1 | 2 | 3 | 4 | 5 | 6 | 7 | 8 | 9 | 10 |

Add brad to each tube at 1 minute intervals

| 1 | 2 | 3 | 4 | 5 | 6 | 7 | 8 | 9 | 10 |

Remove brads after 10 minutes in disinfectant and transfer to nutrient broth

| 1 | 2 | 3 | 4 | 5 | 6 | 7 | 8 | 9 | 10 |

Incubate at 37°C for 48 hours

Figure 83-1. Flow diagram

83. Use-Dilution Testing of Disinfectants

RESULTS AND OBSERVATIONS

Table of results
(+ = growth, – = no growth)

Disinfectant name _____

Control (+ or –) _____

"Clean"

Dilution	Tube No.									
	1	2	3	4	5	6	7	8	9	10
A										
B										
C										

"Dirty"

Dilution	Tube No.									
	1	2	3	4	5	6	7	8	9	10
D										
E										
F										

The safe use dilution under "clean" conditions is _____ .

The safe use dilution under "dirty" conditions is _____ .

QUESTIONS

A. **True or False Statements:** Circle the correct response.

    T   F   1.   Since these are disinfectants, aseptic technique is not required in this experiment.

    T   F   2.   The phenol coefficient is expressed as a ratio.

    T   F   3.   The phenol coefficient tells how effective the test disinfectant is.

    T   F   4.   The use-dilution test is considered to be more practical than the phenol coefficient to describe disinfectant effectiveness.

    T   F   5.   A rough estimation of the use-dilution is obtained by multiplying the phenol coefficient by 100.

B. **Completion:**

6. The use-dilution test performed in England is called the _____ .

7. The use-dilution test used in the United States is described in _____ published by _____ .

8. When the dilution of disinfectant killing a test organism in 10 minutes, but not in 5, is divided by the dilution of phenol with the same effect, the result is called the _____ .

9. A good household disinfectant containing chlorine is _____ .

84 Ames Mutagen Test

OBJECTIVES

The student will be able to:

1. perform the Ames mutagen spot test.

2. indicate the role of the rat microsomal fraction S-9.

3. describe the nature of the test.

Some chemical agents ingested with foods or other substances taken internally have been shown to be potentially hazardous to humans when they cause cancer in man or in animals. Ames described a technique in 1975 for preliminary (Tier one) screening of chemicals for mutagenic activity (i.e., exhibiting the ability to cause **mutation** in a special tester strain of bacteria). Most cancer-producing agents also cause mutagenesis by this test and many other mutagenic agents have been shown to produce cancer in animals when later testing is done (Tier three). Many chemical agents do not cause mutagenesis unless "activated" which in the standard Ames test is brought about by including a specially prepared animal microsomal fraction (S-9) prepared from rat liver. Many agents do not require activation and this exercise takes advantage of that fact.

The bacterial tester strain used here is one of Ames' original *Salmonella typhimurium* strains, an auxotrophic mutant requiring an external supply of histidine in order to grow. Since some mutagenic agents are active only if the cells undergo a few divisions, enough histidine is added to the overlay (step No. 1 below) to permit minimal division. If the chemical agent causes a base-pair substitution mutation, a reversion to histidine independence occurs (i.e., it manufactures its own supply). This is observed by the presence of colonies on the minimal medium. Some *spontaneous reversion* occurs so that a control without chemical treatment is required. In quantitative studies, the number of *spontaneous revertants* needs to be known.

This exercise is designed to illustrate the principle of the Ames qualitative mutagen test without the requirement for the rat microsomal fraction. (References: Ames, B.N. et al. *Mutation Res.* 31:347-364, 1975; Mortelmans, K.E. *J. Food Protection* 41:989-995, 1978.)

MATERIALS (per pair or group)

1. Overnight nutrient broth culture of *Salmonella typhimurium* 1535

2. 3 prepoured minimal glucose agar base plates, sterile

3. 1 sterile 1 ml pipet and safety bulb

4. 3 tweezers

5. Solution of MNNG (N-methyl-N'nitro-N-nitrosoguanidine) — a few ml in a Petri plate to soak disks

6. Solution of EMS (ethyl methane sulfonic acid) — a few ml in a Petri plate to soak disks

7. 3 top agar tubes with L-histidine, sterile

8. Sterile 0.5% NaCl — a few ml in a Petri plate to soak disks

9. Petri plate with sterile filter paper disks, 6.35 mm diameter

10. Special autoclave and hazardous waste disposal bags

PROCEDURE (3 days)

Period 1

1. Prepare 3 top agar overlays by adding 0.1 ml of an overnight nutrient broth culture of *S. typhimurium* 1535 tester strain to each of 3 melted and cooled top agar tubes containing a minimal amount of L-histidine.

2. Mix one at a time by rotating quickly between the hands and pour the contents over a solid minimal glucose agar base plate, tilting and rotating the plate to cover the surface evenly. Repeat for the other two plates.

3. With flamed and cooled tweezers, *carefully* dip a sterile filter paper disk into a sterile solution of 0.5% NaCl for a few seconds. Remove and touch the disk to the side of the container to draw off excess moisture. Then position the disk in the center of one of the overlay plates. Label this plate "control."

> **CAUTION!**
> 4. **Repeat step No. 3 except dip the disk into the mutagenic agent MNNG. Draw off the excess liquid as before and place the disk in the center of the second overlay plate. Label this plate "MNNG."**

5. Flame the tweezers to red heat to burn off any chemical residue.

> **CAUTION!**
> 6. **Repeat step No. 3 with the mutagenic agent EMS and the third plate. Label this plate "EMS."**

7. Flame the tweezers to red heat to burn off any chemical residue.

8. Incubate the plates at 37°C.

OBSERVATIONS

Period 2

9. At 48–72 hours observe the plates looking for rings of *S. typhimurium* colonies around the disks. These are revertants to histidine independence. The control plate establishes the natural or background revertant level.

10. Record the observations on the form provided.

11. After observations are completed, place the plates in the **special discard containers** provided.

THOUGHT QUESTIONS

1. What effect does the rat microsomal S-9 fraction have on chemicals?

2. What are some other test organisms used in mutagen work?

3. If a chemical acts as a mutagen, must it necessarily cause cancer?

Name _____ Date _____ Grade _____

84. Ames Mutagen Test

RESULTS AND OBSERVATIONS

Drawings

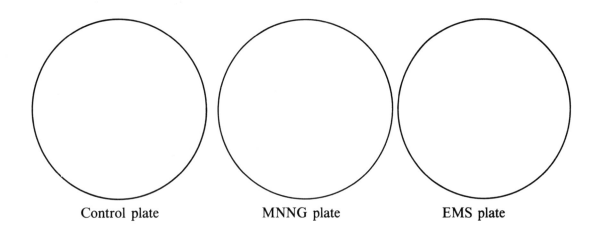

Control plate   MNNG plate   EMS plate

Conclusions:

QUESTIONS

A. True or False Statements: Circle the correct response.

T F 1. Mouth pipetting can be particularly dangerous in this exercise.

T F 2. The S-9 fraction contains microsomes.

T F 3. A mutation in this organism after exposure to a chemical is a certain indication of its ability to cause cancer in man.

T F 4. An actively dividing cell is sometimes necessary to produce a mutation.

T F 5. Any colony of *S. typhimurium* 1535 appearing on the minimal medium is the result of a mutation.

T F 6. Only chemicals cause this type of mutation.

B. Completion:

7. The activation system required to demonstrate mutagenicity for some chemicals is made from

_____ .

8. The bacterium used for mutagen testing in this exercise is a strain of _____

_____ .

9. The type of mutagen detected by this bacterial strain is a _____ .

10. If the number of revertant colonies is known, a _____ test can be performed.

85

Koch's Postulates Demonstrated

OBJECTIVES

The student will be able to:

1. list Koch's postulates.

2. perform a simple experiment to illustrate Koch's postulates.

Robert Koch, a physician, in early studies on the cattle disease anthrax was able to demonstrate that the suspected disease agent could be transferred from animal to animal always causing the same disease. Koch furthermore demonstrated that the disease agent could be isolated from the blood and still cause the disease upon inoculation into an animal. On the basis of these and other observations, Koch described the following criteria, now called **Koch's postulates**, for proving that a specific microbe causes a specific disease:

1. The organism must always be found **associated** with the disease in question and not in healthy hosts.

2. The organism must be **cultivated** in pure culture away from the diseased host.

3. The culture, when **inoculated** into susceptible hosts, causes the same disease.

4. The organism, when **reisolated** from the inoculated host, is the same as the original organism.

Koch's postulates are applicable to diseases of animals, plants, and other changes brought about by microbes such as fermentations and spoilage.

In this exercise you will perform a simple experiment using a plant pathogen causing a rot in carrots to demonstrate the four steps in Koch's postulates.

MATERIALS (per pair)

1. Petri plate with a slice of carrot inoculated earlier with *Erwinia carotovora*

2. 1 Petri plate containing two slices of carrot

3. 2 prepoured nutrient agar plates, sterile

PROCEDURE AND OBSERVATIONS (5 days)

Period 1

1. Examine the soft rot on the carrot piece provided. Poke at the softened area with a **sterile** inoculating loop. Sterilize the loop again and record your observations on the report form.

2. With a sterile loop, touch the soft rot area and streak one of the nutrient agar plates for isolation. Set the other plate aside.

3. Incubate the plate at 20°–25°C for 24 hours.

4. Make a Gram stain from the soft rot area and enter the description on the report form.

Period 2

5. Make a Gram stain of several isolated colonies. Draw the organisms' morphology on the report form and describe the organisms in words.

6. With a sterile loop, streak one of the isolated colonies rather heavily on the center of one of the carrot pieces. Streak a second colony on the second carrot slice.

7. Incubate the carrot plate in a humid environment at 20°–25°C for 48 hours.

Period 3

8. Examine the inoculated carrots for soft rot. If necessary, reincubate for an additional day or two.

9. Make a Gram stain from the soft rot area and enter the description on the report form.

10. From the soft rot area, streak a nutrient agar plate for isolation and incubate the plate at 20°–25°C for 24 hours.

Period 4

11. Make a Gram stain from an isolated colony on the incubated plate. Enter the description and any conclusions on the report form. Normally, some diagnostic media would be used to make a more definitive identification of the organism. This will not be done here.

THOUGHT QUESTIONS

1. If you had not been provided with the identity of the organism used in this exercise, what other tests would normally be done to identify this particular bacterium?

2. Design a flow diagram to illustrate Koch's postulates using a spoiled onion or the making of yogurt.

85. Koch's Postulates Demonstrated

RESULTS AND OBSERVATIONS

Initial observations

Description of soft rot:

Morphology and Gram reaction:

Isolated colony observations

Colony descriptions:

Morphology and Gram reactions:

Reinoculated carrot slice:

Description of inoculated slices

Morphology and Gram reactions:

Conclusions at this point:

Final isolation

Description of colony:

Morphology and Gram reaction:

Final conclusions:

QUESTIONS

A. True or False Statements: Circle the correct response.

T   F   1.   *Erwinia carotovora* causes soft rot of carrots.

T   F   2.   Koch's postulates are criteria that must be satisfied before a specific organism can be proven to be the causative agent of a specific disease.

T   F   3.   Koch's postulates do not apply to viruses and viral diseases.

T   F   4.   A Gram stain and morphology are sufficient to identify the organism used in this exercise.

B. Completion:

5-8.   List Koch's postulates in your own words:

   5.   _____

   6.   _____

   7.   _____

   8.   _____

9.   The family to which this organism belongs is _____ .

10.   The physician generally credited with first using these postulates was _____
   _____ .

11-13.   This early medical microbiologist (from question No. 10) is well known for his work on:

   11.   _____

   12.   _____

   13.   _____

86 Culture and Examination of Clinical Specimens

OBJECTIVES

The student will be able to:

1. perform a culture of a urine specimen and a blood specimen.

2. name the differential and selective media used to cultivate organisms from urinary tract infections (UTIs).

3. explain the mechanism of the selective and differential capability of EMB agar.

4. name the bacterium which is the most common cause of UTIs.

5. name three organisms that are part of the normal urinary tract flora.

6. name the bacterium which is the most common cause of bacterial endocarditis.

7. perform a Gram stain of a clinical specimen and describe the bacteria present.

8. appreciate the decision making process performed by laboratory technologists when they evaluate and report on cultures from hospitalized patients.

Normal urine in the urinary bladder and the organs of the upper urinary tract are sterile. The urethra, however, does contain a normal resident flora that includes *Streptococcus* spp., *Bacteroides* spp., *Mycobacterium* spp., *Staphylococcus* spp., and *Neisseria* spp. Urine can become contaminated with these organisms as it passes through the urethra and is released.

The two main infections of the urinary tract are cystitis (inflammation of the urinary bladder) and pyelonephritis (inflammation of one or both kidneys). The most common cause of urinary tract infections (UTIs) is *Escherichia coli*. This organism usually causes an infection of the urinary bladder which then spreads up the ureters (ascending infection) to the kidneys to cause pyelonephritis. Other organisms capable of causing this type of infection are *Proteus* spp., *Pseudomonas* spp., *Enterobacter* spp., *Candida albicans*, and a few others.

Urinary tract infections are diagnosed by culturing a sample of urine on both blood agar, a good growth medium for many different organisms, and on eosin-methylene-blue (EMB) agar, which is mildly selective for Gram-negative organisms.

Blood cultures are frequently obtained from patients who have developed a fever and are suspected of having bacteria in their bloodstream (blood is usually sterile). Approximately 5 ml of blood is collected at one drawing and added to 50 ml of trypticase soy broth (TSB) giving a 1:11 ratio of blood to broth. This dilution of blood is necessary to lessen the antibacterial factors in blood so the bacteria can easily grow.

While it was stated above that blood is normally sterile, there are periodic instances when transient bacteria appear for a brief period in the circulation. The most common bacteria are the viridans group streptococci. These alpha-hemolytic streptococci are the predominant normal flora of the mouth and enter the circulation through the gums during eating and chewing. Most persons have no problem with eliminating these organisms. However, persons who have damaged heart valves (due to previous injury or congenital defect) are very susceptible to developing an infection of the damaged valves.

The resulting disease develops slowly and is called subacute bacterial endocarditis (SBE). This condition is diagnosed by the presence of intermittent fever, general weakness, a heart murmur, and repeated blood cultures which demonstrate growth of the infecting organisms shed from the infected valves.

In the hospital, culture plates of clinical specimens are examined after overnight incubation by either medical technologists or clinical microbiologists. It is at this initial viewing that the trained professional uses his or her judgment to determine the significance of the growth and what secondary steps should be taken.

The specimens you will culture yourself are illustrative of this decision making process. A laboratory technologist would examine the urine culture and first decide if the growth represented normal flora colony types or if it is suggestive of the morphological types of bacteria known to cause urinary tract infections. If the bacterium does resemble a known urinary pathogen, is the amount of growth suggestive of an active infection or are there just a few colonies which could have resulted from fecal contamination of the specimen? If the amount and type of growth seen is suggestive of an infection, how can it be identified and does antibiotic susceptibility testing need to be performed? And lastly, the technologist must decide on how he/she should report the culture to the attending physician. This decision making process requires good judgment and good training.

The selective and differential media used in the clinical microbiology laboratory are useful tools in identifying and processing microbial growth. Eosin-methylene-blue agar (EMB) contains the dyes eosin-Y and methylene blue. These two dyes are inhibitory to the growth of many Gram-positive organisms and allow Gram-negative organisms to flourish without competition. The carbohydrate lactose is included in the medium to differentiate between organisms capable of lactose fermentation and those which are unable to ferment lactose. The latter types of organisms will form transparent colorless colonies. *Escherichia coli*, which ferments lactose, not only forms colored colonies, but also produces a characteristic green metallic sheen.

Blood agar is a very useful medium which allows uninhibited growth of most bacteria. This medium also helps to differentiate colony types based upon their capability to cause hemolysis.

MATERIALS (per pair)

1. 5% blood agar plate (BAP), sterile
2. Eosin methylene blue plate (EMB), sterile
3. Cotton swabs, sterile
4. Clean microscope slides
5. Gram stain reagents
6. Urine specimen
7. Blood culture specimen

PROCEDURE AND OBSERVATIONS FOR URINE SPECIMEN (2 days)

Period 1

1. Wet a sterile cotton swab in the urine specimen and inoculate a section of a blood agar plate. Repeat for an EMB agar plate. Return the swab to the urine specimen.
2. Streak both plates from the swabbed area for isolation with a sterile loop.
3. Incubate the plates at 37°C for 24 hours. These plates may be refrigerated after 24 hours if necessary to hold for a later laboratory period.
4. Using the swab in the urine specimen, transfer a large drop of urine from the container to a glass slide. *Do not spread it around!* Return the swab to the specimen for later disposal. Allow the drop to air dry (or use *gentle* heating) and then Gram stain.

5. Observe the slide under oil immersion and observe cell morphology and arrangement and Gram reaction. Record your results on the Results and Observations form. It may be necessary to search the slide extensively since there may be very few cells per field.

Period 2

6. Examine the urine culture plates and describe colony morphology, color, background reaction, if any, hemolysis, and any significant culture characteristics which might aid in identification.

7. Make Gram stains of representative colonies and note Gram reaction, morphology, cell arrangement, and any other useful characteristics. Record the results on the form.

PROCEDURE AND OBSERVATIONS FOR BLOOD SPECIMEN (2 days)

Period 1

Use the same procedure, steps No. 1–5 as for the urine specimen except use only a single blood agar plate.

Period 2

As steps No. 6–7 for the urine specimen.

THOUGHT QUESTIONS

1. How does subacute bacterial endocarditis develop?

2. What other organisms may be found in the blood, for example in septicemia?

3. Are there any other urinary tract diseases involving the immune system?

ACKNOWLEDGEMENT

We wish to thank Dr. D. Andy Anderson, Department of Biology, Utah State University for permission to use this exercise.

86. Culture and Examination of Clinical Specimens

RESULTS AND OBSERVATIONS

I. **Urine Specimen**

   1.   Gram stain results:

      a.   How many different types of organisms were seen? _____

      b.   What was the Gram stain reaction, cell shape, and cell arrangement?

         _____

         _____

         _____

      c.   If more than one organism was present, which one was the most numerous?

         _____

   2.   Urine culture results:

      a.   How many different colony types were seen on the blood agar plate? _____

         Describe the colony morphology _____

         _____

         _____

      b.   What is the Gram stain reaction, cell shape, and cell arrangement of the growth on the blood agar plate?

         _____

         _____

         _____

      c.   How many different colony types were seen on the EMB agar plate? _____

      d.   What is the Gram stain reaction, cell shape, and cell arrangement of the growth on the EMB agar plate?

         _____

         _____

         _____

      e.   Do the results of the urine culture plates correlate with the results of the direct Gram stain?

         _____

         _____

         _____

II. Blood Specimen

1. Gram stain results:

   a. How many different types of organisms were seen? _____

   b. What was the Gram stain reaction, cell shape, and cell arrangement?

   _____

   _____

   _____

   c. If more than one organism was present, which one was the most numerous?

   _____

2. Blood culture results:

   a. How many different colony types were seen on the blood agar plate? _____

   Describe the colony morphology _____

   _____

   _____

   b. What is the Gram stain reaction, cell shape, and cell arrangement of the growth on the blood agar plate?

   _____

   _____

   _____

   c. Do the results of the blood culture plate correlate with the results of the direct Gram stain?

   _____

   _____

   _____

QUESTIONS

A. **True or False Statements:** Circle the correct response.

T   F   1.   Normal urine in the urinary bladder is free of bacteria.

T   F   2.   Cystitis is an inflammation of the kidneys.

T   F   3.   *E. coli* usually causes kidney infections by being deposited in kidney tissues from the blood.

T   F   4.   EMB is a mildly selective medium for Gram-positive organisms.

T   F   5.   The proper ratio of blood to broth for a blood culture is 1:5.

T   F   6.   Blood is normally free of bacteria.

T   F   7.   Viridans group streptococci are beta-hemolytic.

T   F   8.   Multiple blood cultures from a febrile patient which show growth merely indicates he is eating food that is too hard.

T   F   9.   In the hospital, culture plates of patient specimens are routinely processed by medical doctors (M.D.s).

T   F   10. When patient urine cultures are examined after overnight incubation, any growth is proof of a urinary tract infection and dictates that antibiotic susceptibilities be performed.

T   F   11. Blood agar usually allows uninhibited growth of most bacteria.

T   F   12. EMB agar selectively allows for the growth of Gram-positive organisms by inhibiting Gram-negatives.

T   F   13. The processing of culture plates from clinical specimens does not require human judgment and can be easily automated to reduce hospital costs.

B. **Completion:**

14.   Name the organism which is the most common infecting agent in urinary tract infections:

_____

15.   Name the organism which is the most common cause of subacute bacterial endocarditis?

_____

16–18. Name three organisms or genera that are part of the normal flora of the urethra.

16. _____

17. _____

18. _____

19–20. Name two professionals that work in the clinical laboratory and process patient cultures.

19. _____

20. _____

21–22. Name the two dyes in EMB agar which are responsible for its inhibitory effect.

21. _____

22. _____

23.   If the bacterium forms pigmented colonies on EMB agar, this suggests that is capable of fermenting the carbohydrate _____ .

Immunology

Immunology began as a science with Louis Pasteur in his classic studies on infectious disease. As the body's first line of defense against disease agents, the immune system has been treated as part of microbiology. Since the early successes against infectious diseases, immunology has moved away from microbiology as a science in its own right. Fundamental discoveries are being made on the nature of the immune system and how it functions. Still students of microbiology will often be called on to perform blood tests of various kinds related to immune function. Some of the immune tests are widely used in identifying microbes or their products. It is essential that some knowledge of this important area be included in a microbiology laboratory manual.

Antibodies produced by B-cells in the blood react with specific antigens. This reaction can be observed in the laboratory using special serological techniques. **Agglutination** results when antibodies and large particles combine to form a large clump. **Precipitation** results when antibody combines with a small antigen forming a fine precipitate. This part introduces the student to a few widely used immunological procedures involving antibodies.

87 Agglutination Reactions: Blood Grouping and the Rh Factor

OBJECTIVES

The student will be able to:

1. explain the agglutination principles involved in blood typing and the Rh factor determination.

2. describe the procedures performed to determine a person's blood type and Rh factor.

3. name the four most common agglutinogens associated with blood groups.

4. give the derivation of the symbol Rh.

The determination of blood group provides a good example of an antigen-antibody reaction (i.e., an agglutination test).

In the ABO blood grouping system, there are two **antigens** (agglutinogens) that may be found on human red blood cells: A and B. A person having antigen A on their red cells is said to belong to group A; a person having antigen B belongs to group B; a person having both antigens belongs to group AB; and a person having neither antigen belongs to group O.

Whatever antigen a person has on his or her red blood cells, the corresponding **isoantibody** (agglutinin) is lacking in the serum. This obviously must be so since if a person of group A had the antibodies against A in the serum, the red cells would be agglutinated. When an antigen is not present, the corresponding isoantibody is present. Thus, a person of group A has no antibody A: but not having antigen B, does have antibody B.

Blood type	Antigenic type of red blood cell (agglutinogens)	Antibodies in plasma or serum (agglutinins)
A	A	B
B	B	A
AB	AB	none
O	none	A and B

Blood typing is performed by adding commercially available **antisera** containing high titers of anti-A and anti-B agglutinins to suspensions of red blood cells. If agglutination (clumping of red blood cells) occurs only in the suspension to which the anti-A serum was added, the blood type is A. If agglutination occurs only in the anti-B mixture, the blood type is B. Agglutination in both samples indicates that the blood type is AB. The absence of agglutination indicates that the blood is type O.

In 1940 it was discovered that rabbit sera containing antibodies for the red blood cells of the Rhesus monkey would agglutinate the red blood cells of 85% of Caucasians. This antigen in humans, first designated as the **Rh factor**, was later found to exist as six antigens which were given the letters C, c, D, d, E, and e. Of these six antigens, the D factor is responsible for the Rh-positive condition. Determination of the Rh factor is accomplished by the addition of high titered commercial antisera containing anti-D agglutinins to a suspension of red blood cells. Agglutination indicates the Rh-positive condition.

MATERIALS (per person)

1. Anti-A, anti-B, and anti-D human antisera
2. 2 clean microscope slides
3. 70% isopropyl alcohol
4. Cotton balls
5. Blood lancet
6. Applicator sticks or toothpicks

PROCEDURE AND OBSERVATIONS (1 day)

A. ABO Blood Typing (Figure 87-1)

1. Divide a slide in half. Label one side A and the other side B.

2. Clean the tip of your finger with a cotton ball soaked in 70% isopropyl alcohol. Allow the alcohol to evaporate.

3. Aseptically unwrap the blood lancet and make a quick stab into the skin about 1-2 mm deep.

4. Wipe off the first drop of blood. Squeeze the finger and allow a drop or two of blood to fall on each side of the slide.

5. Place one drop of anti-A typing serum on the side of the slide marked A.

6. Place one drop of anti-B typing serum on the side of the slide marked B.

7. Immediately mix each side with a different applicator stick or toothpick. Spread the mixture out to the size of a nickel and rock the slide and mixtures back and forth for 2 or 3 minutes.

8. Observe for the occurrence of agglutination (clumps) of red blood cells both macroscopically and microscopically (use the high-dry objective). Determine your blood type using the information included in the introduction to this exercise. *Caution:* Do not confuse drying up of the blood as agglutination.

9. Dispose of all lancets, cotton, applicators or toothpicks *only* as instructed.

B. Rh Factor Determination (Figure 87-2)

1. Place one drop of anti-D typing serum on a slide.

2. Do a finger stick in the same manner as you did in the section on ABO blood typing.

3. Add two large drops of whole blood to the antisera.

4. Mix thoroughly with an applicator stick or toothpick spreading the mixture over most of the slide. Rock the slide gently back and forth for a period not to exceed 2 minutes.

5. Discard all blood contaminated materials exactly as instructed.

6. Observe for macroscopic agglutination. Determine your Rh factor.

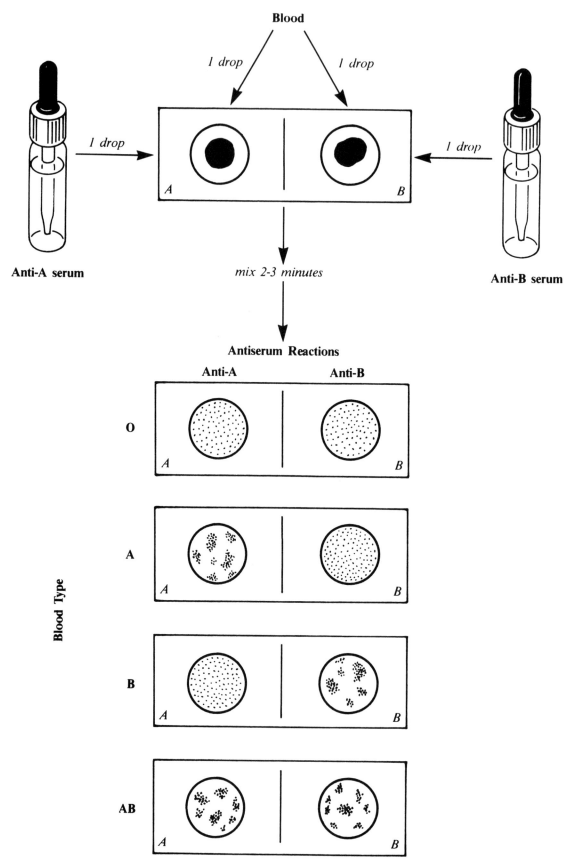

Figure 87-1. ABO blood typing reactions

THOUGHT QUESTIONS

1. What other antigens are found on red blood cells besides those mentioned in the introduction?

2. Do other blood cells have antigens? Of what medical importance are they?

3. What is the chemical nature of the ABO antigens?

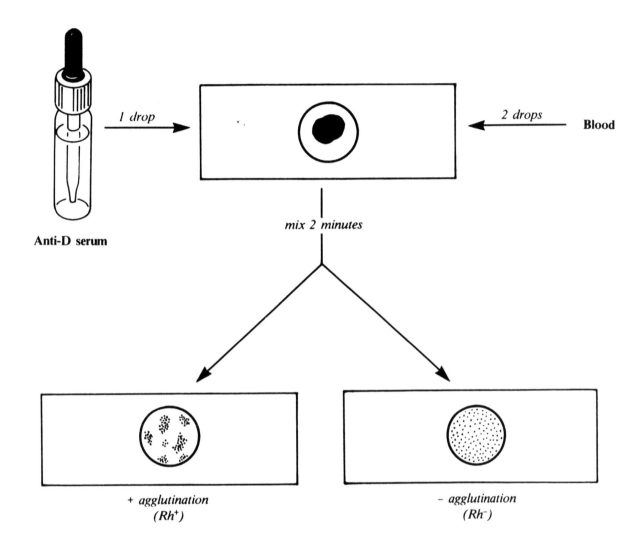

Figure 87-2. Rh factor determination

Name _____ Date _____ Grade _____

87. Agglutination Reactions: Blood Grouping and the Rh Factor

RESULTS AND OBSERVATIONS

Blood type _____

Rh factor _____

QUESTIONS

A. **True or False Statements:** Circle the correct response.

T   F   1.   False positive blood typing results can be caused by the use of outdated or improperly prepared test antisera.

T   F   2.   The Rh factor is an agglutinin.

T   F   3.   An individual with the blood type A has naturally occuring antibodies against blood type B.

T   F   4.   Human red blood cells are antigenic only in other individuals of a different blood type.

B. **Completion:**

5.   About _____ % of the human population is Rh negative.

6.   The typing serum for blood type A can be obtained from the serum of a person with blood type

_____ .

7.   Agglutinogen is synonymous in meaning to the term _____ .

8–9.   The typing sera used to determine all four blood types are called _____

and _____ .

88   Agglutination Reactions: Bacterial Serotyping

OBJECTIVES

The student will be able to:

1. perform a slide agglutination test for identification of *Salmonella* O antigens.

2. determine the group antigen of a *Salmonella* sp.

3. describe the theory of agglutination.

4. describe the serology of the *Salmonella*.

A second example of the reaction between antibody and antigen to form large visible clumps is an agglutination test widely used as an aid in the identification of bacteria (e.g., members of the genus *Salmonella*). *Salmonella* cells contain several types of antigens including the **O** or **somatic** (cell surface) antigens, the **H** or **flagellar** antigens, and the **Vi** antigen which is an envelope surrounding the somatic surface antigens. The genus *Salmonella* contains a number of antigenic **serotypes**, with more than 2000 currently recognized. Although these are often given status as species names, most authorities recognize only a few species on taxonomic grounds. Identification of *Salmonella* in the laboratory requires that the isolate be characterized first biochemically as a member of the genus **then** the serological typing can be done. The serology thus provides subtypes of the few species recognized. The serology is important in **epidemiological** studies of salmonellosis, providing something akin to a fingerprint of the culprit.

This exercise is intended to demonstrate the principle of serological identification of a member of the genus *Salmonella* using a polyvalent antiserum. An unknown organism will be given to you to test.

MATERIALS (per pair)

1. 18-24 hour old nutrient agar slant culture of an unknown organism

2. 2 glass slides

3. Dropper bottle with 0.85% NaCl

4. Dropper bottle with *Salmonella* Poly A-I and Vi antiserum

5. Dropper bottle with *Salmonella* Group B antiserum

6. Dropper bottle with *Salmonella* Group C1 antiserum

7. Fluorescent lamp

PROCEDURE AND OBSERVATIONS (1 day)

1. Mark a glass slide with 2 cm squares with a wax pencil.

2. Place one drop of the 0.85% NaCl in a square near the center of the slide (Figure 88-1).

3. Place a drop of the Poly A-I, Vi antiserum on the square next to the saline.

4. Transfer a portion of a loopful of the unknown culture to the saline drop and emulsify thoroughly.

5. Sterilize the loop and transfer about the same amount of growth to the antiserum drop, emulsifying thoroughly.

6. Rock the slide gently by rotating in a circle to mix the reagents for about one minute. Be careful not to touch the moist areas since the cells are still alive. Avoid evaporation since agglutination cannot be seen. Repeat with larger drops if this happens.

7. Examine the drops under a fluorescent lamp against a dark background for clumps of cells (i.e., agglutination). Record the agglutination degree as follows:

   ++++ all of the cells agglutinate
   +++ 75% of the cells agglutinate
   ++   50% of the cells agglutinate
   +   25% of the cells agglutinate
   ±   <25% of the cells agglutinate
   –   none of the cells agglutinate

8. If your organism agglutinates in the Poly A-I, Vi antiserum, you now must determine which *Salmonella* group it is in.

9. Place the old slide in the container provided for autoclaving and mark a new slide with three squares.

10. Place a drop of the NaCl in the center of the slide (Figure 88-2) and a drop of Group B antiserum in the square on one side and a drop of Group C1 in the square on the other. Emulsify some culture from the slant as in steps No. 4 and 5 above.

11. Rock the slide gently for one minute and read the results as in step No. 7 above.

12. Record your results on the report form and identify the group to which your organism belongs. Find the species or serotype name if possible in Bergey's Manual or the Difco Manual. Ordinarily the specific O antigens present would be determined as well as the flagellar antigens. This will not be done here.

13. Discard this slide in the to-be-autoclaved container, rinse the work area down with disinfectant, and wash your hands thoroughly with disinfectant. The antiserum does not kill these organisms.

THOUGHT QUESTIONS

1. Can this technique be used with all bacteria?

2. Design a test for antibodies in blood using bacterial cells. Does such a test exist?

3. How are the *Salmonella* classified using serotyping? Why is it not proper to consider the serotype as a species?

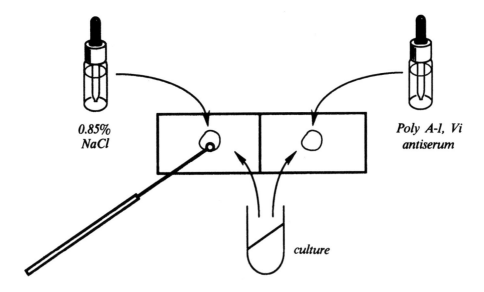

Figure 88-1. First slide set-up

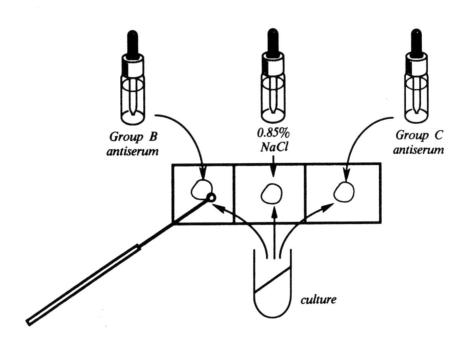

Figure 88-2. Group antigen slide set-up

88. Agglutination Reactions: Bacterial Serotyping

RESULTS AND OBSERVATIONS

Record the level of agglutination for the following:

	Poly A-I, Vi	Saline	B Group	Saline	C1 Group
Unknown result					

Based on the above your organism is in Group _____ and

is identified as *Salmonella* _____ serotype _____

QUESTIONS

A. **True or False Statements:** Circle the correct response.

    T   F   1.   Cell surface antigens are called somatic antigens.

    T   F   2.   Serological typing is usually done before cultural determination is made.

    T   F   3.   A polyvalent antiserum is used first for the *Salmonella*.

    T   F   4.   Many types of O antigens are found.

    T   F   5.   The antiserum kills the bacterium when it attaches to the antigen.

    T   F   6.   The Vi antigen is commonly associate with virulent typhoid organisms.

    T   F   7.   There are only a few serotypes of the *Salmonella* but many species.

B. **Completion:**

    8.   The _____ antigen is found on the outside of the somatic antigens.

    9.   The somatic antigen abbreviation is the letter _____.

    10.   _____ is the study of disease transmission.

    11.   _____ antigens are also called H antigens.

89 Immunodiffusion — Ouchterlony Plate Technique

OBJECTIVES

The student will be able to:

1. perform an immunodiffusion assay using the Ouchterlony technique.

2. interpret the resulting precipitation patterns.

3. describe the theory of immunodiffusion.

4. define equivalence point and precipitin test.

5. name two uses for the immunodiffusion method.

Not all antigens are as large as the red blood cells and the bacteria used in the last two exercises. The reaction of a soluble antigen with an antibody must be visualized in other ways. At the proper ratio of antigen to antibody (the **equivalence zone**), the antigen-antibody complex will form a visible **precipitate**. The **precipitin test** in which dilutions of antigen and antibody are layered one on top of the other and in the suitable antigen/antibody ratio range a fine precipitate is formed. The **Ouchterlony plate** method takes advantage of the diffusion of the soluble antigen and antibody through a gel of agar. At the proper ratios of the two, a visible precipitate forms in the gel (Figure 89-1). The precipitate can be enhanced by staining with Coomassie blue, a protein stain. Several variations of the diffusion method are available. Other methods include single **radial immunodiffusion (RID)**, **radioimmunoassay (RIA)**, and **enzyme immunoassay (EIA)** techniques. An example of the last will be found in Exercise 90.

In the Ouchterlony two-dimensional double diffusion technique, two or more wells are cut into a gel of agar. One well is filled with antibody and the others with antigens of various kinds or vice versa. The antigens and antibodies diffuse toward each other at rates in proportion to their size (decreases rate) and concentration (increases rate). At the point of equivalence, the combination will precipitate if the antibody is specific. The precipitate appears as a continuous line between the antigen and its antibody (Figure 89-2). If the two antigens are identical, then the lines of precipitation will appear as in Figure 89-2A. If the antigens are not identical and the antiserum has antibodies to both, then the lines will appear as an X as in Figure 89-2B. If one well has two antigens and the other only one of them, then the line will be similar to the line of identity except that a tail or spur will be found in the direction of the well without the second antigen (Figure 89-2C). The Ouchterlony immunodiffusion method is widely used to assay antigen and antibody purity and cross reactivity with other molecules.

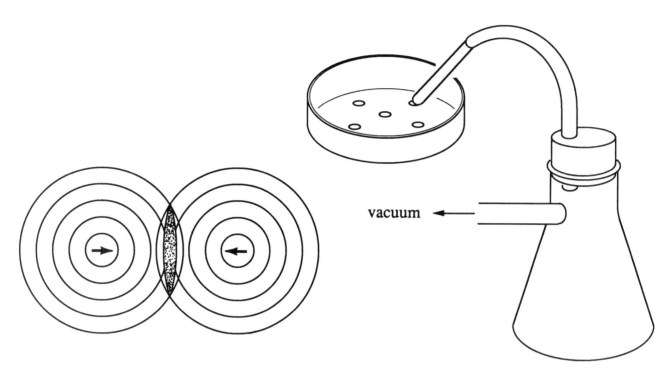

Figure 89-1. Antigen and antibody diffuse uniformly (concentric circles) away from well (arrows). Precipitate occurs in equivalence zone forming a visible band.

Figure 89-3. Plate preparation.

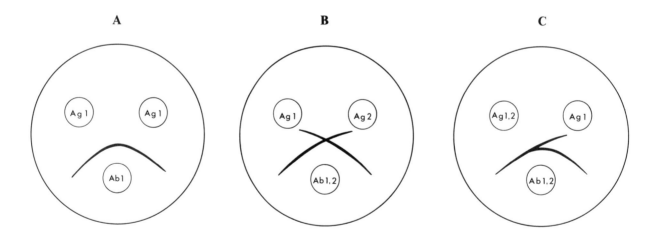

A   B   C

Figure 89-2. Patterns of precipitation lines. A) With a single antibody, the two antigens are identical. B) Antibody to two antigens showing pattern of non-identity of the two antigens. C) With antibody to two antigens, tailing shows one well has both antigens, the other only one, a case of partial identity.

MATERIALS (per pair)

1. 2 diffusion gel agar plates

2. 0.5 ml quantities of the following:

   a. monkey (Rhesus) serum
   b. goat serum
   c. horse serum
   d. human serum
   e. human serum antiserum (rabbit)

3. 0.5 ml of the following diluted:

   a. bovine serum
   b. rabbit serum
   c. human serum
   d. sheep serum
   e. human globin antiserum (rabbit)

4. 10 sterile Pasteur pipets and two safety bulbs

5. 1 plastic bag (Ziploc™ type) for two plates

6. 1 filter paper

7. Glass tube with 3 mm external diameter and about 10 cm long

8. Rubber hose to fit glass tube and vacuum jar to aspirate

PROCEDURE (2–10 days)

Period 1

1. Attach the rubberhose and vacuum flask to the glass tube. Flame the tube gently for about half its length and let it cool. Cut 5 holes with the tube in each of the agar plates 7-10 mm apart as in Figure 89-3. The holes must be equidistant from the center well. As the holes are cut, gently aspirate the plug out. The well must be free of loose agar. Label each plate on the underside with the code number as illustrated in Figure 89-2. Then label one plate serum and the other globin.

2. Each person of the pair does one plate with the reagents listed in No. 2 or 3 of the Materials. Using a separate Pasteur pipet for each reagent, fill the *center* well to the brim of one plate with the human serum antiserum and the center well of the other plate with the human globin antiserum. *Be careful not to overflow the wells.*

3. Fill the remaining wells completely with the antigens for the particular plate as prescribed in the Materials.

4. Wet the filter paper and place it in a plastic bag. Place the two plates in the bag *cover up*, seal the bag edge and place the bag and plates at 4°C.

OBSERVATIONS

Periods 2-11

5. Look at the plates at 24 hours and daily for up the ten days. Do not keep at room temperature any longer than necessary, since warming the plates distorts the lines. Record the precipitation patterns on the report form for each plate showing the location and identity of each antigen and the relationship of the bands.

THOUGHT QUESTIONS

1. What happens in the antigen/antibody ratio area above and below the equivalence zone? Why is there no precipitate?

2. What are some advantages of this technique over the tube precipitin test?

3. Why do bacteria not grow on the diffusion medium?

89. Immunodiffusion — Ouchterlony Technique

RESULTS AND OBSERVATIONS

Record the patterns of precipitation for each plate.

Globin plate   Serum plate

Well contents   Well contents

1   1

2   2

3   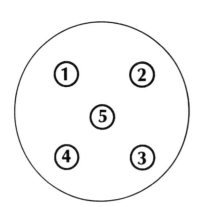   3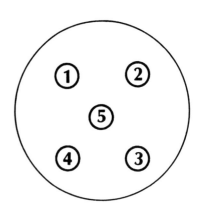

4   4

5   5

Conclusions:

QUESTIONS

A. **True or False Statements:** Circle the correct response.

T   F   1.   The Ouchterlony immunodiffusion method can also utilize bacterial cells as the antigen.

T   F   2.   If an antibody reacts with two antigens, the testing pattern that forms indicates non-identity.

T   F   3.   The appropriate ratio of specific antigen to specific antibody must occur for a visible precipitate to occur.

T   F   4.   Stains such as Coomassie blue can help to better visualize the precipate.

B. **Completion:**

5-6.   Name two uses for the Ouchterlony immunodiffusion method.

5. _____

6. _____

7.   What is the name of the zone of antigen/antibody ratio where precipitation occurs?

_____

8.   Name one other test using precipitation to determine antigen-antibody reactions.

_____

90 Enzyme-Linked Immunosorbent Assay (ELISA)

OBJECTIVES

The student will be able to:

1. perform an indirect enzyme-linked immunosorbent assay.

2. describe the theory of enzyme immunoassays in general.

3. diagram the procedure of the antibody assay used in this exercise.

Agglutination and precipitation reactions are excellent rapid procedures for serological determinations, but they are limited in sensitivity, usually in the 1–100 ng range. By coupling the antibodies or antigens to fluorochromes, radioisotopes, or enzymes, the detection sensitivity can be increased to the picogram range. Enzymes covalently conjugated to antibody or antigen allows the detection of antigen-antibody reactions indirectly through the formation of enzyme product, often colored for easy detection and spectrophotometric quantitation. These are referred to as **Enzyme Immunoassays** or **EIA**. When the antigen or antibody is adsorbed to a surface such as beads or microtiter wells, it is referred to as an **Enzyme-Linked Immunosorbent Assay** or simply **ELISA**. Several ELISA methods are available. In this exercise you will use the indirect method (Figure 90-1) in which an **antigen** is adsorbed onto the walls of microtiter wells, washed, and followed with a specific **antibody** prepared in rabbit. These are allowed to react, the excess antibody washed away and a **rabbit globulin antibody urease** conjugate is added. These react and the excess is washed away. Urea **substrate** containing bromcresol purple at pH 4.8 (yellow color) is added. Enzyme conjugated to the antibody hydrolyzes the substrate releasing ammonia which causes the bromcresol purple to turn its alkaline color, a deep purple. The color then indicates the presence of enzyme, in turn indicating the presence of the antibody to rabbit globin and the antigen-antibody complex. The reciprocal of the antiserum dilution at which the purple color appears is the antibody titer. Several other enzymes (e.g., horseradish peroxidase, alkaline phosphatase, and beta-galactosidase) can be used.

In this exercise you will perform an ELISA for rabbit antibodies to egg albumin using urease conjugated rabbit globin antibodies.

anti-A antibody
antigen A
well side
anti-antibody conjugate
Enzyme substrate
product

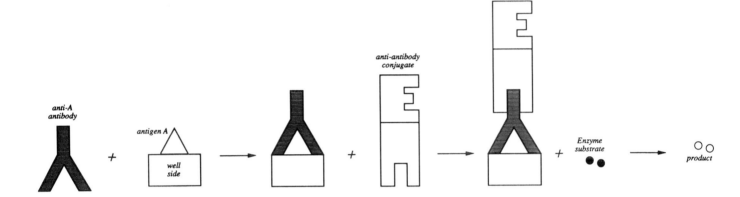

Figure 90-1. Enzyme-linked immunosorbent assay procedure

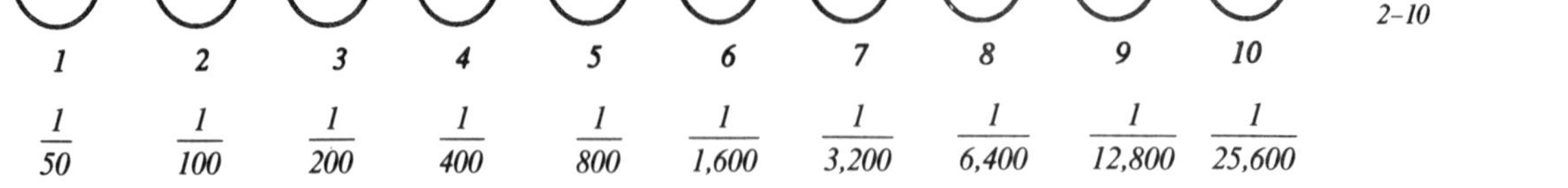

transfer 0.5 ml from tube 1 to 2, mix, etc.
0.5 ml
0.5
0.5
0.5
0.5
0.5
0.5
0.5
0.5
0.5 ml buffer added to tubes 2–10
1
2
3
4
5
6
7
8
9
10
1/50
1/100
1/200
1/400
1/800
1/1,600
1/3,200
1/6,400
1/12,800
1/25,600

Figure 90-2. Antiserum dilution sequence

MATERIALS (per pair)

1. 5 ml chicken egg albumin solution (10 μg/ml) in adsorption buffer

2. 1.0 ml of chicken egg albumin antiserum (rabbit) diluted 1:50 in dilution buffer in a 13 × 100 mm tube

3. 5 ml rabbit globulin antiserum conjugated with urease diluted 1:500 in dilution buffer

4. Wash buffer in a plastic squeeze bottle (100 ml)

5. 5 ml urea-bromcresol purple substrate

6. Microtiter plate, flat bottom

7. 2 sterile 1 ml pipet and safety bulb

8. 5 sterile 0.2 ml pipets

9. Parafilm to cover the microtiter plate

10. Beakers or other containers to receive washings

11. ELISA plate reading spectrophotometer, if available

PROCEDURE AND OBSERVATIONS (2 days)

Period 1

1. Add 0.2 ml of egg albumin (10 μg/ml) to microtiter plate wells A1 to A10 and A12, skipping A11.

2. Add 0.2 ml of adsorption buffer to wells B1 to B10 and B12, skipping B11. This row serves as a control. Cover the plate with parafilm and label.

3. Incubate the plate for 1 hour at room temperature and then at 4°C overnight or until the next lab period to allow the albumin antigen to adsorb to the well walls.

Period 2

4. Label the tube of the egg albumin antiserum No. 1. Make 2-fold dilutions of the egg albumin antiserum (Figure 90-2) as follows:

   a. Add 0.5 ml of dilution buffer to *each* of 9 13 x 100 mm tubes. Label them 2 through 10.

   b. Using the same pipet, transfer 0.5 ml of serum from tube 1 to tube 2 and mix with the pipet.

   c. With the same pipet, transfer 0.5 ml from tube 2 to tube 3 and mix with the pipet.

   d. Continue in like manner through tube 10 and discard the pipet.

5. Remove the parafilm (save it) and invert the plate over a container to empty the wells.

6. Wash the wells by gently filling them with the wash buffer in the plastic squeeze bottle. Cover with the parafilm and allow the tray to sit for 3 minutes. Do this *each* time a wash is done.

7. Empty the wells into the container. Repeat step No. 3 twice more.

8. Add 0.2 ml of the highest dilution of the serum to each of wells A10 and B10. With the same pipet, add 0.2 ml of the next lowest dilution to each of wells A9 and B9. With the same pipet, continue in this manner until the lowest dilution is added to wells A1 and B1.

9. Cover the plate with the parafilm and incubate at room temperature for 1 hour.

10. Wash all wells with wash buffer as in step No. 3 above allowing the plate to sit covered 3 minutes. Wash at least 3 times in this manner.

11. Add 0.2 ml of rabbit globin antiserum (from goat) conjugated to urease (1:500 in dilution buffer) to every well.

12. Cover with parafilm and let sit at room temperature 1 hour.

13. Wash all wells at least 2 times as in step No. 3 with wash buffer followed by 2 similar washes with distilled water to remove all buffer which would interfere with the detection of ammonia.

14. Add 0.2 ml of urea-bromcresol purple substrate to each well. *Be careful **not** to touch the sides of the wells with the pipet.*

15. Cover with parafilm and incubate at room temperature for 1 hour.

16. Read the wells visually. A purple color indicates the presence of egg albumin antibody. The reciprocal of the highest dilution giving a distinct purple color is the antiserum titer for this exercise. Enter the observations on the report form.

17. If an ELISA well reader is available, read at 588 nm using well A12 to zero the instrument and subtracting the absorbance of row B (controls) from each reading. An adjusted absorbance >0.1 is considered positive.

THOUGHT QUESTIONS

1. What advantage does an enzyme-conjugated antibody have over a radioisotope containing antibody?

2. Could this procedure be used in a forensic approach to blood analysis (i.e., distinguish human from animal blood)? How?

3. How would you modify this procedure to search for a particular antigen?

90. Enzyme-Linked Immunosorbent Assay (ELISA)

RESULTS AND OBSERVATIONS

Record the results as + or – for purple color. Note the highest dilution showing purple.

	Tube No.											
	1	**2**	**3**	**4**	**5**	**6**	**7**	**8**	**9**	**10**	**11**	**12**
Antiserum												
Control												

The antiserum titer is _____

QUESTIONS

A. **True or False Statements:** Circle the correct response:

T F 1. An ELISA method is a type of enzyme immunoassay.

T F 2. Bromcresol purple pH indicator turns a yellow color after the enzyme-conjugated antibody hydrolyzes the urea substrate.

T F 3. Enzyme immunoassays are less sensitive than an agglutination reaction.

T F 4. In the enzyme immunoassays, antigen-antibody formation is detected by the use of a radioisotope.

T F 5. Between each of the reagent applications it is necessary to rinse out any excess reagent out of the wells.

B. Completion:

6–7. The products of urea hydrolysis are _____ and _____ .

8–11. Name 4 enzymes conjugated to antibodies used for enzyme immunoassay

   8. _____   10. _____

   9. _____   11. _____

12–15. List the order of reagent application in this test

   12. _____   14. _____

   13. _____   15. _____

16–17. The antirabbit IgG conjugated to the urease was made in _____
   while the albumin antibody was made in _____ .

18. The term ELISA refers to _____ .

91 Fluorescent Antibody Technique

OBJECTIVES

The student will be able to:

1. prepare and observe a fluorescent antibody preparation.

2. describe how the fluorescent antibody technique works.

Certain fluorescent dyes such as fluorescein isothiocyante (FITC) and rhodamine isothiocyanate, when coupled to an antibody, **fluoresce** under the ultraviolet microscope showing the presence of the antigen-antibody complex. The fluorescent antibody (FA) technique has the advantage of giving very rapid results. An antigen, such as a bacterium, when combined with a specific **antibody-fluorescein conjugate** glows green when observed (Figure 91-1). Non-specific staining can occur, especially in tissues.

Two methods are in use, the **direct** method (Figure 91-1) described above and an indirect method which is similar in design to the ELISA test (Exercise 90). In the **indirect** method, an antigen is combined with specific (unlabeled) antibody (e.g., human), the excess washed off, and then fluorescein-labeled antihuman antibody is added. If the complex is present, the fluorescent antibody shows the typical fluorescence. The FA technique is widely used in testing for disease antibodies such as in syphilis, whooping cough, and cerebrospinal infection. It is also widely used as and aid in identifying organisms particularly *Salmonella*, *Staphylococcus aureus*, and *Streptococcus*.

In this exercise you will perform the direct FA technique for coagulase positive *S. aureus*. Note that the organism should be well characterized before the FA technique is used.

MATERIALS (per person or pair)

1. 18–24 hour old suspension (3 mĺ/13 mm tube) of *Staphylococcus aureus* coagulase + and *Staphylococcus aureus* coagulase –

2. *Staphylococcus aureus* FA conjugate

3. Mounting fluid at pH 7.2

4. 1% phosphate–0.85% NaCl buffer adjusted to pH 7.2

5. Coplin or staining jars

6. Applicator stick

7. Petri plate

8. Filter paper to fit Petri plate bottom

9. Fluorescent microscope

10. Microscope slides

11. 95% alcohol

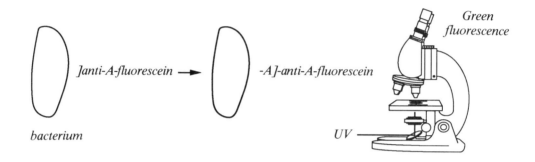

Janti-A-fluorescein ⟶ *-A]-anti-A-fluorescein*

bacterium

Green fluorescence

UV

Figure 91-1. Direct immunofluorescence

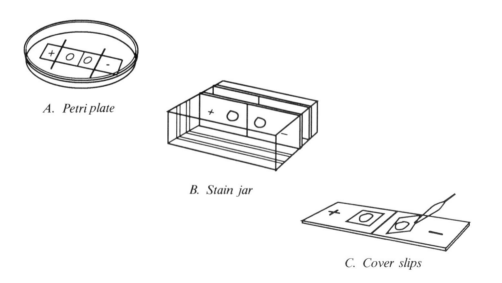

A. Petri plate

B. Stain jar

C. Cover slips

Figure 91-2. Slide preparation

PROCEDURE (1 day)

1. Clean a slide thoroughly with cleansing powder (Comet, Bon Ami, etc.), rinse well, and dry.

2. With a wax pencil, place a line across the center of the slide.

3. Place a large loopful of one of the culture suspensions on the left of the line and a large loopful of the second culture suspension on the other side. Identify each smear as to coagulase + or –.

4. Allow the smear to air dry.

5. Fix the cells to the slide by flooding with 95% alcohol.

6. Wet the filter paper and place it in the Petri plate bottom. Break the applicator stick into two pieces about 4 cm long and place them on the filter paper.

7. Cover each smear with the 1:200 FA conjugate provided and place the slide in the Petri plate on the two pieces of stick (Figure 91-2A).

8. Allow the conjugate and cells to react for 30 minutes.

9. Rinse the slide with buffer and then place it in the staining (Coplin) jar containing buffer for 10 minutes changing the buffer twice during that time (Figure 91-2B).

10. Rinse with distilled water to remove salts.

11. Gently blot dry with absorbent paper.

12. Place a drop of mounting fluid on each smear, drop a coverslip on top of each (Figure 91-2C), and observe with the fluorescence microscope. (*Note:* Do not spend too long looking at any one field since the fluorescence fades quickly.)

OBSERVATIONS

13. Record the intensity of fluorescence as follows:

    4+ maximum — brilliant yellow green; clear cut cell outline; sharply defined cell center

    3+ less yellow green fluorescence — clear cut cell outline; sharply defined cell center

    2+ dim fluorescence — cell outline fuzzy and not well defined

    1+ very dim fluorescence — cell outline not distinguishable from cell center; no fluorescence or negligible

    Record only 3+ or above as positive.

14. Record your observations and conclusion on the report form.

THOUGHT QUESTIONS

1. If your fluorescent antibody shows non-specific reaction with cells other than your test cells, how would you remove this interference?

2. How does the indirect FA method work?

3. Design an experiment using an antigen to find an antibody in human blood. How would you detect the antigen-antibody complex if it occurred?

Name _____ Date _____ Grade _____

91. Fluorescent Antibody Technique

RESULTS AND OBSERVATIONS

Culture	Color	Fluorescence (+ or –)
S. aureus coagulase +		
S. aureus coagulase –		

Conclusions:

QUESTIONS

A. **True or False Statements:** Circle the correct response:

T F 1. Coagulase is an enzyme produced by certain species of *Staphylococcus*.

T F 2. The indirect FA technique is methodologically most similar to the ELISA test.

T F 3. The FA technique uses a fluorescent dye to detect the formation of the antigen-antibody complex.

T F 4. Non-specific staining does not affect the FA test.

B.   Completion:

5.   The reason for putting the slide in a moist Petri plate is to _____ .

6–8.   Name three diseases the FA technique is designed to help detect:

       6.   _____

       7.   _____

       8.   _____

9–11.   Name three groups of bacteria the FA technique is useful in identifying:

       9.   _____

       10.   _____

       11.   _____

12.   Name one advantage the FA technique has over many imunnological assay techniques

_____

13.   The purpose for washing the excess conjugate off of the slide is to _____

_____ .

APPENDIX *I*

Media

All media except 1, 2, 7, 8, 10, 15, 17, 18, 22, 25, 29, 30, 31, 34, 37, 40, 42, 47, 53, 55, 56, 57, 60, and 64 are available commercially.

The "d.w." in the following formulas refers to distilled or demineralized water.

1. *Acetate agar:* Glucose 1 g; yeast extract 2 g; Na acetate · $3H_2O$, 5 g; agar 15 g; d.w. 1 L, pH 5.5.

2. *Ammonium salts medium:* $(NH_4)_2SO_4$ 2 g; K_2HPO_4 1 g; $MgSO_4$ · $7H_2O$ 0.5 g; $FeSO_4$ · $7H_2O$ 0.4 g; $CaCO_3$ 5 g; d.w. 1 L, pH as is. Dissolve by heating but does not require autoclaving.

3. *Blood agar:* Use trypic soy agar 100 ml plus 5 ml sheep red blood cells. Add blood only when agar has cooled to about 45°C. Plates can be purchased ready for use.

4. *Brain heart infusion broth:* Calf brains, infusion from 200 g; beef heart, infusion from 250 g; proteose peptone 10 g; glucose 2 g; NaCl 5 g; Na_2HPO_4 2.5 g; d.w. 1 L, pH 7.4.

5. *Brain heart infusion broth-2% NaCl:* Use Medium No. 4 plus 20 g NaCl.

6. *Brilliant green lactose bile broth:* Peptone 10 g; lactose 10 g; oxgall 20 g; brilliant green 0.133 g; d.w. 1 L, pH 7.2.

Casein agar — See skim milk agar.

Chemotaxis buffer: Formulas for buffer, media, plugs, and cell preparation will be found in the Instructor's Manual.

7. *CT broth:* Casitone 20 g; $MgSO_4$ 0.008M in 0.01M K_2HPO_4–KH_2PO_4 buffer; 1L, pH 7.6.

8. *Deca broth:* Peptone 100 g; yeast extract 50 g; NaCl 25 g; K_2HPO_4 80 g; d.w. 1 L, pH 7.6.

9. *Decarboxylase base Moeller:* Peptone 5 g; beef extract 5 g; dextrose 0.5 g; bromcresol purple 0.005 g; cresol red 0.005 g; pyridoxal 0.005 g; d.w. 1 L, pH 6.0.

    Add 1% (10 g/L) of the appropriate L-amino acid (2% if DL-form). Usually no readjustment of pH is required with lysine or arginine. Ten grams of ornithine in 1 L will require 4.6 ml 1N NaOH to dissolve. Dispense 5 ml amounts in 16 mm screw capped tubes. Sterilize at 121°C for 10 minutes.

10. *Diffusion gel agar:* 2% Ion or Noble agar or agarose in Tris-Tricine buffer at pH 8.6. Keep prepared plates in a moist environment prior to use.

    Tris-Tricine buffer: Tricine 4.3 g; Tris base 9.8 g; Ca lactate 0.1 g; Na azide 0.2 g; d.w. 1 L, pH 8.6.

11. *EC broth:* Tryptose 20 g; lactose 5 g; bile salts No. 3 1.5 g; K_2HPO_4 4 g; KH_2PO_4 1.5 g; NaCl 5 g; d.w. 1 L, pH 6.9.

12. *EMB agar* (Eosin methylene blue agar): Peptone 10 g; lactose 10 g; K_2HPO_4 2 g; eosin Y 0.4 g; methylene blue 0.065 g; agar 15 g; d.w. 1 L, pH 7.1.

13. *mEndo broth MF:* Yeast extract 1.5 g; casitone 5 g; thiopeptone 5 g; tryptose 10 g; lactose 12.5 g; Na desoxycholate 0.1 g; K_2HPO_4 4.375 g; KH_2PO_4 1.375 g; NaCl 5 g; Na lauryl sulfate 0.05 g; $NaSO_3$ 2.1 g; basic fuchsin 1.05 g; d.w. 1 L, pH 7.2.

14. *mFC agar:* Tryptose 10 g; proteose peptone No. 3 5 g; yeast extract 3 g; lactose 12.5 g; bile salts No. 3 1.5 g; NaCl 5 g; aniline blue 0.1 g; agar 15 g; d.w. 1 L, pH 7.4.

15. *Histidine agar (HA):* Tryptone 5 g; yeast extract 5 g; L-histidine · HCl 27 g; NaCl 5 g; $CaCO_3$ 1 g; bromcresol purple 0.06 g; agar 20 g; d.w. to 1 L, pH 5.3. Autoclave at 118°C for 10 minutes. **DO NOT OVERHEAT.**

16. *Kliger iron agar:* Beef extract 3 g; yeast extract 3 g; peptone 15 g; proteose peptone 5 g; lactose 10 g; glucose 1 g; $FeSO_4$ 0.2 g; NaCl 5 g; Na thiosulfate 0.3 g; phenol red 0.024 g; agar 15 g; d.w. 1 L, pH 7.4.

17. *LAB agar:* Lactose 20 g; tryptone 10 g; meat extract 10 g; yeast extract 10 g; tomato juice (filtered) 50 ml; Tween 80 1 g; K_2PO_4 2 g; agar 15 g; d.w. 1 L, pH 6.6.

18. *L broth/agar:* Tryptone 10 g; yeast extract 5 g; NaCl 10 g; glucose 1 g; d.w. 1 L, pH 7.0 with NaOH. For agar, add 15 g/L.

19. *Lactose broth/agar:* Beef extract 3 g; peptone 5 g; lactose 5 g; d.w. 1 L, pH 6.9. For agar, add 15 g/L.

20. *Lauryl sulfate tryptose lactose (LST) broth:* Tryptose 20 g; lactose 5 g; K_2HPO_4 2.75 g; KH_2PO_4 2.75 g; sodium lauryl sulfate 0.1 g; d.w. 1 L, pH 6.8.

21. *Litmus milk:* Skim milk 100 g; litmus 5 g; d.w. 1 L, pH 6.8.

22. *Luminous broth/agar:* NaCl 30 g; K_2HPO_4 3.9 g; KH_2PO_4 2.1 g; NH_4Cl 5 g; yeast extract 5 g; tryptone 5 g; 1 M Tris buffer pH 7.5 50 ml; glycerol 3 g; $MgSO_4 \cdot 7H_2O$ 1 g; KCl 0.75 g; $CaCO_3$ 1 g; d.w. 1 L, pH 7.2. For agar, add 20 g/L.

23. *Manganese agar:* Nutrient agar plus 6 mg/L $MnCl_2 \cdot 4H_2O$.

24. *Mannitol salt agar:* Proteose peptone No. 3 10 g; beef extract 1 g; D-mannitol 10 g; NaCl 75 g; phenol red 0.025 g; agar 15 g; d.w. 1 L, pH 7.4.

25. *Mannitol salts nitrogen-free broth/agar:* K_2HPO_4 0.5 g; $MgSO_4 \cdot 7H_2O$ 0.2 g; $FeSO_4 \cdot 7H_2O$ 0.001 g; NaCl 0.2 g; $MnSO_4 \cdot H_2O$ 0.005g; $CaCO_3$ 10 g; mannitol 10 g; d.w. 1 L, pH as is. For agar, add 15 g/L. Does not need to be sterilized if used within several days. If sterilized, add the mannitol to 100 ml d.w. and the rest of the ingredients to 900 ml. Autoclave separately and then add together aseptically.

26. *Marine broth:* Peptone 5 g; yeast extract 1 g; ferric citrate 0.1 g; NaCl 19.45 g; $MgSO_4$ dried 5.9 g; $NaSO_4$ 3.24 g; $CaCl_2$ 1.8 g; KCl 0.55 g; $NaHCO_3$ 0.16 g; KBr 0.08 g; $SrCl_2$ 0.034 g; boric acid 0.022 g; Na_4SiO_4 0.004 g; NaF 0.0024 g; NH_4NO_3 0.0016 g; Na_2HPO_4 0.008 g; d.w. 1 L, pH 7.6.

27. *Micro culture assay agar* (Difco 0319-01-5): Micro inoculum broth plus agar 10 g/L.

28. *Micro inoculum broth* (Difco No. 0320-01-2): Proteose peptone No. 3 5 g; yeast extract 20 g; glucose 10 g; KH_2PO_4 2 g; sorbitan monooleate complex 0.1 g; d.w. 1 L, pH 6.7.

29. *Minimal glucose base agar (Vogel Bonner E plus glucose):* Solution A — $MgSO_4 \cdot 7H_2O$ 2.0 g; citric acid · H_2O 2.0g; KH_2PO_4 10 g; $NaNH_4PO_4 \cdot 4H_2O$ 3.5 g; d.w. 900 ml. Autoclave. Temper to 45°C. Solution B — Filter sterilize 100 ml of 20% glucose.

Mix Solutions A and B. Pour 30 ml amounts into Petri plates. Plates should be held inverted at room temperature for 1–2 days before use and can be kept up to 3 weeks.

30. *Minimal salts agar (M56):*

Solution A: $Na_2HPO_4 \cdot 7H_2O$ 8.2 g; KH_2PO_4 2.7 g; $(NH_4)_2SO_4$ 1 g; $FeSO_4 \cdot 7H_2O$ 0.25 mg; d.w. 1 L, pH 7.2. Cool to 50°C

Solution B: 10% $MgSO_4 \cdot 7H_2O$

Solution C: 0.5% $Ca(NO_3)_2$

Solution D: 20% glucose

Solution E: 4% L-methionine (8% DL- form)

Solution F: 4% L-leucine (8% DL- form)

Solution G: 4% L-threonine (8% DL- form)

Solution H: 4% L-alanine (8% DL- form)

Solution I: 3.2% agar (32 g/L)

Autoclave all solutions separately. To 1 L of solution A, aseptically add 1 ml of B, 1 ml of C, and 10 ml of D. Then add 1 ml of the required amino acids, temper to 50°C, and mix 1:1 with solution I also tempered to 50°C. Pour in labeled plates. The final concentration of each amino acid in the agar plate is 20 μg/ml.

31. *Morphogenesis solution:* 0.008M $MgSO_4$; 0.5M glycerol; 1% casitone.

32. *Motility test medium:* Tryptose 10 g; NaCl 5 g; agar 5 g; d.w. 1 L, pH 7.2.

33. *MR-VP medium (broth):* Buffered peptone 7 g; glucose 5 g; K_2HPO_4 5 g; d.w. 1 L, pH 6.9.

34. *MS-YE broth:* KCl 1 g; $MgCl_2$ 0.2 g; K_2HPO_4 7 g; KH_2PO_4 5.4 g; $(NH_4)_2SO_4$ 1 g; $CaCl_2$ 0.01 g; yeast extract 1 g; Na_2SO_4 0.2g; glucose 0.25 mM; d.w. 1 L.

35. *Mueller-Hinton agar:* Beef, infusion from 300 g; casamino acids (technical) 17.5 g; starch 1.5 g; agar 17 g; d.w. 1 L, pH 7.3.

36. *Nitrate broth:* Beef extract 3 g; peptone 5g; KNO_3 1 g; d.w. 1 L, pH 7.0.

37. *Nitrite salts medium:* $NaNO_2$ 1 g; K_2HPO_4 1 g; $MgSO_4 \cdot 7H_2O$ 0.3 g; Na_2CO_3 1 g; NaCl 1 g; $FeSO_4 \cdot 7H_2O$ 0.4 g; d.w. 1 L, pH as is. Dissolve by heating but autoclaving is not required.

38. *Nutrient broth/agar:* Beef extract 3 g; peptone 5 g; d.w. 1 L, pH 6.8. For agar, add 15 g/L.

39. *Nutrient gelatin agar:* Nutrient agar plus 10 g gelatin; d.w. 1 L.

40. *Peptone agar:* Peptone 8 g; beef extract 1 g; agar 15 g; d.w. 1 L, pH 7.0.

41. *Peptone water (0.1% or 4%):* Peptone 1 g per 1 L or 4 g per L d.w.

42. *PHB medium:* Solution 1 — Na_2HPO_4 6 g; KH_2PO_4 3 g; NaCl 3 g; NH_4Cl 1 g; Na_2SO_4 0.1 g; $MgCl_2 \cdot 6H_2O$ 0.1 g; $MnCl_2 \cdot 4H_2O$ 0.01g; casamino acids 0.1 g; d.w. 750 ml, pH 7.2. For agar, add 15 g/L.

Solution 2 — glucose 15 g; d.w. 250 ml. Autoclave separately and mix aseptically afterward. Distribute aseptically to sterile tubes.

43. *Phenol red broth:* Trypticase or proteose peptone No. 3 10 g; beef extract (optional) 1 g; phenol red (7.2 ml of 0.25% solution) 0.00018 g; d.w. 1 L, pH 7.3. Carbohydrates 5 g carbohydrate per L added before autoclaving. Autoclave 10 minutes at 118°C.

44. *Plate count agar (Standard plate count agar):* Yeast extract 2.5 g; tryptone 5 g; glucose 1 g; agar 15 g; d.w. 1 L, pH 7.0.

45. *Rose bengal agar:* Prepare plate count agar; rose bengal 0.033 g and autoclave. Cool to 50°C and add 2 ml of the antibiotic mixture. DO NOT remelt.

Antibiotic mixture: chlortetracycline (Aureomycin) 500 mg; chloramphenicol 500 mg in 100 ml of 0.1% peptone water, filter sterilize.

46. *Sabouraud's dextrose or maltose agar:* Polypeptone or neopeptone 10 g; dextrose (or maltose) 40 g; agar 15 g; d.w. 1 L, adjust pH to 5.6 before autoclaving.

47. *Salt agar:* Table salt (NaCl) 200 g (for 20% w/v); $MgSO_4 \cdot 7H_2O$ 20 g; KCl 5 g; $CaCl_2 \cdot 6H_2O$ 0.2 g; yeast extract 3 g; tryptone 5 g; d.w. 1 L, pH 7.2–7.4.

Sheep blood agar — see blood agar

48. *Simmon's citrate agar:* Sodium citrate 2 g; NaCl 5 g; K_2HPO_4 1 g; $NH_4H_2PO_4$ 1 g; $MgSO_4 \cdot 7H_2O$ 0.2 g; bromthymol blue 0.08 g; agar 15 g; d.w. 1 L, pH 6.8.

49. *Skim milk agar:* Skim milk powder 20 g; 100 ml d.w. Autoclave. Mix 20 ml sterile skim milk with 100 ml previously sterilized, melted, nutrient agar, cooled and held at 50°C.

50. *Snyder test agar:* Tryptose 20 g; glucose 20 g; NaCl 5 g; bromcresol green 0.02 g; agar 20 g; d.w. 1 L, pH 4.8.

51. *Spirit blue agar:* Tryptone 10 g; yeast extract 5 g; spirit blue 0.15 g; agar 20 g; d.w. 1 L, pH 6.8. Sterilize. Use lipase reagent (Difco) or prepare lipid as follows: warm 400 ml d.w., add 1 ml of Tween 80, add 100 ml of olive oil (or other lipid) and homogenize vigorously. Add 30 ml of the homogenate to sterile, melted and cooled to 50°C agar.

52. *Starch agar:* Nutrient agar plus 10 g per L of soluble starch.

53. *Starkey modified broth/agar medium:* Solution 1 — K_2HPO_4 0.5 g; NH_4Cl 1 g; $CaCl_2 \cdot 2H_2O$ 0.1 g; Na_2SO_4 1 g; $MgSO_4 \cdot 7H_2O$ 2 g; Na lactate (70%) 5 g; yeast extract 1 g; d.w. 1 L. Autoclave in 350 ml amounts. For agar, add 15 g/L before autoclaving.

Solution 2 — $Fe(NH_4)_2SO_4$ 3.9 g; d.w. 100 ml. Filter sterilize.

Solution 3 — Na ascorbate 1 g; d.w. 1 L. Prepare on day of use. Filter sterilize.

Final medium — broth: To each 350 ml of sterile Solution 1, add 3.5 ml each of sterile Solutions 2 and 3. Mix.

Final medium — agar: To each 100 ml of sterile Solution 1, melted and cooled to 50°C, add 1 ml of Solution 2 and 1 ml of Solution 3. Do this on the day of use. DO NOT remelt.

54. *Thioglycollate broth (with indicator):* Yeast extract 5 g; casitone 15 g; NaCl 2.5 g; L-cystine 0.25 g; thioglycollic acid 0.3 ml; methylene blue 0.002; agar 0.75 g; d.w. 1 L, pH 7.2.

55. *Thioparus broth/agar:* $Na_2S_2O_3 \cdot 5H_2O$ 10 g; $NaHCO_3$ 5 g; $(NH_4)_2SO_4$ 1 g; K_2HPO_4 0.1 g; $MgSO_4 \cdot 7H_2O$ 0.1 g; $CaCl_2 \cdot 2H_2O$ 0.01 g; $FeCl_3 \cdot 6H_2O$ 0.01 g; d.w. 1 L, pH to 6.8 with HCl. Filter sterilize.

For agar, prepare as above except use 500 ml d.w., adjust pH and filter sterilize. Add 15 g of agar to 500 ml d.w., melt, autoclave at 121°C for 15 minutes. Cool to 50°C and combine the two volumes. Hold at 50°C and pour plates as needed. Do not remelt.

56. *Toluidine blue-DNA agar (TB-DNA):* DNA 0.3 g; $CaCl_2$ (anhydrous) 1.1 mg; NaCl 10 g; Tris (hydroxymethyl) aminomethane 6.1 g; agar 10 g; toluidine blue O 0.083 g; d.w. 1 L.

Dissolve TRIS in 1 L d.w. and adjust to pH 9.0. Add remaining ingredients except toluidine blue O and heat to boiling. After agar and DNA are dissolved, add the toluidine blue O and dispense in smaller quantities. DO NOT autoclave. Medium is stable at room temperature for about 4 months and is satisfactory even after several remelting cycles.

57. *Top agar:* Solution A — Make in 100 ml amounts which can be stored. NaCl 0.5 g; agar 0.6 g, d.w. 100 ml. Autoclave. Solution B — L- histidine 10.5 mg, d.w. 100 ml — filter sterilize. Melt 100 ml sterile Solution A and temper to 45-50°C. Add 10 ml of sterile Solution B, mix and maintain at 45-50°C. Pipet 3 ml amounts into sterile 13 × 100 mm tubes. Hold the tubes at 45-50°C until used. **DO NOT** remelt.

58. *Tryptic soy agar:* Tryptone 17 g; soytone 3 g; NaCl 5 g; agar 15; d.w. 1 L, pH 7.3.

59. *Tryptic soy broth:* Tryptone 17 g; soytone 3 g; NaCl 5 g; glucose 2.5 g; K_2HPO_4 2.5 g; d.w. 1 L, pH 7.3.

60. *Tryptone broth (1%):* Tryptone 10 g; d.w. 1 L, pH 7.0.

61. *Tryptose phosphate broth/agar:* Tryptose 20 g; glucose 2 g; NaCl 5 g; Na_2HPO_4 2.5 g; d.w. 1 L, pH 7.3. For agar, add 15 g/L.

62. *Urea broth:* Urea 20 g; yeast extract 0.1 g; KH_2PO_4 9.1 g; Na_2HPO_4 9.5 g; phenol red 0.0001 g (or 4 ml of a .25% aqueous solution); d.w. 1 L, pH 6.8. **FILTER STERILIZE.** DO NOT AUTOCLAVE.

63. *Violet red bile agar:* Yeast extract 3 g; peptone 7 g; bilesalts No. 3 1.5 g; lactose 10 g; NaCl 5 g; neutral red 0.03 g; crystal violet 0.002 g; d.w. 1 L, pH 7.4. **DO NOT AUTOCLAVE.**

64. *Yeast extract tryptone agar:* Yeast extract 2.5 g; tryptone 5 g; agar 7.5 g; d.w. 1 L, pH 7.0.

Reference: Difco Manual, 10th edition. Difco Laboratories, Detroit, MI 48232. 1984.

Reagents

The "d.w." in the following formulas refers to distilled or demineralized water.

1. *Acid-alcohol:* 95% ethyl alcohol plus 3% (v/v) concentrated hydrochloric acid. Dissolve the HCl in the alcohol.

2. *Acidified mercuric chloride:* $HgCl_2$ 15g; d.w. 100 ml; concentrated HCl 20 ml. Mix in this order.

3. *Acridine orange* (0.01%): Acridine orange (Matheson, Coleman, and Bell 364003, color index 788) 0.01 g; d.w. 100 ml. Filter through a 0.2 μm membrane filter on *each* day used to remove any bacteria growing in it during storage.

Barritt's reagents — see Voges-Poskauer A and B

4. *Bromthymol blue* (0.05%): Bromthymol blue 0.05 g; 0.01N NaOH 8 ml; d.w. to 100 ml.

5. *Carbol fuchsin* (Ziehl-Neelsen): Solution A — basic fuchsin 0.3g; 95% ethyl alcohol 10 ml; Solution B — phenol 5 g; d.w. 95 ml. Mix Solutions A and B and let stand for several days before use. Filter through paper into stock bottle.

6. *Gram stain reagents:*

    Gram's crystal violet: Solution A — crystal (gentian) violet 2 g; 95% ethyl alcohol 20 ml; Solution B — ammonium oxalate 0.8 g; d.w. 80 ml. Mix Solutions A and B and store 24 hours. Filter through paper into stock bottle.

    Gram's iodine: Dissolve KI 2 g in 300 ml d.w. When completely dissolved, add I_2 1 g.

    Acetone-alcohol: 95% ethyl alcohol 80 ml; acetone 20 ml.

    Safranin: Safranin O (2.5% in 95% ethyl alcohol) 10 ml; d.w. 100 ml.

7. *Flagella stain* (Lieffson): Solution A — 1.5% NaCl; d.w.

    Solution B — 3.0% tannic acid; d.w.

    Solution C — 0.9% pararosaniline acetate; 0.3% pararosaniline hydrochloride (or 1.2% special flagella stain basic fuchsin); 95% ethyl alcohol. Shake on a shaker several hours to dissolve the dye.

    Mix 1 part Solution A with 1 part Solution B, then add 1 part Solution C. This is best prepared on the day of use but will keep at 4°C for 1–2 months.

8. *Hydrogen peroxide:* 30% H_2O_2 10 ml; add d.w. to make 100 ml.

9. *Indole reagent* (Kovac's): para-dimethyl- aminobenzaldehyde 5 g; amyl or butyl alcohol 75 ml; concentrated HCl 25 ml. Dissolve the reagent in the alcohol, warming gently in a 37°C water bath. When completely dissolved, add the HCl carefully while stirring.

Kovac's reagents — see Indole and Oxidase reagents

10. *Loeffler's methylene blue:* Solution A — methylene blue 0.3 g; 95% ethyl alcohol 30 ml; Solution B — KOH 0.01 g; d.w. 100 ml. Mix Solutions A and B and filter through paper.

11. *Malachite green (5%):* Malachite green 5 g; d.w. to 100 ml. Filter through paper.

12. *Methyl cellulose:* Carboxymethylcellulose (methocel), 15 centipoise (Sigma Chemical Co., St. Louis, MO). Mix 10 g in 45 ml boiling d.w., cool, and add 45 ml d.w.

13. *Methyl red:* Methyl red 0.2 g; 95% ethyl alcohol 500 ml; d.w. 500 ml. Filter if necessary.

14. *Nitrite A:* Sulfanilic acid 0.8 g; acetic acid 5N (1 part glacial to 2.5 parts d.w.) 100 ml.

15. *Nitrite B:* N, N'-dimethyl-1-naphthylamine (dimethyl-α-naphthylamine) 0.5 g; acetic acid 5N (1 part glacial to 2.5 parts d.w.) 100 ml.

16. *Nessler's reagent:* Dissolve 50 g KI in 35 ml cold distilled water. Add a solution of saturated mercuric chloride until a slight precipitate persists. Add 400 ml of a 50% solution of KOH. Add sufficient d.w. to make 1 L, allow to settle, and decant the supernatant for use.

NNDNA: see Nitrite B

17. *Oxidase reagent* (Kovac's): Tetramethyl-para-phenylenediamine HCl 0.5 g; d.w. 50 ml. Prepare the solution on the day of use. If this is not possible, refrigerate to store but warm to room temperature before use. Do not use if more than 5 days old or if a precipitate has formed.

18. *Phenol erythrosin:* Phenol erythrosin 1 g; 5% phenol 100 ml.

19. *Safranin (0.5%):* Safranin 0.5 g; d.w. 100 ml.

20. *Sudan black B:* Sudan black B 0.3 g; ethyl alcohol 100 ml.

Sulfanilic acid reagent: see Nitrite A

21. *Tris-maleic acid buffer:* 2-amino-2-(hydroxymethyl)-1, 3-propanediol (Tris) 6 g; maleic acid 5.8 g; $(NH_4)_2SO_4$ 1 g; $FeSO_4 \cdot 7H_2O$ 0.25 mg; d.w. 900 ml, pH 6.0. Autoclave at 121°C for 15 minutes. Cool to 50°C and aseptically add 100 ml of sterile $MgSO_4 \cdot 7H_2O$ 1 g; $Ca(NO_3)_2$ 50 mg; in 100 ml d.w.

22. *Toluidine blue (1%):* Toluidine blue 1.0 g; d.w. 100 ml.

23. *TPF:* 2,3,5-triphenyl formazan (Sigma Chemical Co. T1383) 0.5 g; methanol 100 ml.

24. *TTC:* 2,3,5-triphenyl tetrazolium chloride (Sigma Chemical Co. T8877) 0.5 g; d.w. 100 ml.

25. *Vaspar:* Equal parts vaseline and paraffin. Sterilize in the oven at 160°C for 3 hours. Avoid browning.

26. *Voges-Proskauer A* (Barritt's A): Alpha-naphthol 5 g; 95% ethyl alcohol 100 ml.

27. *Voges-Proskauer B* (Barritt's B): KOH 40 g; creatine 0.3 g; d.w. 100 ml.

Ziehl-Neelsen carbolfuchsin — see Carbolfuchsin

APPENDIX *III*

List of Organisms

Culture numbers given are from the American Type Culture Collection. Other sources are available for many, especially Carolina Biological Supply Co. (CBS). Substitutions of strains can usually be made except when an asterisk is placed before the name. One or more of the exercises listed requires that particular species or strain. ATCC ##P refers to Preceptrol cultures.

Bacteria and Viruses

Antibiosis kit *B. cereus-Sarcina subflava (Micrococcus luteus)* Carolina Biological Supply 15-4730 (54)
Acinetobacter calcoaceticus ATCC 19606P (29)
Alcaligenes faecalis ATCC 8750P (32)
Aquaspirillum serpens ATCC 11335 (20)
Azotobacter chroococcum ATCC 9043P (64)
Bacillus cereus ATCC 14579P (16, 18, 28)
**Bacillus megaterium* ATCC 14581P (21, 46, 50)
Bacillus sp. ATCC 21592 (45)
Bacillus stearothermophilus ATCC 7953P (42)
Bacillus subtilis ATCC 6051P (9, 10, 25, 32, 36, 38, 51, 82)
Clostridium perfringens ATCC 3624P (46)
Corynebacterium diphtheriae (avirulent) ATCC 11913P (21)
Enterobacter aerogenes ATCC 13048P (30, 31, 34, 40, 41, 61B)
Enterobacter cloacae ATCC 13047P (40, 41)
Enterococcus (Streptococcus) faecalis ATCC 29212P (9. 10, 29, 31, 35, 45, 46)
Erwinea carotovora ATCC 495 (85)
Escherichia coli ATCC 25922P (9, 10, 11, 12, 16, 23, 25, 26, 27, 28, 29, 32, 33, 34, 35, 37, 39, 40, 41, 42, 43, 44, 45, 46, 48, 49, 52, 58, 61B, 81, 82)
*Escherichia coli K12 ATCC 25404P (59)
*Escherichia coli plasmid host ATCC 33525 (60)
*Escherichia coli plasmid pET1 carrier ATCC 39566 (60)
Escherichia coli B ATCC 11303P (57)
E. coli B T-4 phage ATCC 11303-B4P (57)
Halobacterium salinarium ATCC 19700P (44)
Klebsiella pneumoniae ATCC 13883P (19, 41, 61B)
**Lactobacillus plantarum* ATCC 8014 (56) (also Difco 3211-30-3)
Micrococcus luteus ATCC 4698P (9, 10, 11, 12)
**Micrococcus varians* ATCC 15306 (37)
**Morganella morganii* ATCC 25830P (41, 77)
Mycobacterium smegmatis ATCC 14468 (17)
**Myxococcus xanthus* FB ATCC 25232 (55)
Nitrobacter agilis ATCC 14123P (64) see Instructor's Manual
Nitrosomonas europaea ATCC 19718 (64) see Intructor's Manual

Photobacterium phosphoreum ATCC 35080 (72)
Proteus vulgaris ATCC 13315P (20, 33, 39, 40, 41, 53, 61B)
Pseudomonas aeruginosa ATCC 27853P (20, 26, 29, 35, 36, 38, 41, 51, 81)
Pseudomonas fluorescens I ATCC 13525P (42)
Salmonella choleraesuis ATCC 13312P (88, 61B)
Salmonella typhimurium ATCC 14028P (41, 61B, 88)
*Salmonella typhimurium 1535 Ames[a] (84)
Serratia marcescens ATCC 8100P (9, 10, 27, 30, 40, 41, 47, 61B)
Staphylococcus aureus (ATCC 3386 2P) (16, 17, 18, 30, 31, 32, 35, 36, 37, 44, 45, 47, 48, 51, 53, 91)
Staphylococcus aureus ATCC 25923P (81, 82, 83)
Staphylococcus aureus Coagulase negative ATCC 11631P (91)
Staphylococcus epidermidis ATCC 12228P (30)
Thiobacillus thiooxidans ATCC 8085P (65)
*Vibrio marinus ATCC 15381 (42)
Vibrio natriegens ATCC 14048P (24)

Fungi and Yeasts

Aspergillus niger ATCC 16880P (7)
Penicillium chrysogenum ATCC 10002P (7)
Rhizopus stolonifer ATCC 14037P (7)
Saccharomyces cerevisiae ATCC 2341P (7, 44, 45, 81, 82)
Saprolegnia growth kit Carolina Biological Supply 15-5845 (7)

For organisms used as unknowns in Exercise 61A see the Instructor's Manual.

[a] From: Dr. B. Ames, Dept. of Biochemistry, University of California, Berkeley, CA 94720